PENGUIN REFERENCE BOOKS

RI

A DICTIONARY OF SCIENCE

BY E. B. UVAROV AND

D. R. CHAPMAN

A Dictionary of Science

DEFINITIONS AND EXPLANATIONS OF TERMS USED IN
CHEMISTRY, PHYSICS, AND ELEMENTARY MATHEMATICS

BY

E. B. UVAROV
B.SC., A.R.C.S., A.R.I.C., D.I.C.

REVISED WITH THE
ASSISTANCE OF

D. R. CHAPMAN
B.A.

PENGUIN BOOKS
BALTIMORE · MARYLAND

Penguin Books Ltd, Harmondsworth, Middlesex
U.S.A.: Penguin Books Inc., 3300 Clipper Mill Road, Baltimore 11, Md
AUSTRALIA: Penguin Books Pty Ltd, 762 Whitehorse Road,
Mitcham, Victoria

—

First published 1943
Reprinted 1944
Revised Edition 1951
Reprinted 1952, 1954, 1956, 1958, 1959, 1960, 1961, 1962

—

Made and printed in Great Britain
by The Whitefriars Press Ltd
London and Tonbridge
Set in Monotype Baskerville

Foreword to 1951 Edition

THIS edition is a complete revision of the original work which was published in 1943 and reprinted, with minor additions and corrections, in 1944.

The great amount of new knowledge in modern physics which has become available during the past few years made it imperative to obtain the help of a physicist thoroughly familiar with modern developments to revise the physics terms in the Dictionary. This work was undertaken by Mr D. R. Chapman, who has revised and to a great extent re-written all the entries relating to physics and mathematics, and who has added many new entries on atomic energy and related subjects. The opportunity has also been taken to revise all the chemical entries; here, too, every entry has been checked against reliable sources and many additions and amendments have been made.

Much of the new material is such that it cannot be fully explained in simple terms; the fact had to be faced that many concepts of modern physics are such that it is no longer possible to keep a dictionary of this scope self-contained in the sense that every term and idea used is sufficiently explained by cross-references.

To make room for the numerous new entries, it was necessary to omit certain entries which were previously included ; in particular, the brief biographical notes on famous scientists.

It is evident that a work of this size cannot be expected to be a reference book for the specialist; the aim, both in the original editions and in the revision, has been to define and explain scientific terms for the benefit of the layman and the student. At the same time, it is hoped that the information given is sufficiently full and accurate to be of help, on subjects outside his particular field, to the more advanced user.

Very many reference works have been consulted in the compilation of this book, making individual acknowledgements impracticable. In addition, considerable help in the revision has been given by several friends and colleagues; in particular, the author's gratitude is due to Mr L. Cotton, Dr A. S. Carpenter, and Dr R. L. Wormell for their kind assistance.

Abbreviations used in
the Text

A°.	Absolute (temperature)
At. No.	Atomic number
A.W.	Atomic weight
(astr.)	Astronomy; as used in astronomy
b. p.	Boiling point
C.	Centigrade
c.c.	Cubic centimetre
(chem.)	Chemistry; as used in chemistry
conc.	Concentrated
F.	Fahrenheit
gm.	Gram
°K	Degrees on the Kelvin (absolute) scale
lb.	Pound
(math.)	Mathematics; as used in mathematics
mm.	Millimetre
m. p.	Melting point
(phot.)	Used in photography
(phys.)	Physics; as used in physics
q.v.	Which see
S.G.	Specific gravity
temp.	Temperature
wt.	Weight

A Dictionary of Science

ABERRATION (astr.). Variation in the apparent position of a star or other heavenly body, due to the motion of the observer with the Earth.

ABERRATION, CHROMATIC. Formation, by a lens, of an image with coloured fringes, due to the *refractive index* (q.v.) of glass being different for light of different colours. The light is thus dispersed (see *dispersion*) into a coloured band. The effect is corrected by the use of *achromatic lenses* (q.v.).

ABERRATION, SPHERICAL. Distortion of image produced by a lens or mirror due to different rays from any one point of the object making different angles with the line joining that point to the optical centre of the *lens* (q.v.) or mirror (see *mirrors, spherical*) and coming to a focus in slightly different positions.

ABRASION. Rubbing away.

ABRASIVE. A substance used for rubbing or grinding down surfaces; e.g. *emery* (q.v.).

ABSCISSA of a point *P*, in analytical geometry, is the portion of the *x* axis lying between the origin and a point where the line through *P* parallel to the *y* axis cuts the *x* axis.

ABSOLUTE. Not relative; independent. E.g. *absolute zero* (q.v.) of temperature, as distinct from zero on an arbitrary scale such as the Centigrade scale.

ABSOLUTE ALCOHOL. *Ethyl alcohol* (q.v.) containing not less than 99% pure ethyl alcohol by weight.

ABSOLUTE EXPANSION of a liquid. The true expansion, not relative to the containing vessel. The coefficient of absolute expansion is equal to the sum of the coefficient of relative or apparent expansion of the liquid and the coefficient of volume expansion of the containing vessel.

ABSOLUTE THERMODYNAMIC TEMPERATURE. Temperature measured on the absolute or Kelvin scale. This scale is independent of the physical properties of any material substance. It is defined in terms of the heat exchanges in an ideal *Carnot cycle* (q.v.). On this scale the temperature interval between the *ice point* (q.v.) and the *steam point* (q.v.) is defined to be 100 degrees, so that the magnitude of the degrees is the same as on the Centigrade scale. This scale leads to the concept of the *absolute zero* (q.v.) of temperature. To convert temperature on the Centigrade scale to degrees absolute (°A or °K), add 273.

ABSOLUTE UNITS. System of units in which the least possible number of independent *fundamental units* (q.v.) is used.

ABSOLUTE ZERO. Zero on the absolute temperature scale (see *absolute thermodynamic temperature*). The lowest temperature theoretically possible; $0°K = -273 \cdot 16° C$.

ABSORPTION OF GASES. The solution of gases in liquids. Sometimes also applied to the absorption of gases by solids.

ABSORPTION OF RADIATION. Radiant energy (heat and light waves) is partly reflected, partly transmitted and partly absorbed by the surface upon which it falls, the absorption being accompanied by a rise in temperature of the absorbing body. Dull black surfaces absorb the greatest proportion of the incident energy, and brightly polished (reflecting) surfaces the least. Surfaces which are the best absorbers are also the best radiators. See *radiation*.

ABSORPTION SPECTRUM. *Spectrum* (q.v.) consisting of dark lines or bands on a coloured background, formed when a substance is placed between a *white light* (q.v.) source and the spectroscope. The lines or bands are caused by the absorption of the incident light by the substance at certain wave-lengths, and their position is characteristic of the substance.

ABSORPTIVITY of a surface. The fraction of the radiant energy incident on the surface which is absorbed. The absorptivity is a pure numeric, but is often referred to as 'absorptive power'. From *Kirchhoff's law* (q.v.) it follows that the absorptivity is equal to the *emissivity* (q.v.).

ACCELERATION. Rate of change of velocity; measured as a change of velocity per unit time.

ACCELERATION DUE TO GRAVITY, *g*. Acceleration of a body falling freely in a vacuum; varies slightly in different localities as a result of variations in the distance from the centre of mass of the Earth. Standard accepted values = 980·6 cm./sec./sec. at latitude 45°; 981·19 cm./sec./sec. at Greenwich (32·17 and 32·19 ft./sec./sec. respectively).

ACCELERATOR (chem.). A substance which increases the rate of a chemical reaction (i.e., a *catalyst*, q.v.), particularly in the vulcanization of rubber.

ACCELERATOR TUBE. Evacuated tube along which ions (e.g. protons or alpha-particles) can be accelerated to high energies by applying a very large potential difference across its ends.

ACCUMULATOR, storage battery, secondary cell. Device for 'storing' electricity. An electric current is passed between two plates in a liquid; this causes chemical changes (due to *electrolysis*, q.v.) in the plates and the liquid. When the changes are complete, the accumulator is charged. When the charged plates are joined externally by a conductor of electricity, the chemical changes are reversed, a current flows through the conductor till the reversal is complete, and the accumulator is discharged. In the common lead accumulator, the liquid is sulphuric acid of specific gravity 1·20 to 1·28, the positive plate when charged is lead peroxide, PbO_2, and the negative plate is spongy lead. During discharge both plates tend to become lead sulphate, $PbSO_4$, and the specific gravity of the acid solution falls. Discharge should not be continued beyond the point at which the S.G. reaches 1·15, otherwise an insoluble sulphate of lead, not decomposed on re-charging, may be formed. When this occurs, the cell is said to be sulphated.

ACETAL. An organic compound of the general formula $RCH(OR')_2$, where R is hydrogen or an organic radical, and R' is an organic radical. Term is generally applied to $CH_3CH(OC_2H_5)_2$, a liquid, b.p. 104° C.

ACETALDEHYDE. CH_3CHO. Colourless liquid with a pungent fruity smell, b.p. 21° C. Formed by the oxidation of ethyl alcohol; further oxidation gives acetic acid. Used as an intermediate in the manufacture of many organic compounds.

ACETAMIDE. CH_3CONH_2. Colourless crystals, m.p. 81° C., odourless when pure. Used industrially as a solvent, etc.

ACETANILIDE, antifebrin. $C_6H_5NHCOCH_3$. White crystalline solid, m.p. 112° C. Used as an *antipyretic* (q.v.).

ACETATE. A salt or an *ester* (q.v.) of acetic acid.

ACETATE PLASTICS. Plastics made from *cellulose acetate* (q.v.).

ACETATE RAYON. See *cellulose acetate; rayon*.

ACETATE SILK. Obsolete name for cellulose acetate *rayon* (q.v.).

ACETIC ACID. CH_3COOH. The acid contained in vinegar (3 to 6%). Colourless corrosive liquid with a pungent smell; m.p. 16·6° C., b.p. 118·1° C. Solidifies at low temperatures to 'glacial acetic acid'. Commercially obtained from *pyroligneous acid* (q.v.), from vinegar made when alcohol is oxidized by the action of bacteria, and by the oxidation of *acetaldehyde* (q.v.). Used in the manufacture of *cellulose acetate* (q.v.) and in other industries.

ACETIC ETHER. *Ethyl acetate* (q.v.).

ACETONE, dimethyl ketone. CH_3COCH_3. Colourless inflammable liquid with a pleasant smell. B.p. 56·5° C. Used as a solvent, especially in the production of cellulose acetate *rayon* (q.v.).

ACETYLENE, ethyne. C_2H_2. Colourless poisonous inflammable gas. Made by the action of water on calcium carbide, CaC_2, or by the action of an electric *arc* (q.v.) on other hydrocarbons. Used as a starting material for many organic compounds, and in acetylene ('carbide') lamps.

ACHROMATIC LENS. Lens free from chromatic *aberration* (q.v.), giving an image free from coloured fringes. Consists of a pair of lenses, one of crown glass, the other of flint glass, the latter correcting the *dispersion* (q.v.) caused by the former.

ACID. Substance which forms *hydrogen ions* (q.v.) in solution; substance which contains hydrogen which may be replaced by a metal to form a *salt* (q.v.); substance having a tendency to lose *protons* (q.v.). Many acids are corrosive, have a sour taste, and turn litmus red.

ACID AMIDES. See *amides*.

ACID DYES. Group of dyes, nearly all salts of organic acids; used chiefly for dyeing wool and natural silk from an acid dyebath.

ACID RADICAL. A molecule of an acid without the *acidic hydrogen* (q.v.). E.g., the bivalent sulphate radical, SO_4, from sulphuric acid, H_2SO_4, is present in all sulphates.

ACID SALT. An *acid* (q.v.) in which only a part of the *acidic hydrogen* (q.v.) has been replaced by a metal. E.g. sodium bicarbonate, $NaHCO_3$.

ACID VALUE of a fat or oil. Measure of the free *fatty acids* (q.v.) present; the number of milligrams of potassium hydroxide required to neutralize the free fatty acids in one gram of the substance.

ACIDIC. Having the properties of an acid; the opposite of *alkaline* (q.v.).

ACIDIC HYDROGEN. That portion of the hydrogen in an acid which is replaceable by metals to form salts.

ACIDIMETRY. Determination of the amount of acid present in a solution by *titration* (q.v.). See *volumetric analysis*.

ACIDOLYSIS. *Hydrolysis* (q.v.) by means of an acid.

ACOUSTICS. The study of sound.

ACRE. British unit of area. 4,840 square yards.

ACRIFLAVINE, 3:6-diaminomethylacridine chloride hydrochloride. Yellow substance used as an antiseptic.

ACROLEIN. $CH_2:CH.CHO$. Colourless liquid with an irritating smell. B.p. 52·5° C.

ACRYLIC ACID, $CH_2:CH.COOH$. Corrosive liquid, m.p. 13° C., b.p. 141° C. Derivatives form the basis of the important *acrylic resins* (q.v.).

ACRYLIC RESINS. Class of plastics obtained by the *polymerization* (q.v.) of derivatives of acrylic acid. They are transparent, colourless and *thermoplastic* (q.v.); widely used, especially if a clear, transparent material is required.

ACRYLONITRILE, vinyl cyanide. $CH_2:CH.CN$. Colourless liquid, b.p. 78° C. Used in the manufacture of plastics, synthetic rubbers and artificial textile fibres.

ACTINIC RAYS. Portion of the Sun's radiation rich in *ultra-violet rays* (q.v.), having a strong effect on a photographic plate.

ACTINIUM. Ac. Element. A.W. 227. At. No. 89. Radioactive. See *radioactivity*.

ACTIVATED CARBON, active charcoal. Carbon, especially charcoal, which has been treated to remove *hydrocarbons* (q.v.) and to increase its powers of *adsorption* (q.v.). Used in many industrial processes for recovering valuable materials out of gaseous mixtures; as a deodorant; and in *gas masks* (q.v.).

ACTIVE DEPOSIT. Solid radioactive material deposited on surfaces exposed to radioactive emanations by disintegration of the latter. See *radioactivity; radon*.

ACTIVE MASS (chem.), in the Law of *Mass Action* (q.v.) is taken to mean the *molecular concentration* (q.v.) of the substance under consideration.

ACUTE ANGLE. Angle of less than 90°.

ADDITION COMPOUND. Chemical compound formed by the addition of an atom or group of atoms to a molecule. E.g. phosgene, $COCl_2$, is an addition compound of carbon monoxide, CO, and chlorine, Cl_2.

ADHESION. Sticking to a surface. The effect is produced by forces between molecules.

ADHESIVES. Substances used for sticking surfaces together; e.g. glues, cements, etc.

ADIABATIC. Taking place without heat entering or leaving the system.

ADRENALIN, methylamino-ethanol catechol. $C_9H_{13}NO_3$. *Hormone* (q.v.) produced by the suprarenal glands. Used in medicine.

ADSORBATE. The substance which is adsorbed on a surface. See *adsorption*.

ADSORPTION. Concentration of a substance on a surface; e.g. molecules of a gas or of a dissolved or suspended substance on the surface of a solid.

AELOTROPIC. *Anisotropic* (q.v.).

AERIAL, antenna. Electrical circuit which abstracts energy from a passing radio wave as a result of currents induced in it by the magnetic component of the wave. In a transmitting aerial, electromagnetic energy fed into it from the transmitter is radiated from it in the form of wireless waves.

AEROLITES. *Meteorites* (q.v.); especially those consisting of stony material rather than iron.

AERO METAL. Casting alloy consisting chiefly of aluminium, zinc and copper.

AEROSOL. A dispersion of particles in a gas; e.g. smoke.

AFFINITY (chem.). Chemical attraction; force binding atoms together.

AFTER-DAMP. Poisonous mixture of gases, containing *carbon monoxide* (q.v.), formed by the explosion of fire-damp (methane, CH_4) in coal-mines.

AGAR-AGAR. A gelatin-like material obtained from certain seaweeds. Chemically related to the *carbohydrates* (q.v.). A solution in hot water sets to a firm jelly, which is used as a base for culture media for growing bacteria.

AGATE. Natural form of silica, SiO_2. Very hard, used for knife-edges of balances, for mortars for grinding hard materials, and in ornaments.

AGONIC LINE. Line of zero *magnetic declination* (q.v.).

AIR, THE. See *atmosphere*.

AIR THERMOMETER. See *gas thermometer*.

ALABAMINE. Name formerly proposed for element of At. No. 85, the last member of the halogen group. The name *astatine* has now been officially accepted.

ALABASTER. Natural opaque form of hydrated calcium sulphate, $CaSO_4.2H_2O$.

ALBUMENS, ALBUMINS. Group of water-soluble *proteins* (q.v.) occurring in many animal tissues and fluids; e.g. egg-white (egg albumen), milk (lactalbumen) and blood (serum albumen).

ALBUMINOIDS. See *scleroproteins*.

ALCHEMY. Predecessor of scientific chemistry. An art by which its devotees sought, with the aid of a mixture of mysticism, astrology, practical chemistry and quackery, to transmute base metals into gold, prolong human life, etc. Flourished from about A.D. 500 till the Middle Ages, when it gradually fell into disrepute.

ALCOHOL, ETHYL. See *ethyl alcohol*.

ALCOHOLOMETRY. The determination of the proportion of ethyl alcohol in spirits and other solutions; usually performed by measuring the specific gravity of the liquid at a standard temperature by a specially graduated *hydrometer* (q.v.).

ALCOHOLS. Class of organic compounds derived from the *hydrocarbons* (q.v.), one or more hydrogen atoms in molecules of the latter being replaced by hydroxyl groups, OH. E.g. *ethyl alcohol* (ordinary 'alcohol') is C_2H_5OH, theoretically derived from ethane, C_2H_6.

ALDEHYDE. See *acetaldehyde*.

ALDEHYDES, THE. Class of organic compounds of the type $R-C{<}^O_H$ where R is an *alkyl* or *aryl radical* (q.v.).

ALDOL, beta-hydroxybutyraldehyde, $CH_3CH(OH)CH_2CHO$. Thick oily liquid formed by the condensation of *acetaldehyde* (q.v.).

ALGEBRA. Branch of mathematics dealing with the properties of and relationships between quantities by means of general symbols.

ALGEBRAIC SUM. The total of a number of quantities of the same kind, with due regard to sign. Thus the algebraic sum of 3, — 5, and — 2 is — 4.

ALGIN. A loose term for *alginic acid* (q.v.) or its sodium salt.

ALGINIC ACID. A complex organic compound related to the *carbohydrates* (q.v.), found in certain seaweeds. Used for preparing emulsions and as a thickening agent in the food industry; its salts, the *alginates*, can be made into textile fibres which are soluble in alkalies and are used for special purposes.

ALIDADE. Instrument for measuring vertical heights and distances.

ALIPHATIC COMPOUNDS. *Organic* (q.v.) compounds containing open chains of carbon atoms, in contradistinction to the closed rings of carbon atoms of the *aromatic compounds* (q.v.).

ALIZARIN, 1:2 dihydroxyanthraquinone, $C_{14}H_6O_2(OH)_2$. Orange-red crystalline solid, m.p. 289° C. Colouring matter formerly extracted from the root of the madder plant, now made synthetically. Used in dyeing with the aid of *mordants* (q.v.).

ALKALI. Soluble *hydroxide* (q.v.) of a metal, particularly of one of the *alkali metals* (q.v.); term is often applied to any substance which has an alkaline reaction (i.e. turns litmus blue and neutralizes acids) in solution. See also *base*.

ALKALI METALS. The metals lithium, sodium, potassium, rubidium and caesium.

ALKALIMETRY. Determination of the amount of alkali present in a solution, by *titration* (q.v.). See *volumetric analysis*.

ALKALINE. Adjective applied to an *alkali* (q.v.); opposite of acidic.

ALKALINE EARTH METALS. The *bivalent* (q.v.) group of metals comprising beryllium, magnesium, calcium, strontium, barium and radium.

ALKALOIDS. Group of basic organic substances of plant origin, containing at least one nitrogen atom in a ring structure in the molecule. Many have important physiological actions and are used in medicine. E.g. cocaine.

ALKYD RESINS. See *glyptal resins*.

ALKYL RADICALS. Univalent *hydrocarbon* (q.v.) radicals, particularly those derived from hydrocarbons of the *paraffin series* (q.v.), and having the general formula C_nH_{2n+1}. E.g. methyl, CH_3; ethyl, C_2H_5.

ALLOTROPES, allotropic forms. See *allotropy*.

ALLOTROPY. The existence of a chemical *element* (q.v.) in two or more forms differing in physical properties but giving rise to identical chemical compounds. E.g. *sulphur* (q.v.) exists in a number of different allotropic forms.

ALLOY. A composition of two or more metals; an alloy may be a compound of the metals, a solid solution of them, a heterogeneous mixture, or any combination of these.

ALLUVIAL. Deposited by rivers.

ALPHA PARTICLE, α-particle. Helium nucleus; i.e. a close combination of two *neutrons* (q.v.) and two *protons* (q.v.) (see *atom, structure of*), and therefore positively charged. Alpha particles are emitted from the nuclei of certain radioactive elements. See *radioactivity*.

ALPHA RAYS, α-rays. Streams of fast-moving *alpha particles* (q.v.). Alpha rays produce intense ionization in gases through which they pass, are easily absorbed by matter, and produce fluorescence on a fluorescent screen.

ALTAZIMUTH. Instrument for the measurement of the *altitude* (q.v.) and *azimuth* (q.v.) of heavenly bodies.

ALTERNATING CURRENT. A flow of electricity which, after reaching a maximum in one direction, decreases, finally reversing and reaching a maximum in the opposite direction, the cycle being repeated continuously. The number of such cycles per second is the *frequency*.

ALTITUDE. 1. Height. 2. Altitude of the sun, or other heavenly body, is its angle of *elevation* (q.v.).

ALUDEL. See *udell*.

ALUM, potash alum. $K_2SO_4 . Al_2(SO_4)_3 . 24H_2O$. Crystalline potassium, aluminium sulphate. The compound occurs naturally and is used as a *mordant* (q.v.) in dyeing, for fireproofing and other technical purposes.

ALUMINA. Aluminium oxide, Al_2O_3. Occurs naturally as corundum and emery, and in a *hydrated* (q.v.) form as bauxite.

ALUMINIUM. Al. Element. A.W. 26·98. At. No. 13. Light white metal, S.G. 2·7, m.p. 658·7° C., ductile and malleable, good conductor of electricity. Occurs widely in nature in clays, etc.; extracted mainly from *bauxite* (q.v.) by *electrolysis* (q.v.) of a molten mixture of purified bauxite and *cryolite* (q.v.). The metal and its alloys are used for aircraft, cooking utensils, electrical apparatus and for many other purposes where its light weight is an advantage.

ALUMINIUM BRASS. *Brass* (q.v.) containing small amounts of aluminium.

ALUMINIUM BRONZE. Alloy of copper containing 4% to 13% aluminium.

ALUMS, the. Double salts of the general formula
$$M_2SO_4.R_2(SO_4)_3.24H_2O,$$
where M is a univalent metal such as sodium, potassium or ammonium, and R is a tervalent metal such as aluminium or chromium.

ALUM-STONE. See *alunite*.

ALUNITE, alum-stone. Natural compound of potassium and aluminium sulphate and aluminium hydroxide, $K_2SO_4.Al_2(SO_4)_3.4Al(OH)_3$. Used as a source of potash *alum* (q.v.).

AMALGAM. *Alloy* (q.v.) of mercury.

AMALGAMATION PROCESS for gold. Gold-bearing rock or sand, after crushing, is treated with mercury, which forms an amalgam on the surface of the gold. The amalgamated particles are allowed to stick to amalgamated copper plates, the rest of the ore being washed away; they are then removed, the mercury is distilled off in iron retorts, and the remaining gold purified by *cupellation* (q.v.).

AMATOL. Explosive mixture of 80% ammonium nitrate and 20% T.N.T.

AMBER, succinite. A fossil resin, derived from an extinct species of pine. Obtained from mines in East Prussia, and found on seashores. Contains *succinic acid* (q.v.). Yellow to brown solid, used for ornamental purposes.

AMBERGRIS. Grey or black waxy material which occurs (probably as the result of disease) in the intestines of the sperm whale. Used in perfumery.

AMERICIUM. Am. *Transuranic element* (q.v.), At. No. 95. Radioactive.

AMETHYST. Violet variety of *quartz* (q.v.); impure crystalline silica, SiO_2.

AMIDES. Group of organic compounds formed by replacing hydrogen atoms of ammonia, NH_3, by organic acid radicals. E.g. acetamide, CH_3CONH_2.

AMIDOL. Hydrochloride of 2:4-diaminophenol,
$$C_6H_3(OH)(NH_2)_2.2HCl,$$
used in photography as a developer.

AMINES. Compounds formed by replacing hydrogen atoms of ammonia, NH_3, by organic radicals. Classified into primary amines of the type NH_2R; secondary, NHR_2; and tertiary, NR_3. See also *quaternary ammonium compounds*.

AMINO-ACIDS. Group of organic compounds derived by replacing hydrogen atoms in the hydrocarbon groups of fatty acids or other organic acids with *amino groups* (q.v.). E.g. amino-acetic acid, CH_2NH_2COOH. Amino-acids form the constituents of the *proteins* (q.v.).

AMINO GROUP. The univalent group NH_2.

AMMETER. Instrument for the measurement of electric current. In moving iron ammeters, a strip of soft iron is caused to move in the *magnetic field* (q.v.) set up by the current flowing through a coil; for the measurement of direct current, the more accurate moving coil instruments contain a permanent magnet between the poles of which is pivoted a coil carrying the current to be measured. In each type of instrument a pointer attached to the moving portion moves over a scale graduated in amperes.

AMMINES. Complex inorganic compounds formed by the addition of ammonia molecules to molecules of salts or similar compounds.

AMMONAL. Mixture of ammonium nitrate, NH_4NO_3, and aluminium. Used as an explosive.

AMMONIA. NH_3. Pungent-smelling gas, very soluble in water to give an alkaline solution containing ammonium hydroxide, NH_4OH. Obtained synthetically from atmospheric nitrogen (see *Haber process*) and as a by-product of coal-gas manufacture. Used in refrigeration, and for the manufacture of explosives and fertilizers.

AMMONIUM. NH_4. Univalent radical which has not been obtained free, but in compounds behaves similarly to an *alkali metal* (q.v.), giving rise to ammonium salts.

AMMONIUM CHLORIDE, sal ammoniac. NH_4Cl. White soluble crystalline salt, used in dry batteries and Leclanché cells.

AMMONIUM HYDROXIDE. NH_4OH. Compound presumed to exist in aqueous solutions of *ammonia* (q.v.); name is often applied to the solution.

AMMONIUM NITRATE. NH_4NO_3. White soluble crystalline salt, m.p. 169·6° C., decomposes on heating to form nitrous oxide, N_2O, and water. Used in explosives, e.g. *ammonal, amatol* (q.v.).

AMMONIUM SULPHATE, sulphate of ammonia. $(NH_4)_2SO_4$. White soluble crystalline salt, obtained as a by-product of coal-gas manufacture, used as a fertilizer.

AMORPHOUS. Non-crystalline; having no definite form or shape.

AMPERE. Unit of electric current. The *absolute ampere* is 10^{-1} *electromagnetic units* (q.v.) of current. A current may be measured in these latter units by means of the *current balance* (q.v.). The former *international ampere* was defined as the unvarying current which, when passed through a solution of silver nitrate, deposits silver at the rate of 0.00111800 gm. per second. 1 international ampere = 0.99987 absolute amperes.

AMPERE-HOUR. Practical unit of quantity of electricity; the amount of electricity flowing per hour through a conductor when the current in it is one ampere. 3600 *coulombs* (q.v.).

AMPHOTERIC. Chemically reacting as acidic to strong bases and as basic towards strong acids. E.g. the amphoteric oxide ZnO gives rise to zinc salts of strong acids and zincates of the alkali metals.

AMPLITUDE (phys.). If any quantity is varying in an oscillatory manner about an equilibrium value, the maximum departure from that equilibrium value is called the amplitude; e.g. in the case of a pendulum the amplitude is half the length of the swing. For a wave motion, e.g. *electromagnetic waves* (q.v.) or sound waves, the amplitude of the wave determines the amount of energy carried by the wave.

AMYL. The univalent radical C_5H_{11}.

AMYL ACETATE. $CH_3COOC_5H_{11}$. *Ester* (q.v.) of amyl alcohol and acetic acid. Colourless liquid, b.p. $148°$ C., with a smell of pear-drops. Used as a solvent for lacquers, in perfumes and as a flavouring.

AMYL ALCOHOL. $C_5H_{11}OH$. Colourless liquid with a characteristic smell. Exists in several isomeric forms (see *isomerism*). Commercial amyl alcohol consists mainly of *iso*-amyl alcohol,
$$(CH_3)_2:CH.CH_2.CH_2OH,$$
b.p. $131.4°$ C., and is obtained from *fusel oil* (q.v.). Used as a solvent.

AMYLUM. *Starch* (q.v.).

AMYLOPSIN. *Enzyme* (q.v.) of the pancreas, which breaks down or hydrolyses (see *hydrolysis*) complex carbohydrates, e.g. starch, into soluble sugars in the process of digestion.

ANABOLISM. Part of *metabolism* (q.v.), comprising the building-up of complex substances from simpler material, with absorption and storage of energy.

ANAESTHETIC. Substance used in medicine to produce insensibility or loss of feeling.

ANALGESIC. Substance used in medicine to relieve pain.

ANALYSIS (chem.). Decomposition of substances into their elements or constituent parts; term usually applied to chemical or physical methods of determining the composition of substances. See *colorimetric, gravimetric, qualitative, quantitative, spectrum* and *volumetric analysis*.

ANALYTICAL GEOMETRY, co-ordinate geometry. Form of geometry based upon the use of *co-ordinates* (q.v.) to define positions in space.

ANASTIGMATIC LENS. Lens designed to correct *astigmatism* (q.v.).

ANATASE. Crystalline form of natural titanium dioxide, TiO_2.

ANEMOMETER. Instrument for measuring the speed of wind.

ANEROID. Without liquid. The *aneroid barometer* is an instrument for measuring atmospheric pressure; it consists of an exhausted metal box with a thin corrugated metal lid. Variations in atmospheric pressure cause changes in the displacement of the lid; this displacement is magnified and made to actuate a pointer moving over a scale by means of a system of delicate levers.

ANGLE. Formed by two lines (generally straight) meeting at a point. Measured in degrees, 360° being the angle traced by the complete revolution of a line OA about a point O until it returns to its original position, or in radians (see *circular measure*).

ÅNGSTRÖM UNIT, Å.Ū., tenth-metre. 10^{-10} metre, $\frac{1}{10000}$ *micron* (q.v.). Unit of length, especially for measurement of wave-lengths of light.

ANGULAR ACCELERATION. Rate of change of *angular velocity* (q.v.).

ANGULAR DISTANCE. Distance between two bodies, measured in terms of the angle subtended by them at the point of observation; used in astronomy.

ANGULAR VELOCITY. Rate of motion through an angle about an axis. Measured in degrees, radians or revolutions per unit time.

ANHYDRIDE. Anhydride of a substance is that which, when chemically combined with water, gives the substance. E.g. sulphur trioxide, SO_3, is the anhydride of sulphuric acid, H_2SO_4.

ANHYDRITE. Naturally occurring form of calcium sulphate, $CaSO_4$.

ANHYDROUS. Without water; often applied to salts without *water of crystallization* (q.v.).

ANILINE, phenylamine, aminobenzene. $C_6H_5NH_2$. Colourless oily liquid with a peculiar smell, b.p. 184·4° C. Made by the reduction of nitrobenzene, $C_6H_5NO_2$, which is obtained from benzene, C_6H_6, extracted from coal-tar. Used in the manufacture of many important products, including dyes, drugs and plastics.

ANILINE DYES. Organic dyestuffs prepared or chemically derived from *aniline* (q.v.).

ANIMAL CHARCOAL. Material containing 10% carbon and 90% inorganic matter, chiefly calcium phosphate, $Ca_3(PO_4)_2$, obtained by charring bones and other animal substances. Used as a decolorizing agent.

ANIMAL STARCH. See *glycogen*.

ANION. Negatively charged *ion* (q.v.); ion which, during *electrolysis* (q.v.) is attracted towards the anode.

ANISOTROPIC, aelotropic. Possessing different physical properties in different directions; e.g. certain crystals have a different *refractive index* (q.v.) in different directions.

ANNEALING. Very slow regulated cooling, especially of metals, to relieve strains set up during heating or other treatment.

ANNIHILATION RADIATION. On coming into collision, an electron and a positron can annihilate each other, with the emission of energy in the form of gamma-rays. See *mass-energy equation*.

ANNUAL VARIATION of *magnetic declination* (q.v.). Very small regular variation which the magnetic declination undergoes in the course of a year.

ANNULAR. Ringed. E.g. annular eclipse; annular space, i.e. the space between an inner and outer ring.

ANODE. Positive electrode. See *electrolysis*.

ANTENNA. See *aerial*.

ANTHRACENE. $C_{14}H_{10}$. White crystalline hydrocarbon with a blue fluorescence; often yellowish due to impurities. M.p. 217° C. Obtained from coal-tar; used in the manufacture of dyes.

ANTHRACITE. Hard form of coal, containing more carbon and far less *hydrocarbons* (q.v.) than other forms. Probably the oldest form of coal.

ANTI-. Prefix denoting opposite, against. E.g. *antichlor* (q.v.).

ANTIBIOTICS. Chemical substances produced by micro-organisms such as moulds and bacteria, which are capable of destroying bacteria or preventing their growth. Numerous antibiotics have been discovered in recent years, including *penicillin* and *streptomycin* (q.v.).

ANTICHLOR. Substance used to remove chlorine from materials after bleaching. E.g. sodium thiosulphate, $Na_2S_2O_3$.

ANTIDOTE. Remedy for a particular poison, which generally acts chemically upon the poison, thus neutralizing it, making it insoluble or otherwise rendering it harmless.

ANTIFEBRIN. *Acetanilide* (q.v.).

ANTI-FREEZE. Substance added to water in radiators of motor-car engines in order to lower the freezing point of the water. Ethylene glycol, $CH_2OH.CH_2OH$, is frequently used.

ANTIMONY. Sb. (Stibium.) Element. A.W. 121·76. At. No. 51. Brittle crystalline silvery-white metal, S.G. 6·68, m.p. 630° C., expands on solidifying. Occurs as the element, oxide and sulphide (stibnite, Sb_2S_3). Extracted from its ores by roasting the ore and reducing with carbon. Used in *type metal* (q.v.).

ANTINODES. Points of maximum displacement in a series of stationary waves. Two similar and equal wave-trains travelling with equal velocities in opposite directions along a straight line give rise to antinodes and *nodes* alternately along the line. The antinodes are separated from their adjacent nodes by a distance corresponding to a quarter of the *wave-length* (q.v.) of the wave motions.

ANTIPYRETIC, febrifuge. Substance used medically to lower the body temperature.

ANTISEPTIC. Preventing the growth of bacteria.

APATITE. Natural phosphate and fluoride of calcium, $CaF_2.3Ca_3(PO_4)_2$. Used in the manufacture of fertilizers.

APERTURE. Opening; in optical instruments, the size of the opening admitting light to the instrument. In spherical mirrors or lenses, the diameter of the reflecting or refracting surface.

APLANATIC. If any reflecting or refracting surface produces a point image at *B* of a point object at *A* irrespective of the angle at which the rays fall on the surface from A, then that surface is said to be *aplanatic* with respect to A and B.

APOGEE. The moon is said to be *in apogee* when it is at its greatest distance from the Earth.

APOTHECARIES' FLUID MEASURE.

$$1 \text{ minim} = 0.0591 \text{ c.c. (about 1 drop).}$$
$$60 \text{ minims} = 1 \text{ fluid drachm} = 3.55 \text{ c.c.}$$
$$8 \text{ fl. dr.} = 1 \text{ fluid ounce} = 28.41 \text{ c.c.}$$
$$20 \text{ fl. oz.} = 1 \text{ pint} = 568 \text{ c.c.}$$

APOTHECARIES' WEIGHTS. See *Troy weight*.

APPARENT DEPTH of a liquid viewed from above is less than the true depth, owing to the *refraction* (q.v.) of light. The ratio of the true depth to the apparent depth is equal to the refractive index of the liquid.

APPARENT EXPANSION. Relative expansion of a liquid. See *expansion of liquids*.

AQ. (chem.). Symbol denoting water; e.g. H_2SO_4.aq. is aqueous sulphuric acid.

AQUA FORTIS. Concentrated nitric acid, HNO_3.

AQUA REGIA. Mixture of concentrated nitric and hydrochloric acids (1 to 4 by volume). Highly corrosive liquid which dissolves gold and attacks many substances unaffected by other reagents. Turns orange-yellow owing to the formation of nitrosyl chloride, $NOCl$, and free chlorine.

AQUAMARINE. Bluish form of *beryl* (q.v.).

AQUEOUS. Watery. Usually applied to solutions, indicating that water is the solvent.

ARC, ELECTRIC. Highly luminous discharge, accompanied by a temperature of over 3000° C.; produced when a current of electricity flows through a gap between two electrodes, the current being carried by the vapour of the electrode; e.g. the common carbon arc is formed between two carbon rods, and constitutes a very bright source of light. In the same way metallic arcs are formed between two similar metallic surfaces.

ARC LAMP. Technical application of the electric *arc* (q.v.) to produce a very bright light. The *carbon arc* lamp consists of an electric arc between two carbon electrodes, with suitable automatic mechanism for striking the arc and drawing the carbons closer together as they are vaporized away. The *mercury arc* lamp is important for laboratory use.

ARC OF CIRCLE. See *circle*.

ARCHIMEDES' PRINCIPLE. The apparent loss in weight of a body totally or partially immersed in a liquid is equal to the weight of the liquid displaced. See *buoyancy*.

ARE. Metric unit of area, 1 square dekametre, 100 square metres, 119.60 square yards.

AREA. Measure of surface; measured in 'square' units of length, e.g. square inches.

AREA, BRITISH UNITS.

$$1 \text{ square inch} = 6\cdot4516 \text{ square cm.}$$
$$144 \text{ sq. ins.} = 1 \text{ sq. foot} = 929 \text{ sq. cm.}$$
$$9 \text{ sq. ft.} = 1 \text{ sq. yard.}$$
$$30\tfrac{1}{4} \text{ sq. yds.} = 1 \text{ sq. pole.}$$
$$40 \text{ sq. pls.} = 1 \text{ rood.}$$
$$484 \text{ sq. yds.} = 1 \text{ sq. chain.}$$
$$4 \text{ roods} = 4840 \text{ sq. yds.} = 1 \text{ acre.}$$
$$640 \text{ acres} = 1 \text{ sq. mile} = 2\cdot590 \text{ sq. km.}$$

AREA, METRIC UNITS.

$$1 \text{ sq. centimetre} = \cdot155 \text{ sq. inch.}$$
$$10,000 \text{ sq. cm.} = 1 \text{ centare, } 1 \text{ sq. metre.}$$
$$100 \text{ sq. m.} = 1 \text{ are.}$$
$$100 \text{ ares} = 1 \text{ hectare, } 2\cdot4711 \text{ acres.}$$
$$100 \text{ hectares} = 1 \text{ sq. kilometre, } \cdot3861 \text{ sq. mile.}$$

ARGENTIFEROUS. Silver-bearing.

ARGENTITE, silver glance. Natural silver sulphide, Ag_2S. Important ore of silver.

ARGOL, tartar. Reddish-brown crystalline deposit consisting mainly of potassium hydrogen tartrate, which separates in wine-vats.

ARGON. A. Element. A.W. 39·944. At. No. 18. *Inert gas* (q.v.). Occurs in the air (0·8%). Used for filling electric lamps.

ARITHMETICAL PROGRESSION. *Series* (q.v.) of quantities in which each term differs from the preceding by a constant *common difference*. For an A.P. in which the first term is a, the common difference d, the number of terms n, the last term L, and the sum of n terms S,

$$S = \frac{n}{2}\{2a + (n-1)d\}$$
$$S = \frac{n}{2}(a + L)$$
$$L = a + (n-1)d.$$

ARMATURE. The coil or coils, usually rotating, of a *dynamo* (q.v.) or *electric motor* (q.v.).

AROMATIC COMPOUNDS (chem.). Organic compounds derived from *benzene* (q.v.).

ARSENIC. As. Element. A.W. 74·91. At. No. 33. Steel-grey brittle crystalline substance. Occurs combined with sulphur as realgar, As_2S_2, orpiment, As_2S_3; with oxygen as white arsenic, As_2O_3; with some metals and as the element. Compounds are very poisonous, and are used in medicine and for destroying pests.

ARSENICAL PYRITES. *Mispickel* (q.v.).

ARSENIOUS OXIDE, white arsenic, 'arsenic'. As_2O_3.

ARSINE. Hydrogen arsenide, AsH_3; intensely poisonous colourless gas.

ARTIFICIAL RADIOACTIVITY. *Radioactivity* (q.v.) induced in stable elements by bombarding them with *neutrons* (q.v.) or high-energy charged particles. The initial products of *nuclear fission* (q.v.) are also artificially radioactive. Artificially radioactive elements emit beta-and/or gamma-rays.

ARTIFICIAL SILK. Obsolete term for *rayon* (q.v.).

ARYL RADICALS. *Radicals* (q.v.) or groups of atoms derived from *aromatic compounds* (q.v.); e.g. phenyl, C_6H_5.

ASBESTOS. Name given to a variety of fibrous silicate minerals, mainly calcium magnesium silicate. Used as a heat-insulating material and for fire-proof fabrics.

ASCORBIC ACID, vitamin C. $C_6H_8O_6$. White crystalline solid, m.p. 122° C., occurs in fruits and vegetables. See *vitamins*.

ASEPTIC. Free from bacteria.

ASH. Incombustible residue left after the complete burning of any substance. Consists of the non-volatile, inorganic constituents of the substance.

ASPHALT. Black, semi-solid sticky substance composed of *bitumen* (q.v.) with mineral matter. Consists mainly of complex hydrocarbons. Occurs naturally in asphalt lakes or in deposits mixed with sandstone and limestone; made artificially by adding mineral matter to bitumen. Used in road-making and building.

ASPIRATOR. Apparatus for drawing a current of air or other gas through a liquid.

ASPIRIN, acetyl-salicylic acid. $CH_3COOC_6H_4COOH$. White solid, m.p. 133° C. Used in medicine as an *antipyretic* (q.v.) and *analgesic* (q.v.).

ASSAYING. Chemical estimation of metals in ores.

ASSOCIATION (chem.). Under certain conditions, e.g. in solution, the molecules of some substances *associate* into groups of several molecules, thus causing the substance to have an abnormally high molecular weight.

ASTATIC COILS. Arrangement used in sensitive electrical instruments; coils so arranged that the resultant external magnetic field produced by them when an electric current passes through them, and the electro-motive force induced in them by an external magnetic field, are zero.

ASTATIC GALVANOMETER. A type of moving magnet *galvanometer* (q.v.), in which two equal small magnets are arranged parallel but in opposition at the centres of two oppositely wound coils, the system being suspended by a fine torsion fibre. Since the resulting magnetic moment is zero, the Earth's magnetic field exerts no controlling *torque* (q.v.) on the moving system. Instead, the restoring torque is supplied by the suspending fibre and is made very small by using a fine quartz fibre, so making the sensitivity of the galvanometer very large.

ASTATIC PAIR of magnets. Arrangement of magnets used in *astatic galvanometers* (q.v.).

ASTATINE. At. The element At. No. 85, the last member of the *halogen* (q.v.) group.

ASTEROIDS, planetoids, minor planets. A belt of some 1500 small bodies, none exceeding 300 miles in diameter, rotating round the Sun in an orbit between those of Mars and Jupiter.

ASTIGMATISM. Defect of lenses (including the eye) caused by the curvature being different in two mutually perpendicular planes; thus rays in one plane may be in focus while those in the other are out of focus, producing distortion. Astigmatism of the eye is corrected by the use of cylindrical lenses.

ASTRO-COMPASS. Instrument for determining direction relative to the stars. Unaffected by the errors to which magnetic or gyro compasses are subject; used to determine the errors of such instruments.

ASTRONOMY. Scientific study of the heavenly bodies, their motion, relative positions and nature.

ASYMMETRIC. Not possessing *symmetry* (q.v.), having no point, line or plane about which it is symmetrical.

ASYMMETRIC CARBON ATOM. A carbon atom in a molecule of an organic compound with four different atoms or groups attached to its four valencies. Such a grouping permits of two different arrangements in space, leading to the existence of optical isomers. See *stereoisomerism*.

ASYMPTOTE. A line approaching a curve, but never reaching it within a finite distance.

-ATE. Suffix used in the naming of chemical compounds; in the case of salts, denoting a salt of the corresponding *-ic* acid; e.g. sulphate from sulphuric acid.

ATHERMANCY. Property of being opaque to radiant heat; i.e. of absorbing heat radiations.

ATMOLYSIS. Separation of a mixture of gases through the walls of a porous vessel by taking advantage of the different rates of *diffusion* (q.v.) of the constituents.

ATMOSPHERE. Gaseous envelope surrounding the Earth (or other heavenly body).

ATMOSPHERE, composition of the. This varies very slightly in different localities and according to altitude. Volume composition of dry air at sea-level (average values): nitrogen, 78·08%; oxygen, 20·95%; argon, ·93%; carbon dioxide, ·03%; neon, ·0018%; helium, ·0005%; krypton, ·0001%; xenon, ·00001%. Air generally contains, in addition to the above, water vapour, hydrocarbons, hydrogen peroxide, sulphur compounds and dust particles in small and very variable amounts.

ATMOSPHERE, the normal or standard. Unit of pressure. That pressure which will support a column of mercury 760 mm. high (29·92 inches) at $0°$ C., sea-level and latitude $45°$. 1 normal atmosphere $= 1\cdot0132$ bars $= 14\cdot72$ lb./sq. in. (approx.). Atmospheric pressure fluctuates about this value from day to day.

ATMOSPHERICS. Electrical discharges which take place in the atmosphere, causing crackling sounds in radio receivers.

ATOM. Smallest portion of an element which can take part in a chemical reaction; ultimate particle of matter as commonly understood. See *atom, structure of; atomic theory*.

ATOM, STRUCTURE OF. The atom consists of a positively charged central core, the *nucleus*, about which negatively charged *electrons* rotate in various orbits. Almost the whole mass of the atom resides in the nucleus, which is composed of positively charged *protons* and neutral *neutrons*. The proton and the neutron each have a mass nearly equal to that of the hydrogen atom, whereas the mass of the electron is only $\frac{1}{1840}$ that of the hydrogen atom. The charge of the proton is numerically equal to that of the electron, but is of opposite sign. Thus in the neutral atom the number of electrons rotating in the electronic envelope is the same as the number of protons in the nucleus. The chemical behaviour of an atom is determined by the external electronic system, and hence it is the *atomic number* (q.v.) of the atom which determines its chemical properties and characterizes the particular element to which the atom belongs. Atoms of the same element, i.e. of identical atomic number, but differing in the number of neutrons present in the nucleus, are called *isotopes* (q.v.) of that element. The effective radius of a nucleus is approx. 10^{-12} cm., that of the electron approx. 10^{-13} cm., and the radius of the atom as a whole, approx. 10^{-8} cm. Thus the atom has an extremely open structure.

Removal or addition of outer electrons causes the atom to become an *ion* (q.v.) by acquiring an electric charge by the alteration in the number of electrons, which previously balanced the charge on the nucleus. Chemical combination takes place by the transfer or sharing of electrons between combining atoms. See *valency, electronic theory of*.

When a particular isotope of an element is being considered, the following notation is used. To the chemical symbol of the element, the *mass number* of the isotope is added as a superscript. The mass number is given by $n + p$, where n is the number of neutrons and p the number of protons present in the nucleus. The atomic number of the element, p, may be added as a subscript; e.g. $_1H^1$, $_6C^{12}$, $_7N^{14}$, $_{79}Au^{197}$ are the most abundant isotopes of the elements hydrogen, carbon, nitrogen and gold; $_{92}U^{233}$, $_{92}U^{234}$, $_{92}U^{235}$, $_{92}U^{238}$ and $_{92}U^{239}$ are isotopes of uranium.

ATOMIC BOMB. Bomb which makes use of the devastating effect produced when a large amount of *atomic energy* (q.v.) is released in the shortest possible time. Similar in principle to the *atomic pile* (q.v.), both being chain reactors making use of *nuclear fission* (q.v.) to obtain large quantities of energy. The bomb, however, is so designed that the largest possible number of fissions, and consequently the greatest possible energy release, occurs in less than $\frac{1}{100,000}$th of a second. Consists essentially of two masses of suitable fissile material, e.g. the isotope of uranium, $_{92}U^{235}$, or of plutonium, $_{94}Pu^{239}$, each less than a certain critical mass but together greater than that mass, which can be brought into intimate contact very rapidly. A single fission at the moment of contact sets off the whole chain of fissions and so produces the tremendous explosion.

ATOMIC CONSTANTS. Electronic charge, $e = 4.803 \times 10^{-10}$ e.s.u.

Electronic mass, $m = 0.9107 \times 10^{-27}$ gm.

Planck's constant, $h = 6.610 \times 10^{-27}$ erg. sec.

Velocity of light, $c = 2.9978 \times 10^{10}$ cm./sec.

ATOMIC ENERGY. Energy released from an atomic nucleus at the expense of its mass. By the equivalence of mass and energy (see *mass-energy equation*) any mass m may, in certain circumstances, be converted into energy E, given by the relation $E = mc^2$, where c is the velocity of light. As c is very great, the amount of energy made available by the disappearance of 1 gm. of matter is extremely large.

ATOMIC HEAT. The numerical product of the *atomic weight* (q.v.) and the specific heat (see *heat, specific*) of an element. Dulong and Petit's law states that the atomic heat of all solid elements is approx. 6 calories per gram-atom per degree. The law is obeyed by many elements at ordinary temperatures, but at lower temperatures the atomic heat of all elements falls below this value, tending to zero as absolute zero of temperature is approached.

ATOMIC MASS UNIT. Unit used for expressing the masses of individual *isotopes* (q.v.) of elements. Defined so that the most abundant oxygen isotope, $_8O^{16}$, has a mass of 16 atomic mass units. Approximately equal to 1.66×10^{-24} gm.

ATOMIC NUMBER. The number of electrons rotating round the nucleus of the neutral atom of an element, or the number of protons in the nucleus. (See *atom, structure of.*)

ATOMIC PILE, nuclear reactor. Structure consisting of fissile material, e.g. uranium, together with a suitable moderator, e.g. carbon or heavy water, so arranged in a lattice that energy is continuously released in a controlled manner, as the result of *nuclear fission* (q.v.). A suitably designed pile can also be used for the production of plutonium, an element of great importance in connection with the *atomic bomb* (q.v.). In the atomic pile, the uranium atom is excited by capturing a neutron, and undergoes fission. Apart from the elements of approximately equal mass formed as a result of this disintegration, an average of two or more neutrons are also emitted. These neutrons produce further fissions in the uranium atoms, and a *chain reaction* develops. This is controlled by inserting neutron absorbers into the pile, which absorb all neutrons in excess of the number required to maintain the reaction at a constant level. The moderator rapidly slows down the fast neutrons emitted by the fission process, so increasing their chance of capture to produce further fissions.

ATOMIC THEORY. Hypothesis as to the structure of matter, foreshadowed by Democritus, put forward as a formal explanation of chemical facts and laws by Dalton in the beginning of the nineteenth century. Assumes that matter is made up of small indivisible particles called atoms; the atoms of any one element are identical in all respects, but differ from those of other elements at least in weight. Chemical compounds are formed by the union of atoms of different elements in simple numerical proportions. Modern views on the structure of the atom (see *atom, structure of*) diverge considerably from Dalton's simple hypothesis, but it is still of value in affording a simple explanation of the laws of *chemical combination* (q.v.).

ATOMIC WEIGHT. Weight of an atom of an element, expressed on a scale in which the weight of the oxygen atom is exactly 16.

ATOMIC WEIGHT DETERMINATION. Accurate determinations of atomic weights of elements have been carried out mainly by the determination of the combining weights or equivalents of the elements; the atomic weights being simple multiples of these. The correct multiples may be obtained by any of the following methods:

1. The use of *Dulong and Petit's Law* (q.v.).
2. Use of the position of the element in the *Periodic Table* (q.v.).
3. For gaseous elements, using the ratio of the specific heats (see *heat, specific, of gases*) of the gas to ascertain the number of atoms in the molecule, the molecular weight having previously been determined by a knowledge of the *vapour density* (q.v.).
4. By comparison of a compound of the element with an isomorphous (see *isomorphism*) compound consisting of elements of known atomic weights.

ATROPINE. $C_{17}H_{23}NO_3$. Member of the *alkaloids* (q.v.). Colourless crystalline insoluble substance, m.p. 115° C.; extremely poisonous, has a powerful effect upon the nervous system, used in medicine to dilate the pupil of the eye. Occurs in the deadly nightshade and henbane.

AUDIBILITY, LIMITS OF. The limits of frequency of sound-waves which are audible as sound to the human ear. The lowest is approximately 30 vibrations per sec., corresponding to a very deep vibrating rumble, and the highest in the region of 30,000, corresponding to a shrill hiss.

AUER METAL. *Pyrophoric alloy* (q.v.) of 65% *misch metal* (q.v.) (a mixture of cerium and other metals) and 35% iron. Used as 'flint' in lighters.

AURIFEROUS. Gold-bearing.

AURORA BOREALIS, Northern lights. A display of coloured light streamers and glows, mainly red and green, visible in the regions of the North and South Poles. Probably caused by streams of electrified particles from the Sun; most prominent when large *sun-spots* (q.v.) are observed.

AUSTENITE. Solid solution of carbon or of iron carbide in the *gamma*-form of iron; normally stable only at high temperatures, but may be preserved at normal temperatures by certain alloying elements or by rapid cooling.

AUTOCLAVE. Thick-walled vessel with a tightly fitting lid, in which substances may be heated above 100° C. by steam under pressure.

AUXINS, phytamins, plant hormones. Substances promoting or directing the growth of plants.

AVOGADRO'S LAW. Avogadro's hypothesis. Equal volumes of all gases contain equal numbers of molecules under the same conditions of temperature and pressure.

AVOGADRO'S NUMBER. The number of molecules in a *gram-molecule* (q.v.) or of atoms in a gram-atom of a substance; $6 \cdot 02 \times 10^{23}$.

AVOIRDUPOIS WEIGHTS. System of weights used in the English-speaking countries. See *weight, British units of*.

AXIS. An imaginary line about which a given body or system is considered to rotate.

AXIS OF MIRROR. See *mirrors, spherical*.

AXIS OF SYMMETRY. Line about which a given figure is symmetrical; e.g. the diameter of a circle.

AZEOTROPIC MIXTURE, constant boiling mixture. A mixture of two or more liquids which distils at a given constant temperature and has a constant composition, at a given pressure.

AZIMUTH of a heavenly body. The angle at the *zenith* (q.v.) between the meridian and the vertical circle through the body. Measured by the arc intercepted by these two circles on the horizon.

AZLON. Term proposed for all artificial textile fibres made from regenerated proteins.

AZO-DYES. Class of organic dyestuffs, mainly red or yellow, derived from azo-benzene, $C_6H_5N:NC_6H_5$.

AZO GROUP. The bivalent group —N : N—.

AZOTE. Former name for *nitrogen* (q.v.).

AZURITE. Natural basic copper carbonate, blue in colour. $2CuCO_3 . Cu(OH)_2$.

B

BABBITT METAL. A class of alloys with a high proportion of tin, and small amounts of copper and antimony. Part of the tin may be replaced by lead. Used for bearings.

BACK E.M.F. OF CELL. When the poles of a *cell* (q.v.) become polarized (see *polarization, electrolytic*) an *E.M.F.* (q.v.) is set up opposing the natural E.M.F. of the cell.

BACK E.M.F. OF ELECTRIC MOTOR. *E.M.F.* (q.v.) set up in the coil of an electric motor, opposing the current flowing through the coil, when the *armature* (q.v.) rotates.

BACTERICIDE. Substance which kills bacteria.

BAKELITE. (Trade name.) *Thermosetting* (q.v.) plastic material made from *phenol* (q.v.) and *formaldehyde* (q.v.).

BAKING POWDER. Mixture which produces carbon dioxide gas, CO_2, on wetting or heating, thus causing the formation of bubbles in the dough and making it 'rise'. Usually contains sodium bicarbonate, $NaHCO_3$, and tartaric acid or *cream of tartar* (q.v.).

BAKING SODA. Sodium bicarbonate, $NaHCO_3$.

BALANCE. Apparatus for weighing. In principle consists of a lever with two equal arms, with a pan suspended from the end of each arm. Masses placed in the pans are subject to pulls of gravity; when these forces are equal, as indicated by the beam being horizontal, the masses themselves must be equal. Sensitive balances have beam and pans poised on knife-edges of agate resting on agate surfaces. An accurate balance will weigh to the nearest ·0001 gm.; more sensitive balances are available for special work.

BALANCED REACTION. See *chemical equilibrium*.

BALATA. A natural rubber-like material very similar to *gutta-percha* (q.v.).

BALLISTIC GALVANOMETER. Instrument for measuring the total quantity of electricity passing through a circuit due to a momentary current. Any galvanometer may be used ballistically provided that its period of oscillation is long compared with the time during which the current flows.

BALLISTICS. The study of *projectiles* (q.v.).

BALMER SERIES. The visible *spectrum* (q.v.) of hydrogen. Consists of a series of sharp distinct lines, the wave-lengths, λ, of which may be represented by the formula $\dfrac{1}{\lambda} = A\left(\dfrac{1}{2^2} - \dfrac{1}{n^2}\right)$; $n = 3, 4, 5$, etc., A is a constant.

BAND SPECTRUM. Emission or absorption *spectrum* (q.v.) which consists of a number of fluted bands each having one sharp edge. Each band is composed of a large number of closely spaced lines. Band spectra arise from molecules.

BAR. Unit of pressure in C.G.S. units; a pressure of 10^6 dynes per sq. cm. Equivalent to a pressure of 76 cm. of mercury.

BARBITURATES. Class of organic compounds derived from barbituric acid (malonyl urea), $CO(NH.CO)_2CH_2$. Many of these compounds have a powerful and sometimes dangerous soporific effect. Used in medicine.

BARFF PROCESS. Prevention of rusting of iron by the action of steam upon the surface of the red-hot metal, resulting in a surface coating of black oxide of iron, Fe_3O_4.

BARIUM. Ba. Element. A.W. 137·36. At. No. 56. Silvery-white soft metal, tarnishes readily in air. S.G. 3·5, m.p. 850° C. Occurs as barytes, $BaSO_4$, and as the carbonate, $BaCO_3$. Compounds resemble those of *calcium* (q.v.) but are poisonous. Compounds are used in the manufacture of paints, glass and fireworks.

BARKHAUSEN EFFECT. Effect observed when a ferromagnetic substance is magnetized by a slowly increasing magnetic field; the magnetization does not take place continuously, but in a series of small steps. The effect is due to orientation of magnetic domains present in the substance.

BAROGRAPH. Instrument used in *meteorology* (q.v.), recording on paper the variations in atmospheric pressure over a period of time.

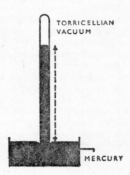

TORRICELLIAN VACUUM

MERCURY

FIG. 1

BAROMETER. (See also *aneroid* barometer.) Instrument for measuring atmospheric pressure. Consists of a long tube closed at the upper end, filled with mercury and inverted in a vessel containing mercury; the vertical height of the mercury column which the atmospheric pressure is able at any time to support being taken as the atmospheric pressure at that time. See Fig. 1.

BARYTA. Barium oxide. BaO. White powder.

BARYTES, heavy spar. Natural barium sulphate, $BaSO_4$. White insoluble solid.

BASALT. Rock of volcanic origin, chemically resembling *felspar* (q.v.).

BASE (chem.). Substance which reacts with an acid to form a salt and water only; substance which has a tendency to accept *protons* (q.v.); substance which yields *hydroxyl ions* (q.v.) if dissolved in water.

BASE EXCHANGE, CATION EXCHANGE. See *ion exchange*.

BASE METALS. In contradistinction to the *noble metals* (q.v.), metals which corrode, tarnish, or oxidize on exposure to air, moisture or heat.

BASIC (chem.). Of the nature of a *base* (q.v.); opposite to acidic; reacting chemically with acids to form salts.

BASIC DYES. Group of *dyes* (q.v.) which are salts of organic bases, and are used for dyeing wool and natural silk, especially if specially bright shades are needed.

BASIC SALT. Salt which has been formed by the partial neutralization of a base; consists of the normal salt combined with a definite molecular proportion of the base. E.g. white lead, basic lead carbonate, $2PbCO_3.Pb(OH)$.

BASIC SLAG. An impure mixture of tetracalcium phosphate, $Ca_4P_2O_9$, calcium silicate, $CaSiO_3$, lime, CaO, and ferric oxide, Fe_2O_3. By-product of steel manufacture; its high phosphorus content makes it a valuable fertilizer.

BATH SALTS. The main constituent is generally sodium sesquicarbonate, $Na_2CO_3.NaHCO_3.2H_2O$, or some other soluble sodium salt to soften the water. See *hard water*.

BATHYMETRY. Measurement of depth, especially of the sea.

BATTERY. A number of primary or secondary cells arranged in series or parallel. In series, they give a multiple of the E.M.F. of the cell; in parallel, they give the same E.M.F. as the cell, but have a greater capacity, i.e. a given current can be supplied for a longer period. The common 'dry batteries' usually consist of *Leclanché cells* (q.v.).

BAUMÉ SCALE. A scale of specific gravity of liquids.

$$\text{Degrees Baumé} = \frac{144\cdot3(\text{S.G.} - 1)}{\text{S.G.}}; \text{S.G.} = \frac{144\cdot3}{144\cdot3 - \text{Degrees Baumé}}.$$

BAUXITE. Natural hydrated aluminium oxide, $Al_2O_3.xH_2O$. The most important ore of *aluminium* (q.v.).

BAUXITE CEMENT, ciment fondu. A rapid-hardening cement consisting mainly of calcium aluminate; made from bauxite and lime in an electric furnace.

BEAM (phys.). *Electromagnetic waves* (q.v.) (light, wireless, etc.) radiated in a particular direction.

BEAM TRANSMISSION. Radio transmission in which the electromagnetic wireless waves are sent in a particular direction in a beam instead of being radiated in all directions.

BEARING (math.). The direction of a point B from a fixed point A; stated either in terms of the angle the line AB makes with the line running due North and South through A (e.g. 20° East of North); or in terms of the angle the line AB makes with the line running due North through A, considered in a clockwise direction.

BEATS (phys.). A periodic increase and decrease in loudness which is heard when two notes of nearly the same *frequency* (q.v.) are sounded simultaneously. Caused by *interference* (q.v.) of sound-waves; the number of beats produced per second is equal to the difference in frequencies of the two notes.

BECKMANN THERMOMETER. Sensitive thermometer for measuring small differences or changes in temperature. The quantity of mercury in the bulb can be varied by causing it to overflow into a reservoir at the top, thus enabling the thermometer to be used over various ranges of temperature. The scale covers 6–7 degrees and is graduated to ·01 degree.

BEET SUGAR, sucrose. $C_{12}H_{22}O_{11}$. Obtained from the sugar beet; chemically identical with cane sugar.

BEL. Ten *decibels* (q.v.).

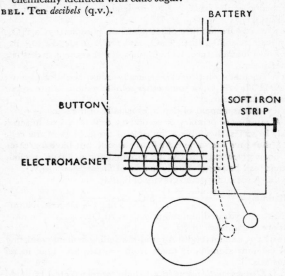

FIG. 2.

BELL, ELECTRIC. Simple device making use of the magnetic effect of an electric current. Pressing the button causes a current, provided by a Leclanché cell, to flow through a small electromagnet. This then attracts a piece of soft iron attached to a hammer, causing the latter to strike the gong of the bell. The movement of the iron breaks the circuit; the current ceases to flow through the electromagnet, and the iron and attached hammer spring back into their original position, thus closing the circuit again; this process continues as long as the button is depressed. See Fig. 2.

BELL METAL. Alloy of copper (60–85%) and tin.

BENTONITE. A clay-like material similar to *fuller's earth* (q.v.).

BENZENE, benzol. C_6H_6. *Hydrocarbon* (q.v.) found in coal-tar. Colourless liquid, b.p. 80·1° C. Used as a solvent, in motor fuel, and in the manufacture of numerous organic compounds.

BENZINE. Mixture of hydrocarbons of the *paraffin* (q.v.) series, boiling

50–65° C. Used for dry cleaning and as a solvent.

BENZOL, benzole. *Benzene* (q.v.).

BENZYL. The univalent radical —$CH_2.C_6H_5$.

BERGIUS PROCESS. A process for the manufacture of oil from coal. Coal, made into a paste with heavy oil, is heated with hydrogen under a pressure of 250 atmospheres to a temperature of 450–470° C., in the presence of a *catalyst* (q.v.). The carbon of the coal reacts with the hydrogen to give a mixture of various *hydrocarbons* (q.v.).

BERKELIUM. Bk. *Transuranic element* (q.v.). At. No. 97.

BERTHOLLIDE COMPOUNDS. Chemical compounds the composition of which does not conform to a simple ratio of atoms in the molecule.

BERYL. Natural beryllium aluminium silicate, $3BeO.Al_2O_3.6SiO_2$.

BERYLLIUM, glucinum. Be. Element. A.W. 9·013, At. No. 4. Hard white metal, S.G. 1·85, m.p. 1350° C. Occurs as *beryl* (q.v.), from which it is obtained by electrolysis. Used for light, corrosion-resisting alloys.

BESSEMER PROCESS. A process for making steel from cast iron. Molten iron from the *blast furnace* (q.v.) is run into the Bessemer converter, a large egg-shaped vessel with holes below. Through these, air is blown into the molten metal, and the carbon is oxidized. The requisite amount of *spiegel* (q.v.) is then added to introduce the correct amount of carbon for the type of steel required.

BETA PARTICLES, β-particles. Term applied to swiftly moving *electrons* (q.v.), β^-, and *positrons* (q.v.), β^+, when emitted by radioactive substances.

BETA RAYS, β-rays. Stream of beta particles; possess greater penetrating power than *alpha rays* (q.v.) and are emitted with velocities in some cases exceeding 98% of the velocity of light.

BETATRON. Apparatus for accelerating *electrons* (q.v.) to very high energies. The electric field induced by a time-varying magnetic field provides the accelerating force. The electrons move in stable circular orbits in an evacuated 'doughnut'-shaped chamber, perpendicular to the plane of which the varying magnetic field is applied.

BI-. Prefix denoting two; in chemical nomenclature indicating an *acid salt* (q.v.) of a *dibasic acid* (q.v.). E.g. sodium bisulphate, $NaHSO_4$.

BICARBONATE. *Acid salt* (q.v.) of carbonic acid, H_2CO_3; carbonic acid in which half the acidic hydrogen has been replaced by a metal. E.g. sodium bicarbonate, $NaHCO_3$.

BICHROMATE OF POTASH. $K_2Cr_2O_7$. See *potassium dichromate*.

BILLION. Million million, 10^{12} (British); thousand million, 10^9 (American).

BINARY COMPOUND. A chemical compound of two elements only. Denoted by the suffix -ide; e.g. calcium carbide, CaC_2.

BINOCULAR. Any optical instrument designed for the simultaneous use of both eyes; e.g. binocular field-glasses.

BINOMIAL. Mathematical expression consisting of the sum or difference of two terms; e.g. $a^2 - 3b$.

BINOMIAL THEOREM. The expansion of

$$(x + y)^n = x^n + nx^{n-1}y + \frac{n(n-1)}{\lfloor 2}x^{n-2}y^2 + \ldots + y^n,$$

n being a positive integer. In general, for n not a positive integer, the following expression is valid if the numerical value of x is less than unity: $(1 + x)^n = 1 + nx + \frac{n(n-1)}{\lfloor 2} x^2 + \ldots$ to ∞ .

BIOCHEMISTRY. The chemistry of living matter.

BIOLOGY. The science of life.

BIOMETRY. The application of mathematical and statistical methods to the study of biology.

BIOPHYSICS. The application of physics to the study of biology.

BI-PRISM. Optical device for obtaining *interference* (q.v.) fringes; consists of two acute-angled prisms placed base to base.

BIRKELAND AND EYDE PROCESS. Process for the fixation of atmospheric nitrogen (see *fixation of nitrogen*), becoming obsolete. Nitrogen and oxygen from the atmosphere are made to combine to form nitric oxide, NO, by the action of an electric arc.

BISECTION. Division into two equal parts.

BISECTOR. Line dividing into two equal parts.

BISMUTH. Bi. Element. A.W. 209·00. At. No. 83. White crystalline metal with a reddish tinge. S.G. 9·8; m.p. 271°. Brittle, rather poor conductor of heat and electricity. Expands on solidifying. Occurs as the metal, or as the oxide, Bi_2O_3. Extracted by roasting the ore and heating with coal. Used in alloys of low melting point (see *Rose's metal, Wood's metal*); compounds used in medicine.

BITTERN (chem.). *Mother-liquor* (q.v.) remaining after the crystallization of common salt, NaCl, from sea-water. Source of compounds of magnesium, bromine and iodine.

BITUMEN. Term covering numerous mixtures of *hydrocarbons* (q.v.), more particularly solid or tarry mixtures, soluble in carbon disulphide.

BITUMINOUS. Containing, or yielding upon distillation, bitumen or tar.

BIVALENT, divalent. Having a *valency* (q.v.) of two.

BLACK ASH. Impure sodium carbonate obtained in the *Leblanc process* (q.v.).

BLACK BODY RADIATION. Full or complete *radiation* (q.v.); radiation of all frequencies, such as would be emitted by an ideal 'black body' which absorbs all radiations falling upon it. Such radiation is a function of the temperature only.

BLACK DAMP. Carbon dioxide (in coal mines).

BLACKLEAD, plumbago, graphite. Natural crystalline form of carbon. Soft grey-black solid; used for making vessels to resist high temperatures, in pencils, and as a lubricant.

BLANC FIXE. Artificial barium sulphate, $BaSO_4$. Used as an *extender* (q.v.) in the paint industry.

BLAST FURNACE. Furnace for the smelting of iron from iron oxide ores. Constructed of refractory bricks covered with steel plates. Charged from above with a mixture of the ore, limestone ($CaCO_3$) and coke. The coke is ignited at the bottom of the furnace by a blast of hot air; the carbon monoxide so produced reduces the iron oxide to iron, while the heat of the action decomposes the limestone into carbon dioxide and lime, CaO. The lime combines with the sand and other impurities in the ore to form a molten slag. The molten iron and the slag are tapped off at the bottom of the furnace, The resulting 'pig' iron or cast iron contains up to 4.5% carbon.

BLASTING GELATIN. Jelly-like mixture of *gun-cotton* (q.v.) with *nitro-glycerin* (q.v.). A very powerful explosive.

BLEACHING. Removing the colour from coloured materials by chemically changing the dyestuffs into colourless substances. *Bleaching powder* (q.v.) and other oxidizing agents, and sulphur dioxide and other reducing agents are often used.

BLEACHING POWDER, chloride of lime. Whitish powder, consisting mainly of calcium oxychloride, $CaOCl_2$, with water; prepared by the action of chlorine on slaked lime, $Ca(OH)_2$. The action of dilute acids liberates chlorine which acts as an oxidizing agent and so bleaches the material.

BLENDE. Natural zinc sulphide, ZnS.

BLOWN OIL. A thickened oil made by blowing air through a natural vegetable or animal oil.

BLOWPIPE. Device for producing a jet of flame by forcing an inflammable gas mixed with air or oxygen through a nozzle at high pressure.

BLUE VITRIOL, bluestone. Crystalline copper sulphate, $CuSO_4.5H_2O$. Used for spraying plants.

BLUE-PRINT, cyanotype. Device much used for reproducing electrical circuit diagrams, engineering designs, etc. Sensitive paper, coated with an organic ferric salt and potassium ferricyanide, $K_3Fe(CN)_6$, is used; the original drawing is placed over this and the whole exposed to light. The sensitive paper is then developed by washing with water; this gives an image of white lines on a blue background. The blue colour is caused by the reduction of the ferric salt to a ferrous salt by the action of light, and the interaction of the ferrous salt with the potassium ferricyanide to give Prussian Blue.

BLUESTONE. See *blue vitriol*.

BOARD OF TRADE UNIT, B.O.T. unit. Legal British unit of electrical energy, the kilowatt-hour. The work done when a rate of working of one *kilowatt* (q.v.) is maintained for one hour.

BOART. See *bort*.

BOG IRON ORE. Impure form of hydrated iron oxide, $Fe_2O_3.xH_2O$, found in bogs and marshes.

BOHR THEORY of hydrogen atom spectrum. Theory of the atom put forward by Bohr to explain the *line spectrum* (q.v.) observed for hydrogen (see *Balmer series*). Based on three postulates: 1. The electrons rotate in certain orbits round the nucleus of the atom without radiating energy in the form of electromagnetic waves (i.e. visible light, ultra-violet and infra-red rays). 2. These orbits are such that the angular momentum of the electron about the nucleus is an integral multiple of $h/2\pi$, where h = Planck's constant. 3. Emission or absorption or radiation occurs when an electron jumps from one of these so-called 'stationary' states of energy E_1 to another of energy E_2, the frequency ν of the emitted (or absorbed) light being given by $E_1 - E_2 = h\nu$. If E_1 is greater than E_2, light is emitted; conversely, light is absorbed. This theory has now been superseded by the application of *wave mechanics* (q.v.), which has shown that for the hydrogen atom spectrum, Bohr's theory is a very good approximation. Wave mechanics has the advantage of requiring no *ad hoc* assumptions and can deal more effectively with the problem of atoms with two or more electrons.

BOILED OIL. Linseed oil boiled with, or containing, a drying agent such as litharge, PbO. Used in paints.

BOILING, ebullition. The state of a liquid at its *boiling point* (q.v.) when the maximum vapour pressure of the liquid is equal to the external pressure to which the liquid is subject, and the liquid is freely converted into vapour.

BOILING POINT, b.p. of a liquid. The temperature at which the maximum vapour pressure of the liquid is equal to the external pressure; the temperature at which the liquid boils freely under that pressure. Boiling points are normally quoted for standard atmospheric pressure, i.e. 760 mm. of mercury.

BOLOMETER. Extremely sensitive instrument for measuring heat radiations. Consists essentially of two very thin, blackened platinum gratings, forming two arms of a *Wheatstone bridge* (q.v.) circuit. Radiant heat falling upon one of the gratings raises its electrical resistance, thus causing a deflection of the needle of a galvanometer in the circuit.

BOLTZMANN'S CONSTANT. $K = \dfrac{R}{N} = 1 \cdot 381 \times 10^{-16}$ erg. deg.$^{-1}$

where R = the gas constant $\left(\dfrac{PV}{T}\text{for 1 gm.-mol. of a perfect gas}\right)$

N = *Avogadro's number* (q.v.).

BOMB CALORIMETER. Strong metal vessel used for measuring *heats of reaction* (q.v.), especially heats of combustion; e.g. for determining the *calorific value* (q.v.) of a fuel. To do this, a known weight of the substance under test is burnt in the vessel, and by measuring the quantity of heat produced, the calorific value is calculated.

BOND, valency bond, linkage. Representation of a *valency* (q.v.) link by which one atom is attached to another in a chemical compound.

BONE ASH. Ash obtained by heating bones in air. Consists mainly of calcium phosphate, $Ca_3(PO_4)_2$.

BONE BLACK. *Animal charcoal* (q.v.).

BONE CHAR. See *animal charcoal.*

BONE OIL, Dippel's oil. Product obtained by the destructive distillation of bones. Dark, oily, evil-smelling liquid; source of *pyridine* (q.v.).

BORACIC ACID. *Boric acid* (q.v.).

BORAX. Sodium pyroborate, $Na_2B_4O_7.10H_2O$. White, soluble crystalline salt, occurs naturally as tincal. On heating, loses water and melts to a clear glass-like solid (see *borax bead test*). Used as an antiseptic, in fire-proofing, soldering, glass, ceramics and other industries.

BORAX BEAD TEST. Chemical test for the presence of certain metals. A bead of *borax* (q.v.) fused in a wire loop will react chemically with the salts of a number of metals, often producing colours which help to identify the metal; e.g. manganese compounds give a violet bead, cobalt a deep blue.

BORDEAUX MIXTURE. Mixture of copper sulphate (blue vitriol, $CuSO_4$), lime, CaO, and water. Used for spraying plants as a fungicide for plant diseases.

BORIC ACID, boracic acid. H_3BO_3. White crystalline soluble solid. Occurs naturally in volcanic regions; also manufactured from *borax* (q.v.). Used as a mild antiseptic and in various industries.

BORON. B. Element. A.W. 10·82. At. No. 5. Brown amorphous powder or yellow crystals; S.G. 2·3, m.p. 2300° C. Occurs as *borax* and *boric acid* (q.v.). Used for hardening steel.

BORT, boart. Impure or discoloured *diamond* (q.v.), useless as gem, but as hard as pure diamond, and used for drills, cutting tools, etc.

BOSCH PROCESS. Industrial process for the manufacture of hydrogen. *Water gas* (q.v.), a mixture of carbon monoxide and hydrogen, is mixed with steam and passed over a heated *catalyst* (q.v.). The steam reacts chemically with the carbon monoxide to give carbon dioxide, CO_2, and hydrogen. The CO_2 is then removed by dissolving it in water under pressure.

BOTANY. The scientific study of plants.

BOURDON GAUGE. Pressure gauge for steam boilers, etc. Depends on the tendency of a partly flattened curved tube to straighten out when under internal pressure.

BOYLE'S LAW. At a constant temperature, the volume of a given quantity of any gas is inversely proportional to the pressure upon the gas; i.e. $V \propto \dfrac{1}{p}$, or $PV =$ constant. True for a *perfect gas* (q.v.).

BRAKE HORSE-POWER. *Horse-power* (q.v.) of an engine measured by the degree of resistance offered by a brake; represents the useful horse-power that the engine can develop.

BRASS. Large class of alloys, consisting principally of copper and zinc.

BREWING. The making of beer. *Malt* (q.v.) is ground and mixed with water. In the resulting 'mash' chemical changes take place, the chief of which is the conversion of starch into *maltose* (q.v.), forming a sweetish liquid known as *wort*. This is boiled with the addition of hops. After cooling and removal of solids, yeast is added and *fermentation* (q.v.) occurs.

BREWSTER'S LAW. The tangent of the angle of *polarization* (q.v.) is numerically equal to the refractive index of the reflecting medium.

BRIGHTNESS. The brightness at any point of an extended source, in a given direction, is the quotient of the *luminous intensity* (q.v.) of a small element of the source containing the point, by the area of the element projected on to a plane perpendicular to the given direction. Measured in *candelas* (q.v.) per unit area.

BRIMSTONE. Sulphur fused into blocks or rolls.

BRINELL TEST. Test for the hardness of metals. A ball of chrome steel, or other hard material, of standard size, is pressed by a heavy load into the surface of the metal, and the diameter of the depression is measured.

BRITANNIA METAL. Alloy of variable composition, containing 80–90% tin, with some antimony and copper, and sometimes also zinc and lead.

BRITISH THERMAL UNIT. Quantity of heat required to raise the temperature of 1 lb. of water through 1° Fahrenheit. 252 *calories* (q.v.).

BROMIDE. Salt of hydrobromic acid, HBr; binary compound with bromine. 'Bromide' of pharmacy is potassium bromide, KBr.

BROMIDE PAPER. Photographic paper containing silver bromide, AgBr.

BROMINE. Br. Element. A.W. 79·916. At. No. 35. Dark red fuming liquid with a choking, irritating smell, b.p. 58·8° C. Occurs as magnesium bromide, $MgBr_2$, in *bittern* (q.v.) from sea-water; in the *Stassfurt deposits* (q.v.); in marine plants and animals and in some inland lakes. Used as a disinfectant and in the manufacture of some organic compounds. Compounds used in photography and medicine.

BRONZE. Class of alloys of copper and tin; term is also sometimes applied to alloys containing no tin, e.g. aluminium bronze, an alloy of copper and aluminium.

BROWNIAN MOVEMENT. Erratic zig-zag movements performed by microscopic particles in a *disperse phase* (q.v.); e.g. particles in suspension in a liquid or smoke particles in air. Caused by the continuous irregular bombardment of the particles by the molecules of the surrounding medium.

BRUNSWICK GREEN, cupric oxychloride. $CuCl_2.3Cu(OH)_2$. Used as a pigment.

BRUSH DISCHARGE. Discharge of electricity from sharp points on a conductor. The surface density (i.e. quantity of electricity per unit area) is greatest at sharp points; the high charge at such points causes a displacement of the charge on the air particles near the points, and hence an attraction to the points. On reaching the points, the particles acquire some of the charge on the points and are repelled. This causes a stream of charged air particles to leave the vicinity of the points.

BUCHNER FUNNEL. Funnel, usually of porcelain, with a flat circular base perforated with small holes. Used for filtering by suction.

BUFFER SOLUTION. A solution the *hydrogen ion concentration* (q.v.) of which, and hence the acidity or alkalinity, is practically unchanged by dilution, and which resists a change of pH on the addition of acid or alkali.

BULK MODULUS. *Elastic modulus* (q.v.) applied to a body having uniform stress distributed over the whole of its surface. Its value is given by the expression $\dfrac{pV}{v}$ where p = intensity of stress, V = original volume of the body, and v = change in volume.

BUNA N, GR-N. 'Synthetic rubber'; co-polymer of butadiene and acrylo-nitrile, containing about 35% of the latter; vulcanized in a similar way to natural rubber. See *polymerization*.

BUNA S, GR-S. 'Synthetic rubber', co-polymer of butadiene and styrene, containing about 35% of the latter; vulcanized in a similar way to natural rubber. See *polymerization*.

BUNSEN BURNER. Burner for coal-gas, used in laboratories. Consists of a metal tube with an adjustable air-valve for burning a mixture of gas and air.

BUOYANCY. The upward thrust exerted upon a body immersed in a fluid; equal to the weight of the fluid displaced (Archimedes' Principle). Thus a body weighs less when weighed in water, the apparent loss in weight being equal to the weight of the water displaced. For accurate weighing of bodies in air, a small allowance has to be made to correct for the buoyancy of the body.

BURETTE. Graduated glass tube with a tap, for measuring the volume of liquid run out from it. Used in *volumetric analysis* (q.v.).

BURNING, combustion. Generally understood to be chemical combination of the burning substance with oxygen of the air; heat, light and flame being produced. Any chemical action accompanied by the evolution of light and heat.

BURNT ALUM. White porous mass of anhydrous potassium aluminium sulphate, $K_2SO_4 . Al_2(SO_4)_3$, obtained by heating *alum* (q.v.).

BUTADIENE, $CH_2 : CH . CH : CH_2$. Gas, used in the manufacture of synthetic rubber, e.g. *Buna* (q.v.).

BUTANE. C_4H_{10}. *Hydrocarbon* (q.v.) of the *paraffin series* (q.v.). Gas at ordinary temperatures.

BUTTER OF ANTIMONY. Antimony trichloride, $SbCl_3$. White crystalline substance, m.p. 73° C.

BUTYL. Univalent *alkyl radical* (q.v.). C_4H_9.

BUTYL RUBBER. Co-polymer of butadiene and *iso*-butene, containing about 90% of the latter. Vulcanized in a similar way to natural rubber. See *polymerization*.

BUZZER, electric. Device similar in principle to the electric *bell* (q.v.), but without a hammer or gong. The rapid vibration of the arm produces a definite buzzing note when the current flows.

BY-PRODUCT. Substance obtained incidentally during the manufacture of some other substance. Often as important as the manufactured substance itself. E.g. the by-products of coal-gas manufacture include ammonia, coal-tar and coke.

C

CABLE, COAXIAL. Cable consisting of central conducting wire together with a concentric cylindrical conductor, the space between the two being filled with a *dielectric* (q.v.) substance, e.g. polythene, air, etc. The outer conductor is normally connected to earth. Its main use is to transmit high-frequency power from one place to another with minimum energy loss; e.g. from a transmitter to its aerial.

CADMIUM. Cd. Element. A.W. 112·41. At. No. 48. Soft silvery-white metal, S.G. 8·642, m.p. 320·9° C. Occurs together with zinc. Used in the manufacture of *fusible alloys* (q.v.) and for electroplating.

CADMIUM CELL. Standard primary cell. See *Weston cell*.

CAESIUM. Cs. Element. A.W. 132·91. At. No. 55. Silvery-white metal resembling sodium in its physical and chemical properties. S.G. 1·90, m.p. 28·5° C. Highly reactive. Compounds are very rare.

CAFFEINE, theine. $C_8H_{10}O_2N_4$. Member of the *purine* (q.v.) group of organic compounds. White crystals, m.p. 235° C. Occurs in tea-leaves, coffee-beans and other plant material. Has a powerful action on the heart; used in medicine.

CALAMINE. Natural zinc carbonate, $ZnCO_3$.

CALCIFEROL, vitamin D_2. $C_{28}H_{43}OH$. Formed by the action of ultra-violet radiation on *ergosterol* (q.v.). See *vitamins*.

CALCINATION. Strong heating; conversion of metals into their oxides by heating in air.

CALCITE, calcspar. Natural crystalline calcium carbonate, $CaCO_3$.

CALCIUM. Ca. Element. A.W. 40·08. At. No. 20. Soft white metal, tarnishes rapidly in air; S.G. 1·55, m.p. 810° C. Compounds are very abundant, widely distributed and essential to life. Occurs as the carbonate, $CaCO_3$ (limestone, marble and chalk); sulphate, $CaSO_4$ (gypsum, anhydrite); essential constituent of bones and teeth. Compounds are of great industrial importance; e.g. *lime* (q.v.).

CALCIUM CARBIDE, 'carbide'. CaC_2. Greyish solid, colourless when pure; prepared by heating lime, CaO, with carbon in the electric furnace. Reacts with water to give *acetylene* (q.v.).

CALCIUM CARBONATE. $CaCO_3$. White insoluble solid; occurs naturally as chalk, limestone, marble and calcite.

CALCIUM CYANAMIDE, 'cyanamide', Nitrolime. $CaCN_2$. Artificial fertilizer made by heating calcium carbide, CaC_2, in nitrogen at

1000° C. Water in the soil converts it into ammonia. Also used as the starting point in the manufacture of various chemical products.

CALCIUM HYDROXIDE, slaked *lime* (q.v.), $Ca(OH)_2$.

CALCIUM OXIDE, quicklime, CaO. See *lime*.

CALCULUS, the. Branch of mathematics, divided into two main parts, *differential* and *integral* calculus. Deals with variable quantities and their rates of change. Affords a powerful method of solving numerous mathematical problems.

CALIBRATION. The *graduation* (q.v.) of an instrument to enable measurements in definite units to be made with it; thus the arbitrary scale of a *galvanometer* (q.v.) may be calibrated in amperes, thus converting the instrument into an ammeter for measuring electric current.

CALICHE. Impure natural sodium nitrate $NaNO_3$, found in Chile.

CALIFORNIUM. Cf. *Transuranic element* (q.v.). At. No. 98.

CALLIPERS, calipers. Instrument for measuring the distance between two points, especially on a curved surface; e.g. for measuring the internal and external diameters of tubes.

CALOMEL, mercurous chloride. Hg_2Cl_2. White insoluble substance used in medicine.

CALORESCENCE. Absorption of light radiations by a surface, their conversion into heat, and the consequent emission of heat radiation.

CALORIE. Unit of quantity of heat. The amount of heat required to raise the temperature of 1 gm. of water through 1° C. The 15° calorie is defined as the amount of heat required to raise the temperature of 1 gm. of water from 14.5° C. to 15.5° C.

CALORIE, LARGE, kilogram-calorie. 1000 *calories* (q.v.). Written Calorie. Used for quoting energy values of foods.

CALORIE, MEAN. One-hundredth of the quantity of heat required to raise the temperature of 1 gm. of water from 0° C. to 100° C. Very nearly equal to the *calorie* (q.v.) as defined above.

CALORIFIC VALUE of a fuel. The quantity of heat produced by a given weight of the fuel on complete combustion. Usually given as the number of *British Thermal Units* (q.v.) evolved by the complete combustion of 1 lb. of the fuel. Determined by the *bomb calorimeter* (q.v.).

CALORIMETER. Instrument for determining quantities of heat evolved, absorbed or transferred. In its simplest form consists of an open cylindrical vessel of copper or other substance of known specific heat (see *heat, specific*).

CAMERA, PHOTOGRAPHIC. In principle consists of a light-proof box with a lens at one end. The lens, when opened to the outside by means of a shutter, and properly focused, throws an image of the object at which the lens is pointed upon the back of the box. A plate or film sensitive to light is placed here. Focusing is carried out by varying the distance of the lens from the sensitive plate by a suitable device. In 'box' cameras, the lens is fixed relative to the film so as to be in focus for an object at a theoretically infinite distance, but clear definition is obtained at all distances not too close to the lens. See *photography*.

CAMPHOR. $C_{10}H_{16}O$. White crystalline solid with a characteristic smell. M.p. 178° C. Occurs in the camphor tree. Used in the manufacture of *celluloid* (q.v.) and in other industries.

CANAL RAYS. Positively charged *ions* (q.v.) produced during the discharge of electricity in gases, driven to the cathode by the applied potential difference and allowed to pass through canals bored in the cathode.

CANDELA, 'new candle'. Unit of luminous intensity. So defined that the brightness of a *black body* (q.v.) radiator at the temperature of solidification of platinum equals 60 candela/sq. cm. The candela now replaces the *international candle* (q.v.) as unit of luminous intensity.

CANDLEPOWER of a light source, in a given direction, is the *luminous intensity* (q.v.) of the source in that direction expressed in terms of the *candela* (q.v.). Formerly expressed in terms of the *international candle* (q.v.).

CANDLE WAX. Usually either *paraffin wax* (q.v.) or *stearine* (q.v.).

CANE SUGAR, sucrose, saccharose. $C_{12}H_{22}O_{11}$. Obtained from the sugar-cane. Chemically identical with beet sugar.

CANTON'S PHOSPHORUS. Impure calcium sulphide, CaS, having the property of *phosphorescence* (q.v.) after exposure to light. Used in luminous paints.

CAOUTCHOUC. Raw *rubber* (q.v.).

CAPACITY, ELECTRICAL. The relation between the charge placed upon an electrical conductor and the potential acquired by it is of the form, charge $= C \times$ potential, where C is a constant called the *capacity* of the conductor. The practical unit of capacity is the *farad*; a body having a capacity of 1 farad requires a charge of 1 coulomb to raise its potential 1 volt. 1 farad $= 9 \times 10^{11}$ electrostatic units.

CAPACITY, THERMAL; heat capacity. The quantity of heat required to raise the temperature of a body 1° C. Product of the mass of the body in grams and its *specific heat* (q.v.).

CAPILLARY ACTION. General term for phenomena observed in liquids due to unbalanced inter-molecular attraction at the liquid boundary; e.g. the rise or depression of liquids in narrow tubes, the formation of films, drops, bubbles, etc.

CAPILLARY TUBE. Tube of small internal diameter.

CARAMEL (chem.). Brown substance of complex composition, formed by the action of heat on sugar.

CARAT. 1. Measure of weight of diamonds and other gems; formerly 3·17 grains (0·2053 gm.), now standardized as the *international carat*, 0·200 gm. 2. Measure of *fineness* (q.v.) of gold, expressed as part of gold in 24 parts of the alloy. Thus, 24 carat gold is pure gold, 18 carat gold contains 18 parts in 24 or has a fineness of 750.

CARBAMIDE. See *urea*.

CARBIDE. *Binary compound* (q.v.) of carbon; loose term for *calcium carbide* (q.v.).

CARBOCYCLIC COMPOUNDS. Organic compounds containing a closed ring of carbon atoms within the molecule. E.g. benzene, C_6H_6, has a molecule of six carbon atoms joined in a ring, with a hydrogen atom attached to each.

CARBOHYDRATES. Large group of organic compounds composed of carbon, hydrogen and oxygen only. Usually the hydrogen and oxygen atoms are in a ratio of 2 to 1, as in water. Group includes the sugars, gums, starches and cellulose. Many carbohydrates are used in the body as a source of energy, and are usually formed by plants, by *photosynthesis* (q.v.).

CARBOLIC ACID, C_6H_5OH. See *phenol*.

CARBON. C. Element. A.W. 12·01. At. No. 6. Occurs in several allotropic forms (see *allotropy*) including diamond and graphite (crystalline); and as amorphous carbon in the forms of lamp-black, gas carbon, etc. Compounds occur as the metallic *carbonates* (q.v.), carbon dioxide in the air, mineral oil, coal, etc. Essential to life; contained in all living things. Animals obtain their energy by the oxidation of carbon compounds eaten as food.

CARBON DIOXIDE, carbonic acid gas. CO_2. Colourless gas with faint tingling smell and taste. Occurs in the atmosphere; formed by the oxidation of carbon and carbon compounds. Utilized by plants. See *photosynthesis*.

CARBON DISULPHIDE, carbon bisulphide, CS_2. Colourless inflammable liquid, b.p. 46° C., with a high *refractive index* (q.v.). Made by heating carbon with sulphur in a retort. Used as a solvent in the vulcanization of rubber, in the manufacture of viscose *rayon* (q.v.) and for killing pests.

CARBON MONOXIDE. CO. Colourless, almost odourless gas. Very poisonous; when breathed, combines with the *haemoglobin* (q.v.) of the blood to form bright red *carboxyhaemoglobin*. This is chemically stable, and thus the haemoglobin is no longer available to carry oxygen. Burns with a bright blue flame to form carbon dioxide. Formed during the incomplete combustion of coke, charcoal and similar fuels. Occurs in coal-gas and in the exhaust fumes of motor engines.

CARBON TETRACHLORIDE. CCl_4. Heavy colourless liquid with a sweetish smell, b.p. 76·8° C. Used as a non-inflammable solvent and in fire extinguishers ('pyrene').

CARBONADO. Black, discoloured or impure variety of *diamond* (q.v.), useless as a gem but very hard and used for drills, etc.

CARBONATE. Salt of carbonic acid, H_2CO_3.

CARBONIC ACID. H_2CO_3. Very weak acid probably formed in small amounts when carbon dioxide dissolves in water. Term often applied to carbon dioxide itself. Never obtained pure; breaks up almost completely into carbon dioxide and water when obtained in a chemical reaction. Gives rise to two series of salts, the *carbonates* and *bicarbonates* (q.v.).

CARBONYL CHLORIDE. See *phosgene*.

CARBONYL GROUP. The divalent group CO.

CARBONYLS. Compounds of metals with carbon monoxide; e.g. nickel carbonyl, $Ni(CO)_4$.

CARBORUNDUM, silicon carbide, SiC. Dark crystalline solid, nearly as hard as diamond, used as an abrasive and as a refractory material. Made by heating silica, SiO_2, with carbon in an electric furnace.

CARBOXYL GROUP. The univalent group COOH, characteristic of the organic *carboxylic acids*.

CARBURETTOR. Device in the internal-combustion petrol engine for mixing air with petrol vapour preliminary to explosion.

CARNALLITE. Natural potassium magnesium chloride,
$$KCl.MgCl_2.6H_2O,$$
found in the *Stassfurt deposits* (q.v.). Important source of potassium salts.

CARNOTITE. Uranium potassium vanadate of variable composition. Ore of uranium.

CARNOT'S CYCLE. An ideal reversible cycle of operations for the working substance of a heat engine. The four steps in the cycle are: (a) *isothermal* (q.v.) expansion, the substance taking in heat and doing work; (b) *adiabatic* (q.v.) expansion, without heat change, external work done; (c) isothermal compression, heat given out, work done on the substance by external forces; (d) adiabatic compression, no heat change, work done on the substance.

CARNOT'S PRINCIPLE. The efficiency of any reversible heat engine depends only on the temperature range through which it works and not upon the properties of any material substance. If all the heat is taken up at absolute temperature T_1 and all given out at absolute temperature T_2 (as in *Carnot's cycle*, q.v.), the efficiency is $\dfrac{T_1 - T_2}{T_1}$.

CARO'S ACID, permonosulphuric acid. H_2SO_5.

CAROTENE. $C_{40}H_{56}$. Yellow *unsaturated* (q.v.) *hydrocarbon* (q.v.) present in carrots and butter. Converted into vitamin A (see *vitamins*) in the animal organism.

CARRIER (chem.). Substance assisting a chemical reaction by combining with part or all of the molecule of one of the reacting substances to form a compound which is then easily decomposed again by the other reacting substance; the carrier is thus left unchanged. See *catalyst*.

CARRIER WAVE. A continuous electromagnetic wave motion, of constant amplitude and frequency, emitted by a radio transmitter. By *modulation* (q.v.) of the carrier wave, impulses caused by sounds at the transmitting end are conveyed by it to the receiver.

CARRON OIL. Mixture of vegetable oil (olive or cotton-seed) with lime-water. Used as an application for burns.

CASCADE LIQUEFIER. Apparatus used for liquefying air, oxygen, etc. A gas cannot be liquefied until it is brought to a temperature below its *critical temperature* (q.v.). In the cascade liquefier the critical temperature of the gas is reached step by step, using a series of gases having successively lower boiling points. The first of these, which can be liquefied by compression at ordinary temperatures, is allowed to evaporate under reduced pressure; this produces a temperature below the critical temperature of the second gas, which can then be liquefied. This is similarly allowed to evaporate, and the step is repeated until finally the desired liquefaction is reached.

CASEIN. Main *protein* (q.v.) of milk. Pale yellow solid obtained from milk by the addition of acid ('acid casein'), by controlled souring ('self-soured casein') or by curdling with *rennet* (q.v.) ('rennet casein'). Used in paper-coating, paints, adhesives, plastics and for making artificial textile fibres.

CASEINOGEN. British term for *casein* (q.v.) before precipitation. The American terms are *casein* before precipitation, and *para-casein* after.

CASSIOPEIUM. See *lutetium*.

CASSITERITE. SnO_2. Natural tin oxide. Principal ore of tin.

CAST IRON, pig iron. Impure, brittle form of iron, such as produced in the *blast furnace* (q.v.). Contains from 2% to 4·5% carbon in the form of *cementite* (q.v.) and usually also some manganese, phosphorus, silicon and sulphur. Generally not used direct, but converted into steel or wrought iron.

CATABOLISM, katabolism. Part of *metabolism* (q.v.) dealing with the chemical decomposition of complex substances into simple ones, with a release of energy.

CATALASE. An *enzyme* (q.v.) which decomposes hydrogen peroxide.

CATALYSIS. The alteration of the rate at which a chemical reaction proceeds, by the introduction of a substance (*catalyst*) which remains unchanged at the end of the reaction. Small quantities of the catalyst are usually sufficient to bring the action about or to produce a vast increase in its speed.

CATALYST. Substance which alters the rate at which a chemical reaction occurs, but is itself unchanged at the end of the reaction. Catalysts are widely used in chemical industry; metals in a finely divided state, and oxides of metals, are frequently used. The *enzymes* (q.v.) are organic catalysts produced by living cells.

CATAPHORESIS. See *electrophoresis*.

CATENARY. Curve formed by a chain or string hanging from two fixed points.

CATHETOMETER. Telescope mounted on a graduated vertical pillar along which it can move. The instrument is used for measuring lengths and displacements at a distance of a few feet.

CATHODE, kathode. Negative electrode. Negatively charged conductor in *electrolysis* (q.v.) and in vacuum tubes. See *discharge in gases*.

CATHODE RAY OSCILLOSCOPE. Apparatus consisting essentially of an 'electron gun' producing a beam of electrons which passes through horizontal and vertical deflecting plates, to fall upon a fluorescent screen. The whole is enclosed in an evacuated glass envelope, one end of which is coated with a fluorescent material and serves as the screen. The point at which the electrons strike the screen can be seen by the fluorescence produced by them. Potentials applied to the deflecting plates cause a deflection of the electron beam. The oscilloscope has many uses, the most important being the analysis of transient and rapidly changing potentials.

CATHODE RAYS. Stream of *electrons* (q.v.) emitted from the negatively charged electrode or cathode when an electric discharge takes place in a vacuum tube, i.e. a tube containing a gas at very low pressure. See *discharge in gases*.

CATION, kation. Positively charged *ion* (q.v.); ion which, during *electrolysis* (q.v.), is attracted towards the negatively charged cathode.

CAUSTIC. Corrosive towards organic matter (but term is not applied to acids). E.g. caustic soda.

CAUSTIC (phys.). Parallel rays of light falling on a concave spherical mirror do not form a point image at the focus (see *mirrors, spherical*). Instead, there is a region of maximum concentration of the rays forming a curve or surface of revolution, called a *caustic*, the apex or cusp of which is at the focus of the mirror. A similar caustic occurs in the image formed by a convex *lens* (q.v.) receiving parallel light. Such a curve may be seen on the surface of a liquid in a cup, formed by the reflection of light upon the curved wall of the cup.

CAUSTIC ALKALI. Sodium or potassium hydroxide.

CAUSTIC POTASH. *Potassium hydroxide* (q.v.), KOH.

CAUSTIC SODA. *Sodium hydroxide* (q.v.), NaOH.

CELESTIAL EQUATOR (astr.). Circle in which the plane of the Earth's equator meets the *celestial sphere* (q.v.).

CELESTIAL SPHERE (astr.). The imaginary sphere to the inner surface of which the heavenly bodies appear to be attached; the observer is situated at the centre of the sphere.

CELL (phys.). Device for producing a current of electricity by chemical action. See *accumulator, primary cell*.

CELLULOID. Plastic material made from *cellulose nitrate* (q.v.) and *camphor* (q.v.).

CELLULOSE. $(C_6H_{10}O_5)_n$. Structural tissue which forms the cell-walls of plants; the principal constituent of the cotton fibre. Used in the manufacture of paper, collodion, rayon, plastics and explosives. Obtained from wood pulp, cotton and other plant sources.

CELLULOSE ACETATE. *Ester* (q.v.) obtained by the action of acetic anhydride on cellulose. A white solid, used in the manufacture of *rayon* (q.v.) and plastics.

CELLULOSE NITRATE, nitrocellulose. Nitric acid *ester* (q.v.) of cellulose. Range of compounds formed by treatment of cellulose with a mixture of nitric and sulphuric acids; properties depend on the extent to which the hydroxyl groups of the cellulose are esterified. Used in the manufacture of plastics, lacquers and explosives.

CELTIUM. See *hafnium*.

CEMENT. Powder which, after mixing with water, sets to a hard mass. *Portland cement* is made by heating a mixture of limestone and clay and grinding the product. Consists of calcium silicates and aluminates; complex chemical changes occur during setting.

CEMENTATION. Early process for steel manufacture. Bars of wrought iron were heated for several days in charcoal at red heat.

CEMENTITE, iron carbide. Fe_3C. Hard, brittle compound which is responsible for the brittleness of cast iron. Present in steel.

CENTI-. Prefix denoting one-hundredth of, in metric units. E.g. centi-metre, one-hundredth of a metre.

CENTIGRADE DEGREE. One-hundredth of the difference between the temperature of melting ice and water boiling under standard atmo-spheric pressure (760 mm.).

CENTIGRADE SCALE of temperature. Temperature scale in which the m.p. of ice is taken as zero, and the b.p. of water as $100°$ C. Used in scientific work, and is almost universal for all purposes except in the English-speaking countries.

CENTRE OF CURVATURE of a spherical mirror. The centre of the sphere of which the mirror forms a part.

CENTRE OF GRAVITY of a body is the fixed point through which the resultant force due to the Earth's attraction upon it always passes, irrespective of the position of the body.

CENTRIFUGAL FORCE. The outward force acting on a body rotating in a circle round a central point. The *centripetal force* is the radial force imposed by the constraining system, necessary to keep the body moving in its circular path. The centrifugal and centripetal forces are equal and opposite.

CENTRIFUGE. Apparatus for separating particles from a *suspension* (q.v.). Balanced tubes containing the suspension are attached to the opposite ends of arms rotating rapidly about a central point; by *centrifugal force* (q.v.) the suspended particles are forced outwards, and collect at the bottoms of the tubes.

CENTRIPETAL FORCE. See *centrifugal force*.

CERARGYRITE. *Horn silver* (q.v.).

CERESIN. Hard, brittle *paraffin wax* (q.v.) with a melting point in the range of $70-100°$ C.

CERIUM. Ce. Element. A.W. 140·13. At. No. 58. Steel-grey soft metal, S.G. 6·7, m.p. $640°$ C. Occurs in several rare minerals, e.g. monazite sand. Use in *pyrophoric alloys* (q.v.) for lighter 'flints'; compounds are used in the manufacture of gas mantles.

C.G.S. system, centimetre-gram-second system. A system of physical units derived from the centimetre, gram mass and the second. E.g. velocities in C.G.S. units may be measured in centimetres per second.

CHABASITE. A natural *zeolite* (q.v.), calcium aluminium silicate. See *ion exchange*.

CHAIN REACTION, NUCLEAR. See *atomic pile*.

CHALCEDONY. Variety of natural impure silica, SiO_2. Has a fibrous structure and a waxy lustre. Used for ornaments.

CHALK. Natural calcium carbonate, $CaCO_3$, formed from the shells of minute marine organisms. Blackboard chalk sticks are calcium sulphate, $CaSO_4$.

CHALYBEATE, chalybite. Natural ferrous carbonate, $FeCO_3$.

CHANGE OF STATE (phys.). The conversion of a substance from one of the physical states of matter (solid, liquid or gas) into another. E.g. the melting of ice.

CHARACTERISTIC (math.). The integral or whole-number part of a *logarithm* (q.v.).

CHARCOAL. General name for numerous varieties of carbon, usually impure; generally made by heating vegetable or animal substances with exclusion of air. Many forms are very porous and adsorb various materials readily. See *activated carbon*.

CHARGE, ELECTRIC. See *electric charge*.

CHARLES' LAW. See *gas laws*.

CHEDDITE. Class of explosives containing sodium or potassium chlorate with dinitrotoluene and other organic substances.

CHEMICAL AFFINITY. See *affinity*.

CHEMICAL CHANGE. Change in a substance involving an alteration in its chemical composition, due to an increase, decrease or re-arrangement of atoms within its molecules. See *equation, chemical; molecule*.

CHEMICAL COMBINATION, LAWS OF:

Law of constant composition. A definite chemical compound always contains the same elements chemically combined in the same proportions by weight.

Law of multiple proportions. When two elements unite in more than one proportion, for a fixed weight of one element there is always a simple relationship with the weight of the other element present.

Law of combining weights (also termed the *law of reciprocal proportions, law of equivalents*). Elements combine in the ratio of their combining weights or chemical equivalents; or in some simple multiple or submultiple of that ratio.

CHEMICAL EQUILIBRIUM. Many chemical reactions do not go to completion; in such cases a state of equilibrium or balance is reached when the original substances are reacting at the same rate as the new substances are reacting with each other to form the original substances. Thus, if two substances A and B react to form C and D, the state at equilibrium is denoted by the balanced equation $A + B \rightleftharpoons C + D$. If one of the substances is removed, the system readjusts the equilibrium; thus, if C is constantly removed as soon as formed, more A and B react until the action is completed. An equilibrium reaction which could thus be made to complete itself in either direction is termed a *reversible reaction*. E.g. if steam is passed over red-hot iron, iron oxide and hydrogen are formed, the latter being constantly removed by more steam which passes through; the reaction thus goes to completion according to the equation $4H_2O + 3Fe = Fe_3O_4 + 4H_2$. If, however, hydrogen is passed over red-hot iron oxide, the reverse action takes place, $Fe_3O_4 + 4H_2 = 4H_2O + 3Fe$. If the reaction is allowed to proceed in an enclosed space, a state of equilibrium is reached, all four substances being present.

CHEMICAL EQUIVALENTS, combining weights. Combining proportions of substances by weight, relative to hydrogen as a standard. *Equivalent* of an element is the number of grams of that element which will combine with or replace 1 gm. of hydrogen or 8 gm. of oxygen. *Gram-equivalent, equivalent weight*, is the equivalent expressed in grams. Equivalent weight of an acid is the weight of the acid containing unit weight of replaceable *acidic hydrogen* (q.v.). Equivalent weight of a base is the weight of the base required to neutralize the equivalent weight of an acid. The combining proportions of substances by weight are in the ratio of their equivalents, or in some simple multiple or submultiple of that ratio. For an element, the *atomic weight* (q.v.) is equal to the product of its equivalent and its *valency* (q.v.).

CHEMICAL REACTION. The interaction of two or more substances, resulting in *chemical changes* (q.v.) in them.

CHEMILUMINESCENCE. Cold flame; evolution of light accompanied by little heat during a chemical reaction.

CHEMISTRY. Study of the composition of substances, and of their effects upon one another.

CHERT. A natural form of silica, SiO_2, resembling flint.

CHILE SALTPETRE. Impure *sodium nitrate* (q.v.), $NaNO_3$. Occurs in huge deposits in Chile.

CHINA CLAY, kaolin. Pure natural form of hydrated aluminium silicate, $Al_2Si_2O_5(OH)_4$. On heating loses water and changes chemical composition. Used for making porcelain.

CHINESE WHITE. Zinc oxide, ZnO.

CHITIN. Complex organic substance, related to the carbohydrates but containing nitrogen. Forms an essential part of the shells of crustaceans and insects. Also found in some fungi.

CHLORAL. $CCl_3.CHO$. Pungent-smelling, colourless oily liquid, b.p. $97 \cdot 7°$ C.

CHLORAL HYDRATE. $CCl_3CH(OH)_2$. White crystalline solid, m.p.

47

57° C. Prepared from *chloral* (q.v.) by the action of water. Used in medicine as a soporific.

CHLORARGYRITE. *Horn silver* (q.v.).

CHLORIDE. *Binary compound* (q.v.) with chlorine; salt of *hydrochloric acid* (q.v.), HCl.

CHLORIDE OF LIME. Calcium oxychloride, $CaOCl_2$. See *bleaching powder*.

CHLORINE. Cl. Element. A.W. 35·457. At. No. 17. Greenish-yellow gas with a choking irritating smell. Poisonous; first poison gas to be used in warfare (by Germany, Ypres, 1915). Compounds occur as common salt (sodium chloride), NaCl, in sea-water and as rock salt; and as chlorides of other metals. Manufactured almost entirely by the *electrolysis* (q.v.) of brine. Used in the manufacture of bleaching powder, disinfectants, hydrochloric acid.

CHLOROFORM. $CHCl_3$. Volatile colourless heavy liquid with a powerful sweet smell, b.p. 61° C. Made from acetone, acetaldehyde or ethyl alcohol by the action of bleaching powder, or by the action of chlorine on methane, CH_4. Used as an anaesthetic and industrial solvent.

CHLOROPHYLL. Green pigment contained in the leaves of green plants. Absorbs energy from sunlight to enable the plant to build up sugar (see *photosynthesis*). Has recently been shown to consist of at least two distinct substances: chlorophyll-*a*, $C_{55}H_{72}O_5N_4Mg$; and chlorophyll-*b*, $C_{55}H_{70}O_6N_4Mg$.

CHLOROPICRIN. CCl_3NO_2. Oily liquid, b.p. 112° C. Highly poisonous and chemically active. Used as a disinfectant and fungicide.

CHOKE, choking coil. A coil of low resistance and high *inductance* (q.v.) used in electrical circuits to pass direct currents whilst suppressing alternating currents.

CHOKE-DAMP. See *after-damp*.

CHOLESTEROL. $C_{27}H_{45}OH$. Organic compound belonging to the *sterol* (q.v.) group. White waxy substance present in the tissues of the human body, in which it performs a number of vital functions.

CHORD (math.). Straight line joining two points on a curve. See *circle*.

CHROMATIC ABERRATION. See *aberration, chromatic*.

CHROMATOGRAPHY. Method of chemical analysis developed from the fact that if a liquid mixture is allowed to trickle through a column of adsorbing material (e.g. chalk) the components of the mixture may be adsorbed in separate layers in the column.

CHROME ALUM. Chromium potassium sulphate,
$$K_2SO_4 . Cr_2(SO_4)_3 . 24H_2O.$$
Dark purple crystalline soluble salt; used in dyeing, calico-printing, tanning.

CHROME IRON ORE, chrome ironstone, chromite. Ferrous chromite, $FeO . Cr_2O_3$. Source of chromium metal and its compounds.

CHROME RED. Basic lead chromate, $PbO . PbCrO_4$. Used as a pigment in paints.

CHROME YELLOW. Lead chromate, $PbCrO_4$. Used as a pigment.

CHROMITE. See *chrome iron ore.*

CHROMIUM. Cr. Element. A.W. 52·01. At. No. 24. Hard white metal resembling iron; S.G. 6·92, m.p. 1615° C. Occurs as chrome iron ore. Extracted by reducing the oxide with aluminium (see *Goldschmidt process*). Used in the manufacture of stainless steel and for chromium plating.

CHROMIUM PLATING. Deposition of a thin, resistant film of chromium metal by *electrolysis* (q.v.) from a bath containing a solution of chromic acid, CrO_3.

CHROMIUM STEEL. Steel containing varying amounts of chromium; strong and tough, used for tools, etc.

CHROMOSPHERE. Layer surrounding the *photosphere* (q.v.) of the Sun; visible during a total eclipse.

CHRONOGRAPH. Accurate time-recording instrument.

CHRONOMETER. Accurate clock; term now applied mainly to instruments used in navigation.

CIMENT FONDU. See *bauxite cement.*

CINNABAR. Natural mercuric sulphide, HgS. Bright red crystalline solid, S.G. 8·1. Ore of mercury.

CIRCLE (math.). Plane figure contained by a line, the *circumference*, which is everywhere equidistant from a fixed point, the *centre*. Distance from the centre to the circumference is the *radius*; a straight line joining any two points on the circumference is a *chord*; a chord passing through the centre, equal in length to twice the radius, is a *diameter*; any portion of the circumference is an *arc*; a portion cut off by a chord is a *segment*; a portion cut off by two radii is a *sector*. Ratio of circumference to diameter, denoted by π ('pi') = 3·14159 ... (approx. 3⅐). Length of circumference = $2\pi r$; area = πr^2, where r = radius.

CIRCUIT, ELECTRICAL. The complete path traversed by an electric current.

CIRCULAR MEASURE of angles. Measurement of angles in *radians* (q.v.), the size of an angle stated as the ratio of the length of arc cut off by the angle at the centre of a circle to the radius of the circle. Thus

$$180° = \pi \text{ radians}; \quad 1 \text{ radian} = \frac{180}{\pi} \text{ degrees} = 57° \ 17·7'.$$

CIRCULARLY POLARIZED LIGHT. Light which can be resolved into two vibrations lying in planes at right angles, of equal amplitude and frequency and differing in *phase* (q.v.) by 90°. The electric vector of the wave describes, at any point in the path of the wave, a circle about the direction of propagation of the light as axis. (See also *polarization of light*.)

CIRCUMFERENCE. See *circle.*

CIS-FORM. See *cis-trans isomerism.*

CIS-TRANS ISOMERISM. Form of *isomerism* (q.v.) associated with compounds containing a *double bond* (q.v.). Like groups in such compounds may be either on the same side of the plane of the double bond (*cis-*

form) or on opposite sides (*trans*-form). E.g. $H - C - COOH$, maleic

$$H - C - COOH$$

acid, and $H - C - COOH$, fumaric acid, are respectively *cis-* and

$$HOOC - C - H$$

trans-forms.

CITRATE. Salt of *citric acid* (q.v.).

CITRIC ACID. $C_6H_8O_7$. White crystalline soluble organic tribasic acid, m.p. 153° C. Has a sour taste, occurs as the free acid in lemons (6%) and other sour fruits. Used in the preparation of effervescent salts.

CLARK CELL. Standard primary cell, used as a standard of *E.M.F* (q.v.). Voltage is given by the equation E.M.F. $= 1·433 - 0·0012(t - 15)$ volts, where t is the Centigrade temperature.

CLATHRATE COMPOUNDS. Chemical compounds formed not by the action of valency *bonds* (q.v.), but by 'molecular imprisonment', the combined molecules being held together mechanically by virtue of their configuration in space.

CLAY. A class of complex *silicates* (q.v.) e.g. kaolinite or *china clay* (q.v.).

CLEAVAGE. Manner of breaking of a crystalline substance.

CLINICAL THERMOMETER. See *thermometer, clinical*.

CLOTTING. Formation of solid deposits or clots in liquids, often due to the *coagulation* (q.v.) of soluble proteins dissolved in the liquid.

CLOUD CHAMBER. Apparatus used to study the tracks of ionizing radiations, e.g. alpha-, beta-, gamma- and X-rays. Makes use of the fact that water vapour condenses more readily on charged ions than on uncharged molecules. The rays under investigation are allowed to pass through a chamber super-saturated with water vapour. The ions produced by them in their passage serve as nuclei for the condensation of the water vapour. The path of the ray is thus made visible as a track of tiny droplets of water.

COAGULATION OF PROTEINS. When solutions of water-soluble proteins (*albumens*, q.v.) are heated, the protein becomes 'denatured' at a definite temperature; it then becomes insoluble and either remains in suspension or is precipitated as a clot or curd. Other types of proteins, e.g. *globulins* (q.v.) may be denatured and coagulated by heat, or by the addition of acids or alkalies. A denatured protein cannot be easily reconverted into the original compound, and the nature of the process is not definitely understood.

COAL. Material, occurring in large underground deposits, consisting of carbon and various carbon compounds. Formed by the decomposition of vegetable matter during periods of many thousands of years. The formation is said to have taken place in the following stages: peat, lignite, ordinary or bituminous coal, anthracite.

COAL-GAS. Fuel gas manufactured by the *destructive distillation* (q.v.) of coal in closed iron retorts; often supplemented with *water-gas* (q.v.). Composition by volume (average values): hydrogen 50%, methane, CH_4, 30%, carbon monoxide, CO, 8%, other hydrocarbons 4%, nitrogen, carbon dioxide and oxygen 8%.

COAL-GAS BY-PRODUCTS. Amongst the valuable substances obtained during the manufacture of coal gas are coke, coal-tar, ammonia, sulphuric acid and pitch.

COAL-TAR. Thick black oily liquid obtained as a by-product of coal-gas manufacture. Distillation and purification yields, amongst other valuable products: benzene, C_6H_6; toluene, $C_6H_5CH_3$; xylene, $C_6H_4(CH_3)_2$; phenol, C_6H_5OH; naphthalene, $C_{10}H_8$; cresol, $CH_3C_6H_4OH$, and anthracene, $C_{14}H_{10}$. Pitch is left as a residue.

COAL-TAR DYES. Organic compounds, used as dyestuffs, prepared or derived from substances such as benzene occurring in coal-tar.

COAXIAL. Having a common axis.

COBALT. Co. Element. A.W. 58·94. At. No. 27. Hard silvery-white magnetic metal resembling iron. S.G. 8·9, m.p. 1480° C. Occurs combined with sulphur and with arsenic. Extracted by converting the ore into the oxide and reducing with aluminium, or with carbon in the electric furnace. Used in many alloys; compounds used to produce a blue colour in glass and ceramics.

COBALT STEEL. Steel containing cobalt, and often other metals such as wolfram (tungsten), chromium and vanadium. The addition of cobalt results in greater hardness and brittleness, improves the cutting power of *high-speed steel* (q.v.) tools, and alters the magnetic properties.

COCAINE. $C_{17}H_{21}O_4N$. Member of the *alkaloids* (q.v.); occurs in the coca plant. White solid, m.p. 98° C. Powerful *anaesthetic* (q.v.). A dangerous habit-forming drug.

COCHINEAL. Natural red dyestuff obtained from the dried body of the *Coccus cacti* insect.

CODEINE. $C_{18}H_{21}O_3N$. Member of the *alkaloids* (q.v.) chemically closely related to *morphine* (q.v.), but is not a powerful narcotic. Occurs in opium; used in the treatment of coughs.

COEFFICIENT (math.). A number or other known factor written in front of an algebraic expression. E.g. in the expression $3x^4$, 3 is the coefficient of x^4.

COEFFICIENT (phys.). Factor or multiplier which measures some specified property of a given substance, and is constant for that substance under given conditions. E.g. coefficient of expansion. (See *expansion*, *coefficient of*.)

COERCIVE FORCE of a substance. The strength of the magnetic field to which a ferromagnetic substance undergoing an *hysteresis cycle* (q.v.) must be subjected in order to demagnetize the substance completely. If the substance is magnetized to saturation during the cycle, the coercive force is called the *coercivity*.

COERCIVITY. See *coercive force*.

COFFEY STILL. Apparatus for the fractional distillation of solutions of ethyl alcohol as obtained by *fermentation* (q.v.) on an industrial scale; the product is known as rectified spirit.

COHESION. Holding together; force holding a solid or liquid together owing to attraction between the molecules. Decreases with rise in temperature.

COINAGE METALS. The metals copper, silver, gold.

COKE. Greyish, porous brittle solid containing about 80% carbon. Obtained as a residue in the manufacture of *coal-gas* (q.v.) ('gas coke'); also made specially in coke ovens, in which the coal is treated at lower temperatures than in gas manufacture.

COLCOTHAR, rouge, red iron oxide. Ferric oxide, Fe_2O_3. Used as a pigment and for polishing.

COLLAGEN. Organic substance which is the chief constituent of cartilage and connective tissues of animals. On boiling with water, gives rise to *gelatin* (q.v.).

COLLARGOL. Powder containing protein material and finely divided silver; with water forms a colloidal solution of silver.

COLLIGATIVE PROPERTIES. Those properties of a substance (e.g. a solution) which depend only on the concentration of particles (molecules or ions) present and not upon their nature; e.g. *osmotic pressure* (q.v.).

COLLIMATOR. Tube containing a convex *achromatic lens* (q.v.) at one end and an adjustable slit at the other, the slit being at the focus of the lens. Light rays entering the slit thus leave the collimator as a parallel beam of light.

COLLODION. Solution of *cellulose nitrate* (q.v.) in a mixture of alcohol and ether.

COLLOID. Substance present in solution in the *colloidal state* (q.v.). The original division, made by Graham, of all substances into crystalloids and colloids according to the ability of their solutions to pass through a *semi-permeable membrane* (q.v.) is not generally accepted now, since most substances can be brought into the colloidal state by suitable means.

COLLOIDAL METALS. *Colloidal solutions* (q.v.) or *suspensions* (q.v.) of metals, the metal being distributed in the solvent in the form of very small electrically charged particles. May be prepared by striking an electric arc between poles made of the metal, under water; or by the chemical reduction of a solution of a salt of the metal. Used in medicine.

COLLOIDAL SOLUTION, sol. A solution in which the solute is present in the *colloidal state* (q.v.). Common examples include solutions of starch, albumen, colloidal metals, etc. The solvent is termed the *dispersion medium* and the dissolved substance the *disperse phase*. Several types of colloidal solution are possible, depending upon whether the dispersion medium and the disperse phase are respectively liquid and solid (*suspensoid sols*), liquid and liquid (*emulsoid sols*), gas and solid, etc. If the disperse phase, when removed from solution by evaporation or coagulation, returns to the colloidal state on merely mixing with the dispersion medium, it is termed a reversible or *lyophilic* colloid, and the solution a *reversible sol*. If the disperse phase does not return to the colloidal state on simple mixing, it is termed an *irreversible* or *lyophobic* colloid.

COLLOIDAL STATE. A system of particles in a *dispersion medium* (q.v.), with properties distinct from that of a true solution because of the larger size of the particles. The presence of these particles, which are approximately 10^{-5} to 10^{-7} cm. across, can often be detected by means of the *ultramicroscope* (q.v.). As a result of the grouping of the molecules, a solute in the colloidal state cannot pass through a suitable *semi-permeable membrane* (q.v.) and gives rise to negligible *osmotic pressure* (q.v.), *depression of freezing point* (q.v.) and *elevation of boiling point* (q.v.) effects. The molecular groups or particles of the solute carry a resultant electric charge, generally of the same sign for all the particles.

COLOPHONY. See *rosin*.

COLORIMETER. Apparatus used in *colorimetric analysis* (q.v.) for comparing intensities of colour.

COLORIMETRIC ANALYSIS. Determination of the amounts of substances by comparing the intensity of colour produced by them with specific reagents, with the intensity of colour produced by a standard amount of the substance.

COLOUR. The sensation of a particular colour is the effect upon the human eye of light of a particular wave-length. See *colour vision*.

COLOUR VISION. White light, such as daylight, consists of a mixture of wave-motions (see *electromagnetic waves*) of various wave-lengths. A surface which reflects all of these will appear white; some surfaces, however, have the property of absorbing some of the radiations they receive, and reflecting the rest. Thus, a surface which absorbs all light radiations excepting those corresponding to green, will appear green by reflecting only those radiations. In the cases of colour seen by transmitted light, as in coloured glass, the glass absorbs all the radiations except those which are visible, and which pass through. See *surface colour; pigment colour*.

COLUMBIUM, Cb. See *niobium*.

COLZA OIL, rapeseed oil. Yellow oil obtained from the seeds of various *Brassica* plants. Used as an edible oil, illuminant, lubricant and in the quenching of steel. '*Mineral colza*' oil is a mixture of paraffin *hydrocarbons* (q.v.) with a boiling range of 250–350° C.

COMBINATION, LAWS OF CHEMICAL. See *chemical combination, laws of*.

COMBINATION (math.). A selection of a specified number of different objects from some larger specified number. The number of combinations of r different objects selected from n objects (i.e. the number of combinations of n objects taken r at a time) is denoted by the expression ^nC_r, and is equal to $\dfrac{\lfloor n}{\lfloor r \cdot \lfloor n-r}$. (See *factorial*.)

COMBUSTION. See *burning*.

COMET. Heavenly body, moving under the attraction of the Sun. Consists of a hazy gaseous cloud containing a brighter nucleus and a fainter tail.

COMMUTATOR. Device for altering or reversing the direction of an electric current; used in the dynamo to convert the alternating current into a direct one if required.

COMPASS, MAGNETIC. In its simplest form consists of a magnetized needle pivoted at its centre so that it is free to move in a horizontal plane. The effect of the Earth's magnetic field is to cause the needle to set along the magnetic meridian. The needle is usually placed at the centre of a circular scale marked with the points of the compass. As such a compass is also affected by magnetic fields other than that of the Earth, for navigation the *gyro-compass* (q.v.) is used.

COMPLEMENTARY ANGLES. Angles together totalling 90° or one right angle.

COMPLEMENTARY COLOURS. Pairs of colours which, when combined, give the effect of white. See *colour vision*.

COMPLETE RADIATION. See *black body radiation*.

COMPLEX NUMBER. A complex number consists of two parts, 'real' and 'imaginary', and can be expressed in the form $x + iy$, where both x and y are real quantities and i is the square root of -1, i.e. $i^2 = -1$. The real part of the complex number is 'x' and the imaginary part 'iy'. Such numbers obey the ordinary laws of algebra except that in equations containing them the real and imaginary parts are equated separately.

COMPONENT (chem.). Term in the *phase rule* (q.v.). The number of components in a system is the least number of substances from which every *phase* (q.v.) of the system may be constituted. E.g. each of the phases ice, water, water vapour in equilibrium is composed of one component, H_2O.

COMPONENT FORCES AND VELOCITIES. Two or more forces or velocities which produce the same effect upon a body as a single force or velocity, known as the *resultant*.

COMPOUND (chem.). Substance consisting of two or more elements chemically united in definite proportions by weight.

COMPRESSIBILITY. The coefficient of compressibility (isothermal) of a substance is given by $c = -\dfrac{1}{V} \cdot \dfrac{\delta V}{\delta p}$, where δV is the change in the volume V of the substance resulting from a change of pressure δp, the temperature remaining constant.

CONCAVE. Curving inwards; thus, a concave (or bi-concave) lens is thinner at the centre than at the edges.

CONCENTRATED (chem.). As applied to reagents, containing the minimum of water or other solvent; the opposite of dilute.

CONCENTRATION of any substance in a given space, or in another substance, is the amount of it present per definite amount of space or of the other substance. Concentration of aqueous solutions is usually expressed in grams, gram-molecules or gram-equivalents per litre.

CONCENTRIC. Having the same centre. E.g. two concentric tubes would appear, in cross-section, as two concentric circles.

CONCHOIDAL FRACTURE. Type of break or fracture characteristic of an *amorphous* (q.v.) solid; an irregular break with a curved face exhibiting concentric rings.

CONCRETE. Building material composed of stone, sand, cement and water.

CONDENSATION (chem.). Chemical change in which two or more molecules react with the elimination of water or of some other simple substance. E.g. acetic anhydride, $(CH_3CO)_2O$, may be regarded as a condensation product of acetic acid, CH_3COOH, a molecule of the anhydride being formed when two molecules of the acid combine with the elimination of one molecule of water. See also *polymerization*.

CONDENSATION OF VAPOUR. Change of vapour into liquid. Takes place when the pressure of the vapour becomes equal to the maximum vapour pressure of the liquid at that temperature.

CONDENSATION PUMP. Apparatus used to obtain high vacua, i.e pressures of the order of 10^{-6} mm. mercury. Mercury or oil vapour issuing as a jet through the orifice O exhausts the system attached to the tube A. Gas molecules in A diffuse through the layer of mercury vapour around the orifice and are carried down with the vapour stream by molecular bombardment. The mercury vapour is cooled at the jet causing it to condense, so preventing it from diffusing back into the system which is being exhausted. See Fig. 3.

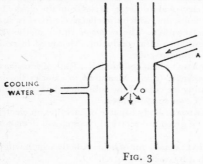

COOLING WATER →

FIG. 3

CONDENSER (chem.). Liebig condenser. Apparatus for converting vapour into liquid during *distillation* (q.v.). In its simplest form consists of a tube along which the vapour passes and is cooled, usually by cold water flowing through an outer jacket surrounding the tube.

CONDENSER, ELECTRICAL. In its simplest form consists of two parallel metal plates separated by a thin layer of air or other non-conducting material (dielectric). Device for holding or 'storing' static electricity. The *capacity* (q.v.) of a parallel plate condenser is given by the expression $\frac{Sk}{4\pi d}$, where S = area of plate, d = thickness of the dielectric, and k = its *specific inductive capacity* (q.v.).

CONDENSER MICROPHONE. *Microphone* (q.v.) consisting essentially of a condenser, one plate of which is fixed and the other plate forms the diaphragm upon which the sound waves fall. The vibrations of the diaphragm vary the capacity of the condenser, which in turn alters the potential across a high resistance. This varying potential is then amplified in the normal way.

CONDENSER, OPTICAL. Device used in optical instruments to converge rays of light; e.g. in the microscope a condenser lens is used to converge light upon the object to be viewed.

CONDUCTANCE, ELECTRICAL. The *reciprocal* (q.v.) of the *resistance* (q.v.) of a conductor. Measured in 'reciprocal ohms', or *mhos*.

CONDUCTION, THERMAL. The transmission of heat from places of higher to places of lower temperature in a substance, by the interaction of molecules possessing greater *kinetic energy* (q.v.) with those possessing less. In gases the heat energy is transmitted by collision of the gaseous molecules, those possessing the greater kinetic energy imparting, on collision, some of their energy to molecules having less. Conduction in liquids is mainly due to the same process. In solid electrical conductors, the chief contribution to thermal conduction arises from a similar process taking place between the free electrons present. The interaction of the molecules responsible for thermal conduction in solid electrical insulators arises from the elastic binding forces between the molecules, which are effectively fixed in space.

CONDUCTIVITY, ELECTRICAL. The *reciprocal* (q.v.) of the *resistivity* (q.v.) or specific resistance of a conductor. Measured in reciprocal ohms or mhos per centimetre cube.

CONDUCTIVITY, THERMAL; heat conductivity. Rate of transfer of heat along a body by *conduction* (q.v.). Measured in calories flowing per second across a centimetre cube of the substance, having a temperature difference of $1°$ C. on opposite faces.

CONDUCTOR, ELECTRICAL. Body capable of carrying an electric current; a body which, if given an electrical charge, will distribute that charge over itself.

CONDUCTOR, THERMAL; conductor of heat. A body which will permit heat to flow through it by *conduction* (q.v.).

CONDY'S FLUID. Solution of sodium and calcium (or sometimes aluminium) permanganate, $NaMnO_4$. Used as a disinfectant.

CONE (math.). Solid figure traced by a straight line passing through a fixed point, the *vertex*, and moving along a fixed circle. For a cone of vertical height h, slant height s, and radius of base r, the volume is given by $V = \frac{1}{3}\pi r^2 h$, and the area of the curved surface $A = \pi rs$.

CONGRUENT FIGURES. Geometrical figures equal in all respects.

CONIC SECTIONS. Curves obtained by the intersection of a plane with a cone; include the *circle, ellipse, parabola* and *hyperbola*.

CONJUGATE POINTS of a lens. Points on either side of the lens, such that an object placed at either will produce an image at the other.

CONJUNCTION (astr.). A planet (or other heavenly body) is said to be in *superior conjunction* when it is in a straight line with the Sun and the Earth; a planet with its orbit inside that of the Earth is in *inferior conjunction* when it is between the Sun and the Earth and in line with them.

CONSERVATION OF MASS AND ENERGY. The sum total of energy and mass $\times c^2$ (where c = velocity of light) is constant for any system and cannot increase or decrease. The *principle of conservation of energy*, i.e. that energy cannot be created or destroyed, and the *principle of conservation of matter*, i.e. that matter cannot be created or destroyed, valid in Newtonian mechanics, are very close approximations for all motions involving velocities which are small compared with the velocity of light. The use of these principles in such circumstances leads to very valuable results.

CONSERVATION OF MOMENTUM, principle of. For a perfectly elastic collision, the total *momentum* (q.v.) of two bodies before impact is equal to their total momentum after impact. When velocities comparable to the speed of light are being considered, the variation of mass with velocity (see *relativity*, theory of) must be taken into account, and the expression for the momentum becomes

$$\text{Momentum} = mv = \frac{m_0}{\sqrt{1 - \dfrac{v^2}{c^2}}} \times v, \text{ where } \begin{array}{l} m_0 = \text{rest mass and} \\ v = \text{velocity of the body.} \end{array}$$

CONSTANT (math., phys.). Any quantity which does not vary; e.g. π ('pi'), the ratio of the circumference to the diameter of any circle.

CONSTANT BOILING MIXTURE. See *azeotropic mixture*.

CONSTANT COMPOSITION, LAW OF. See *chemical combination, laws of*.

CONSTANTAN. Alloy of copper containing 10–55% nickel; electrical resistance does not vary with temperature; used in electrical equipment.

CONTACT ANGLE, for solid-liquid interface. The angle included between the tangent plane to the surface of a liquid and the tangent plane to the surface of a solid at any point along their line of contact.

CONTACT POTENTIAL DIFFERENCE. If two dissimilar metals, *a* and *b*, are in contact (see Fig. 4), then in general a potential difference exists

FIG. 4

between point *A*, just outside conductor *a*, and a point *B*, just outside conductor *b*. This is the contact potential difference of the two conductors.

CONTACT PROCESS. Industrial process for the manufacture of sulphuric acid, H_2SO_4. Sulphur dioxide, SO_2, is made to combine with oxygen by passing over a heated *catalyst* (q.v.), usually platinum or platinized asbestos. The sulphur trioxide, SO_3, which is formed is combined with water to give sulphuric acid.

CONTINUOUS SPECTRUM. See *spectrum*.

CONTINUUM. A continuous series of component parts passing into one another; e.g. the three space dimensions and the time dimension are considered to form a four-dimensional continuum.

CONVECTION. Transference of heat through a liquid or gas by the actual movement of the fluid. Portions in contact with the source of heat become hotter, expand, become less dense and rise; their place is taken by colder portions, thus setting up *convection currents*.

CONVERGENCE. Coming to a point.

CONVERGING LENS. Lens capable of bringing to a point a beam of light passing through it; a convex lens.

CONVERSE. The transposition of a statement consisting of a fact or datum and a consequent conclusion. Thus the converse of the proposition 'equal chords of a circle are equidistant from the centre' is 'chords which are equidistant from the centre of a circle are equal.' A converse of a statement is not necessarily true.

CONVEX. Curving outwards; e.g. a convex lens, one thicker at the centre than at the edges.

CO-ORDINATE GEOMETRY. See *analytical geometry*.

CO-ORDINATES, CARTESIAN. The two distances of any point, *P*, from two axes in its plane intersecting (generally at right angles) at a point *O*, the *origin*. The distance from the horizontal or *x*-axis (measured along the vertical or *y*-axis) is termed the *ordinate* of *P*; the distance from the *y*-axis is the *abscissa*.

CO PAL. Natural resin obtained from certain trees. Used in varnishes.

CO-PLANAR (math.). In the same plane.

CO-POLYMERIZATION. See *polymerization*.

COPPER. Cu. Element. A.W. 63·54. At. No. 29. Red metal, m.p. 1084° C. S.G. 8·95. Very malleable and ductile; after silver, the best conductor of electricity. Unaffected by water or steam. Occurs as the free metal, and as cuprite or ruby ore, Cu_2O; copper glance, Cu_2S; copper pyrites, $CuFeS_2$. Extracted from sulphide ores by alternate roasting and fusing with sand, thus removing iron and volatile impurities, and leaving a mixture of cuprous oxide and sulphide. This is then heated in a reverberatory furnace, giving impure copper, which is then refined by various methods. Used for steam boilers, electrical wire and apparatus in electrotyping and in numerous alloys, e.g. bronze, brass, speculum metal, gun metal, bell metal, Dutch metal, manganin, constantan, nickel silver, German silver, etc.

COPPER SULPHATE, cupric sulphate, blue vitriol. $CuSO_4.5H_2O$. Blue crystalline soluble salt, used in plant spraying.

COPPERAS, green vitriol, ferrous sulphate. $FeSO_4.7H_2O$.

CORAL. Deposit of impure calcium carbonate, $CaCO_3$, formed of the hard skeletons of various marine organisms.

CORDITE. Explosive prepared from *nitrocellulose* (q.v.) and *nitroglycerine* (q.v.).

CORONA. White irregular halo surrounding the sun, visible during a total eclipse.

CORPUSCULAR THEORY. Theory that light consists of minute corpuscles in rapid motion. The original corpuscular theory was abandoned in the middle of the nineteenth century in favour of the wave theory of light, first put forward by Huygens in 1678. Later research has shown that all light phenomena can be interpreted in terms of *photons* or waves, so that the two descriptions are merely two different ways of viewing one and the same reality.

CORROSION. Surface chemical action, especially on metals, by the action of moisture, air or chemicals.

CORROSIVE SUBLIMATE, mercuric chloride. $HgCl_2$. White crystalline soluble salt, m.p. 275° C. Very poisonous; used as a germicide.

CORUBIN. Crystalline aluminium oxide, Al_2O_3. Obtained as a by-product of the *thermit* (q.v.) process.

CORUNDUM. Natural aluminium oxide, Al_2O_3. Crystalline substance nearly as hard as diamond, used as an abrasive.

COSECANT. See *trigonometrical ratios*.

COSINE. See *trigonometrical ratios*.

COSMIC DUST. Small particles of matter, probably ranging in size from one-hundredth to one ten-thousandth of a millimetre, distributed throughout space.

COSMIC RAYS. Very energetic radiation falling upon the Earth from outer space, and consisting chiefly, if not entirely, of charged particles. The majority of these are most probably *protons* (q.v.), although *electrons* (q.v.) may also be present. There is also evidence that a small component of the primary radiation consists of heavy atomic nuclei.

The primary particles, when incident upon our atmosphere, cause several secondary processes. Proton-neutron collisions in the top tenth of the atmosphere give rise to *mesons* (q.v.), several different types of which are now known. High-energy electrons are created in the atmosphere by meson decay, by interaction of high energy protons with nuclei, by 'knock-on' collisions of mesons with electrons, etc. (An ionizing particle passing through a gas very occasionally makes a close collision with an electron and knocks it out of its atom with high energy. This is termed a *knock-on collision*.) These high-energy electrons give rise to *cosmic ray showers* (q.v.) resulting in the creation of photons, positrons and further electrons. Energies as high as 10^{17} electron-volts have been observed with cosmic ray particles. The origin of cosmic rays is not known with certainty. See also *east-west asymmetry*.

COSMIC RAY SHOWERS, cascade showers. High-energy electrons passing through the atmosphere lose energy rapidly, chiefly by the process of 'collision radiation'; i.e. the electron, on passing through the electric field of an atomic nucleus, emits a *photon* (q.v.). This photon, after travelling a short distance, is absorbed by interaction with a nuclear electric field giving rise to a *positron* (q.v.) and an electron. The conversion of a photon into an electron and positron in this manner is called '*pair production*'. This pair of newly-created particles produce two further photons by collision radiation. These photons are again absorbed, giving rise to more electrons and positrons. This process continues, producing a cascade or shower of particles, until the final electrons and positrons created possess insufficient energy to emit the 'collision radiation'.

COSMOGONY. Theories as to the origin of the heavenly bodies.

COTANGENT. See *trigonometrical ratios*.

COULOMB, THE. Unit of quantity of electricity; quantity of electricity transferred by 1 *ampere* (q.v.) in one second. *Absolute coulomb* = 1 absolute ampere in one second; 10^{-1} *electromagnetic units* (q.v.); 3×10^9 *electrostatic units* (q.v.).

COUPLE (phys.), torque. Two equal and opposite parallel forces acting upon a body. The moment of a couple is the product of either force and the perpendicular distance between the line of action of the forces.

CRACKING (chem.), pyrolysis. Decomposition of a chemical substance by heat; especially the conversion of mineral oils of high boiling point into more volatile oils suitable for petrol engines, by 'cracking' the larger molecules of the heavy oils into smaller ones.

CREAM OF TARTAR. Potassium hydrogen tartrate. $C_4O_6H_5K$. Sparingly soluble white solid, obtained from *argol* (tartar) (q.v.).

CREOSOTE. A distillation product obtained from tar; term often restricted to the product from the tar obtained by the destructive distillation of wood. Oily, transparent liquid containing *phenol* (q.v.) and *cresol* (q.v.). Used for preserving timber.

CRITH. Weight of 1 litre of hydrogen at 0° C. and a pressure of 760 mm.; approximately ·09 gm.

CRITICAL ANGLE of a medium (phys.). The least angle of incidence at which *total internal reflection* (q.v.) occurs. When a ray of light passing from a denser to a less dense medium, e.g. glass to air, meets the surface, a portion of the light does not emerge, but is internally reflected. As the angle of incidence increases, the intensity of the internally reflected beam also increases until an angle is reached when the whole beam is thrown back, total internal reflection taking place.

CRITICAL DAMPING. A measuring instrument is said to be *critically damped* when it takes up its equilibrium deflection in the shortest possible time, the oscillations of the indicator (needle) about the equilibrium position being quickly damped out. Galvanometers are normally used critically damped.

CRITICAL POTENTIAL, excitation potential. An *ionization* or *radiation potential* (q.v.).

CRITICAL PRESSURE. The pressure of the saturated vapour of a substance at the *critical temperature* (q.v.).

CRITICAL TEMPERATURE of a gas. The temperature above which the gas cannot be liquefied by pressure alone.

CRITICAL VELOCITY. The velocity at which the flow of a liquid ceases to be streamline (see *streamline flow*) and becomes turbulent.

CRITICAL VOLUME of a substance is the volume occupied by 1 gm. of the substance at the *critical temperature* (q.v.) and under the *critical pressure* (q.v.).

CROSS-LINKAGE (chem.). The joining of polymer molecules (see *polymerization*) to each other by *valency bonds* (q.v.). A polymer may be imagined, in the simplest case, to consist of very long chain-like *molecules* (q.v.); cross-linkage would have the effect of joining adjacent chains by lateral links.

CROSS-SECTION. Term used in nuclear physics to represent the effective area which an atom of an element presents to an incident beam of elementary particles (neutrons, protons, etc.) in various atomic processes; e.g. the scattering of the incident beam by the element (scattering cross-section); capture of the incident particles by the element (capture cross-section). Thus, if the capture cross-section of an element for neutrons is α, and a volume containing x atoms of it is exposed to a uniform beam of neutrons, the number of neutrons captured by the element will be $\dfrac{x\alpha}{\text{area of beam}} \times$ total number of neutrons in the beam. The value of the cross-section for any particular process depends on (a) the element being bombarded; (b) the bombarding particles; (c) the energy of the bombarding particles.

CROWN GLASS. Variety of *glass* (q.v.) containing potassium or barium in place of sodium; less fusible than ordinary soda glass; used in optical instruments.

CRUCIBLE. Vessel of heat-resisting material used for high-temperature chemical reactions.

CRYOGEN. *Freezing mixture* (q.v.).

CRYOHYDRATES. Crystalline substances, containing the solute with a definite molecular proportion of water, which crystallize out from solutions cooled below the freezing point of pure water.

CRYOLITE. Natural sodium aluminium fluoride, Na_3AlF_6. Used in the manufacture of *aluminium* (q.v.).

CRYOPHORUS. Apparatus used to demonstrate the cooling effect of evaporation.

CRYOSTAT. Vessel in which a specified low temperature may be maintained.

CRYOSCOPIC METHOD for the determination of molecular weights; freezing-point method. The determination of the molecular weight of a dissolved substance by noting the depression of freezing point produced by a known concentration. See *depression of freezing point*.

CRYSTAL. Substance solidified in a definite geometrical form. Most solid substances, when pure, are obtainable in a definite crystalline form.

CRYSTAL DETECTOR. See *detector*. Consists of a fine wire ('cat's whisker') in contact with a crystal of galena (PbS) or other suitable substance. This arrangement is a good conductor of electricity in one direction, and suppresses most of the flow of electricity in the other direction.

CRYSTAL OSCILLATOR. A source of electrical oscillation of very constant frequency determined by the physical characteristics of a quartz crystal. See *quartz clock*.

CRYSTALLOGRAPHY. Study of the geometrical form of crystals.

CRYSTALLOIDS. Substances which, in solution, are able to pass through a *semi-permeable membrane* (q.v.); substances which do not usually form *colloidal solutions* (q.v.).

CUBE. 1. A regular hexahedron; regular solid figure with six square faces. 2. The third power of a number. E.g. 8 is the cube of 2, 2^3.

CUBE ROOT, $\sqrt[3]{}$, of a number A is the quantity which, when 'cubed' (i.e. raised to the third power), gives A. Thus 2 is the cube root of 8.

CUBIC CENTIMETRE. c.c. Metric unit of volume. 1000 c.c. = 1 *litre* (q.v.) very nearly. Term used synonymously with millilitre, ml., one-thousandth of a litre.

CUPEL. Dish used in the extraction of the noble metals by *cupellation* (q.v.).

CUPELLATION. Separation of silver, gold and other noble metals from impurities which are oxidized by hot air. The impure metal is placed in a cupel, a flat dish made of porous refractory material, and a blast of hot air is directed upon it in a special furnace. The impurities are oxidized by the air and are partly swept away by the blast and partly absorbed by the cupel.

CUPRIC. Compound of *bivalent* (q.v.) copper. Most of the commoner copper compounds are cupric salts.

CUPROUS. Compound of *univalent* (q.v.) copper.

CUPROUS OXIDE, red copper oxide, Cu_2O. Red insoluble powder, formed when *Fehling's solution* (q.v.) is reduced.

CURARE. Very poisonous material, containing certain *alkaloids* (q.v.). Obtained from various South American trees.

CURIE, the. Measure of the activity of a radioactive substance (see *radioactivity*). Originally defined as the quantity of radon in radioactive equilibrium with 1 gm. of radium. Now extended to cover all radioactive isotopes by the definition 'that quantity of a radioactive isotope which decays at the rate of 3.7×10^{10} disintegrations per second'.

CURIE POINT, Curie temperature. The temperature for a given *ferromagnetic* (q.v.) substance above which it becomes merely *paramagnetic* (q.v.).

CURIUM. Cm. *Transuranic element* (q.v.), At. No. 96. Radioactive.

CURRENT, electric. See *electric current*.

CURRENT BALANCE. Instrument for the determination of a current in absolute *electromagnetic units* (q.v.). Consists of two similar coils attached to the extremities of a balance arm. Above and below each of these coils is a fixed coil. The six coils are connected in series in such a way that when the current is allowed to pass through them, the beam experiences maximum torque. The beam is restored to its horizontal equilibrium position by means of a known torque supplied by a rider sliding along the arm. From the known torque and the geometry of the system the current can be calculated.

CURRENT DENSITY, in *electrolysis* (q.v.). Current per unit area of electrode.

CURSOR. Transparent slider with a fine hair-line; used in *slide-rules* (q.v.).

CYANAMIDE. NH_2CN. Colourless crystals, m.p. $42°$ C. Name often applied to *calcium cyanamide* (q.v.).

CYANIDE. Salt of hydrocyanic acid, HCN. All cyanides are intensely poisonous.

CYANIDE OF POTASSIUM. KCN.

CYANIDE PROCESS for gold. Extraction of gold from its ores by dissolving the gold in a solution of potassium cyanide, KCN, reducing the resulting potassium aurocyanide, $KAu(CN)_2$, with zinc, filtering off, melting down and cupelling (see *cupellation*) the metal.

CYANOGEN. C_2N_2. Colourless, very poisonous gas with a smell of bitter almonds. In its chemical properties resembles the *halogens* (q.v.), forming cyanides analogous to the chlorides, etc.

CYANOTYPE. See *blueprint*.

CYBERNETICS. The theory of communication and control mechanisms in living beings and machines.

CYCLE (phys.). Any series of changes or operations performed by or on a system, which brings it back to its original state. E.g. the frequency of an alternating current is measured in cycles per second.

CYCLIC FIGURE (math.). Figure through all the vertices or corners of which a circle may be drawn; figure inscribed in a circle.

CYCLIC HYDROCARBONS. Organic compounds of carbon and hydrogen only; some or all of the carbon atoms in the molecule being linked in a closed ring structure; e.g. *benzene* (q.v.).

CYCLIC QUADRILATERAL. Four-sided plane rectilinear figure through the vertices of which a circle may be drawn. The pairs of opposite angles are supplementary (i.e. total 180°).

CYCLOID. Figure traced out in space by a point on the circumference of a circle which rolls without slipping along a fixed straight line.

CYCLONITE, hexogen, R.D.X. $(CH_2N.NO_2)_3$. A very powerful explosive made from *hexamine* (q.v.).

CYCLOTRON. An apparatus for imparting to charged particles of atomic magnitudes, energies of several million *electron-volts* (q.v.). The ions or charged particles are caused to traverse a spiral path between two hollow semi-circular electrodes, called *dees*, by means of a suitable magnetic field applied perpendicularly to the plane of the dees. At each half-revolution the particles receive an energy increase of some tens of thousands of electron-volts from an oscillating voltage applied between the dees.

CYLINDER. Solid figure traced out by a rectangle rotating round one side as axis. For a cylinder having vertical height h and radius of base r, the volume is $\pi r^2 h$ and the total surface area $2\pi r(h + r)$.

D

DAILY VARIATION of the Earth's magnetic field. Small variation of the horizontal intensity, magnetic declination and dip recurring over a period of a day. See *magnetism, terrestrial.*

DALTON'S ATOMIC THEORY. See *atomic theory.*

DAMPING. Decrease in the *amplitude* (q.v.) of an oscillation or wave motion with time.

DANIELL CELL. Primary cell having a negative pole of amalgamated zinc, standing in a porous pot containing dilute sulphuric acid. This pot stands in copper sulphate solution, which also contains the positive pole, a copper plate. On completion of the external circuit, a current flows and the following reactions take place: at the negative pole, zinc is dissolved, zinc sulphate being formed; at the positive pole, copper is deposited. The E.M.F. is 1·1 volt.

DARK GROUND ILLUMINATION. Device used in microscopy, whereby transparent or unstained objects are made to appear as bright particles on a black background.

DASH-POT. Mechanical damping device. Depends upon the fact that when a body moves through a fluid medium, viscous forces are set up which damp the motion of the body.

DAVY LAMP. See *safety lamp*.

D.D.T. $(C_6H_4Cl)_2:CHCCl_3$. White powder with a fruity smell. Used as insecticide.

DE BROGLIE WAVE-LENGTH. A moving particle, whatever its nature, has wave properties associated with it. For a particle of mass m moving with velocity v, the wave-length of the associated *de Broglie wave* is given by $\lambda = \dfrac{h}{mv}$, where h is *Planck's constant* (q.v.).

DEBYE AND HUCKEL'S THEORY of electrolysis. An explanation of the phenomena of *electrolysis* (q.v.) put forward to overcome certain difficulties which arise in the interpretation of the phenomena on the classical theory of electrolytic dissociation. It is assumed that strong electrolytes are completely dissociated, and that the increase in equivalent conductivity which is observed with dilution is due not to an increase in the fraction ionized, but to an increase in the mobility of the ions, due to the decrease of electrostatic forces.

DECANTATION. Separation of a solid from a liquid by allowing the former to settle and pouring off the latter.

DECAY CONSTANT. See *transformation constant*.

DECAY, PERIOD OF. See *half-value period*.

DECIBEL. The decibel is a unit used to compare, or indicate changes in, levels of intensity. Two quantities of intensities I_1 and I_2 are said to differ in intensity by x decibels where

$$x = 10 \log_{10} \frac{I_2}{I_1}.$$

The unit is often used to express sound intensities. In this case I_2 is the intensity of the sound under consideration and I_1 the intensity of some reference level, usually the intensity of the lowest audible note of the same frequency.

DECINORMAL SOLUTION. A solution containing one-tenth of a gram-equivalent per litre.

DECLINATION (astr.). The angular distance of a heavenly body from the equator.

DECLINATION, MAGNETIC. See *magnetic declination*.

DECOMPOSITION (chem.). Breaking up of a chemical compound. E.g. mercuric oxide, HgO, decomposes on heating into mercury and oxygen.

DECREPITATION. Bursting or cracking of crystals of certain substances on heating, mainly due to expansion of water within the crystals.

DEFICIENCY DISEASES. Diseases produced by lack of a particular *vitamin* (q.v.) or other essential food factor in the diet; e.g. scurvy, caused by the deficiency of vitamin C.

DEFORMATION. Alteration in the size or shape of a body.

DEGAUSSING. De-magnetization of a magnetized substance. Achieved by surrounding the substance with a coil carrying an alternating current of ever-decreasing magnitude.

DEGREE. Subdivision of an interval in a scale of measurement; e.g. the *Centigrade degree* (q.v.).

DEGREE, measure of angle. See *angle.*

DEGREES OF FREEDOM (chem.). Term used in the *phase rule* (q.v.); the least number of independent variables defining the state of a system (e.g. the temperature and pressure in the case of a gas) which must be given definite values before this state is completely determined.

DEGREES OF LATITUDE AND LONGITUDE. See *latitude, longitude.*

DEHYDRATION. Elimination or removal of water; term usually applied to the removal of chemically combined water. E.g. concentrated sulphuric acid, H_2SO_4, acts as a dehydrating agent on substances which contain hydrogen and oxygen in the proportions in which they occur in water.

DEKA-. Prefix denoting ten times, in metric units.

DELIQUESCENT. Having the property of picking up moisture from the air to such an extent as to dissolve in it; becoming liquid on exposure to air.

DELTA METAL. Alloy of copper (55%) and zinc (43%) with small amounts of iron and other metals.

DELTA RAYS. *Electrons* (q.v.) moving at relatively low speeds. Emitted in large numbers by surfaces exposed to *alpha rays* (q.v.).

DENOMINATOR (math.). The number below the line in a vulgar fraction; e.g. 4 in $\frac{3}{4}$.

DENSITOMETER. Instrument for the measurement of the density of an image produced by light, X-rays, gamma rays, etc., on a photographic plate.

DENSITY (phys.). Measured as mass per unit volume; expressed in grams per c.c. in metric (C.G.S.) units. In these units, numerically equal to the *specific gravity* (q.v.).

DENSITY, OPTICAL. If one medium has a greater refractive index than another for light of a given wave-length, then it has the greater *optical density* for that wave-length.

DEPILATORY. Substance used for removing hair.

DEPOLARIZATION. Prevention of electrical *polarization* (q.v.) in a cell. In the *Leclanché cell* (q.v.) polarization is reduced by surrounding the positive carbon pole with manganese dioxide, MnO_2. This oxidizes the hydrogen liberated at the pole, the chief cause of polarization.

DEPRESSION, ANGLE OF. If B is a point below the level of another point A, the angle of depression of B from A is the angle which AB makes with the horizontal plane AX through A. See Fig. 5.

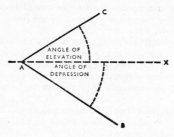

FIG. 5.

DEPRESSION OF FREEZING POINT. Lowering of the freezing point of a liquid when a solid is dissolved in it. With certain exceptions, the depression is proportional to the number of molecules or ions present, and the depression produced by the same molecular concentration of any substance is a constant for a given solvent. This gives rise to the *cryoscopic method* (q.v.) for the determination of molecular weights.

DERIVATIVE (chem.). Substance derived or prepared from some other substance, usually retaining the general structure of the parent substance. E.g. nitrobenzene, $C_6H_5NO_2$, is a derivative of benzene, one of the hydrogen atoms in every molecule of the latter being replaced by a nitro group, NO_2.

DERIVATIVE (math.). Derived function; result of *differentiation* (q.v.) of a mathematical function.

DERIVED FUNCTION. See *derivative*.

DERIVED UNITS. Units of physical measurement, other than the *fundamental units* (q.v.) of length, mass and time, but derived from these. E.g. the unit for velocity is derived from the units for length and time, velocity being expressed as length per unit time, e.g. feet per second.

DESICCATION. Drying; removal of moisture.

DESICCATOR. Apparatus used in laboratories for drying substances and for preventing *hygroscopic* (q.v.) substances from picking up moisture. Consists of a glass vessel with a close-fitting ground lid, and containing some hygroscopic substance, e.g. phosphorus pentoxide, P_2O_5.

DESTRUCTIVE DISTILLATION. Heating a complex substance to produce chemical changes in it, and distilling off the volatile substances so formed. E.g. the destructive distillation of coal produces *coal-gas* (q.v.) and many other valuable products.

DETECTOR, rectifier. Device for rectifying alternating currents induced in a conductor by a modulated radio-frequency wave, to give a direct current varying in accordance with the modulation envelope of the original wave. The purpose is achieved by the *crystal detector* (q.v.) the *rectifying valve* (q.v.), etc.

DETERGENT. A cleaning agent; term usually restricted to substances used in solution for cleaning a solid surface by action other than simple dissolution; e.g. by using a *surface-active agent* (q.v.).

DETINNING. Recovery of metallic tin from scrap tin-plate by the action of chlorine, which combines with the tin to form volatile stannic chloride, $SnCl_4$.

DETONATING GAS. Mixture of hydrogen and oxygen in a volume ratio of $2:1$; i.e. in the volume ratio required to form water. Extremely explosive when lit or sparked.

DETONATION. Extremely rapid and powerful *explosion* (q.v.).

DEUTERIUM. D, $_1H^2$, heavy hydrogen. *Isotope* (q.v.) of hydrogen. Atomic mass is $2 \cdot 0147$, mass number (see *isotopic weight*) $= 2$. Occurs in small amounts in water as the oxide, D_2O (*heavy water*, q.v.). Obtained chiefly by the fractional electrolysis of water.

DEUTERON. Nucleus of *deuterium* (q.v.) atom.

DEVARDA'S ALLOY. Alloy of 50% copper, 45% aluminium, 5% zinc.

DEVELOPING, PHOTOGRAPHIC. The action of certain chemicals, usually organic reducing agents, on an exposed photographic plate or film in order to bring out the latent image. The developer reduces those areas of the silver salts which had been exposed to light to metallic silver. This remains as a black deposit. See *photography*.

DEVITRIFICATION of glass. Crystallization of glass, which is normally an amorphous mixture in a *metastable* (q.v.) state; when crystallization takes place, the glass loses its characteristic state of clear transparency.

DEW. Liquid water produced by *condensation* (q.v.) of water vapour in the air when the temperature falls sufficiently for the vapour to reach saturation.

DEW POINT. The temperature at which the water vapour present in the air saturates the air and begins to condense, i.e. dew begins to form.

DEWAR FLASK. Glass vessel used for keeping liquids at temperatures differing from that of the surrounding air. This is done by reducing to a minimum the transfer of heat between the liquid and the air. Consists of a double-walled flask with the space between the two walls exhausted to a very high vacuum, to minimize transfer of heat by *convection* (q.v.) and conduction. The inner surfaces of the walls are silvered to reduce transfer of heat by radiation; areas of contact between the two walls are kept at a minimum to keep down *conduction* (q.v.) of heat. See Fig. 6.

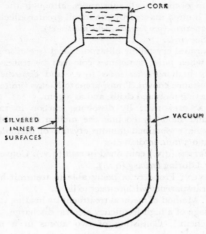

CORK

SILVERED INNER SURFACES

VACUUM

FIG. 6.

DEXTRIN. British gum, starch gum. Mixture of gummy *carbohydrates* (q.v.) obtained by the partial *hydrolysis* (q.v.) of starch.

DEXTROROTATORY. Rotating or deviating the plane of vibration of polarized light to the right (observer looking against the oncoming light).

DEXTROSE. See *glucose*.

DIAGONAL. Line joining the intersections of two pairs of sides of a rectilinear figure.

DIALYSIS. Separation of *colloids* (q.v.) in solution from other dissolved substances (crystalloids) by selective diffusion through a *semi-permeable* membrane (q.v.). Such a membrane is slightly permeable to the molecules of the crystalloids, but not to the larger molecules or groups of molecules in the colloidal state.

DIALYZED IRON. A *colloidal solution* (q.v.) of ferric hydroxide, $Fe(OH)_3$. Deep red liquid, used in medicine.

DIALYZER. Arrangement for effecting *dialysis* (q.v.). The solution to be dialyzed is placed in a vessel in which it is separated from water by a *semi-permeable membrane* (q.v.); this is not permeable to the substance in the colloidal state, which will eventually remain as a pure solution on its side of the membrane.

DIAMAGNETIC. Term applied to a substance having a small negative *magnetic susceptibility* (q.v.). This type of magnetism is due to a change in the orbital motion of the electrons in the atoms of the substance consequent on the application of an external magnetic field. The phenomenon occurs in all substances, although the resulting diamagnetism is often masked by the much greater effects due to para- or ferromagnetism (see *ferromagnetic substances*).

DIAMETER. See *circle*.

DIAMOND. Natural crystalline allotropic form (see *allotropy*) of carbon. Colourless when pure, sometimes coloured by traces of impurities. Has a very high *refractive index* (q.v.) and *dispersive power* (q.v.). Hardest substance known. Transparent to X-rays (imitations are not). Used for cutting tools and drills, and as a gem.

DIAMONDS, ARTIFICIAL. By dissolving carbon in molten iron at 3500° C. and suddenly cooling the molten mass, Moissan (1893) claimed to have obtained minute crystals of diamond, the largest being about 0·5 mm. in diameter.

DIASTASE. *Enzyme* (q.v.) contained in *malt* (q.v.). Converts starch into *maltose* (q.v.) during *brewing* (q.v.).

DIATHERMANCY. Property of being able to transmit heat radiation; similar to transparency with respect to light.

DIATHERMY. Method of medical treatment by heating the body-tissues by the passage of a high-frequency electric discharge.

DIATOMIC (chem.). Consisting of two atoms in a molecule; e.g. hydrogen gas, H_2.

DIAZO COMPOUNDS. Organic compounds of the general formula $RN:NR'$. Many are important in the manufacture of dyes.

DIBASIC ACID. Acid containing two atoms of *acidic hydrogen* (q.v.) in a molecule; acid giving rise to two series of salts, normal and acid salts; e.g. sulphuric acid, H_2SO_4, which gives rise to normal sulphates and bisulphates.

DICHROMATE CELL, bichromate cell. Primary cell having a positive pole of carbon and a negative pole of zinc in a liquid consisting of a solution of sulphuric acid, H_2SO_4, and potassium dichromate, $K_2Cr_2O_7$, the latter acting as a depolarizing agent by its oxidizing action.

DICHROMATE OF POTASH. See *potassium dichromate*.

DICHROMATISM. A medium is said to show dichromatism when the colour of light transmitted by it depends on the thickness of the medium.

DIELECTRIC. Non-conductor of electricity, insulator. Substance in which an *electric field* (q.v.) gives rise to no net flow of electric charge but only to a displacement of charge.

DIELECTRIC CONSTANT. See *specific inductive capacity*.

DIESEL ENGINE. Type of internal combustion engine which burns heavy oil. Air which is mixed with the oil is compressed and thereby heated to the ignition temperature of the oil.

DIFFERENTIAL COEFFICIENT, derived function. See *differentiation*.

DIFFERENTIATION (math.). Operation, used in the calculus, of obtaining the differential coefficient; if $y = x^n$, the differential coefficient, $\frac{dy}{dx} = nx^{n-1}$.

DIFFRACTION. When a beam of light passes through an aperture or past the edge of an opaque obstacle and is allowed to fall upon a screen, patterns of light and dark bands (with monochromatic light) or coloured bands (with white light) are observed near the edges of the beam, and extend into the geometrical shadow. This phenomenon, which is a particular case of *interference* (q.v.) is due to the wave nature of light, and is known as diffraction. The phenomenon is common to all wave motions.

DIFFRACTION GRATING. Device used to disperse a beam of light, X-rays or other *electromagnetic waves* (q.v.) into its constituent wavelengths, i.e. for producing its *spectrum* (q.v.). It may consist of any device which acts upon an incident wave front in a manner similar to that of a regular array of parallel slits where the slit width is of the same order as the wave-length of the incident radiation. Such gratings may be prepared by ruling equidistant parallel lines on to a glass (transmission grating) or metal surface (reflection grating). The grating may be plane or concave, the latter having self-focusing properties.

DIFFUSION OF GASES. Molecules of all gases move freely and tend to distribute themselves equally within the limits of the vessel enclosing the gas; thus all gases diffuse within the limits of any enclosing walls, and are all perfectly miscible with one another. The rates of diffusion of gases through porous bodies are inversely proportional to the square roots of their densities. (*Graham's law*, q.v.)

DIFFUSION OF LIGHT. Scattering or alteration of direction of light rays, such as is produced by transmission through frosted glass, fog, etc., or by irregular reflections at matt surfaces such as blotting paper.

DIFFUSION OF SOLUTIONS. Molecules or ions of a dissolved substance move freely through the solvent, the solution becoming uniform in concentration; the phenomenon is similar to *diffusion of gases* (q.v.).

DIGIT (astr.). One-twelfth of the diameter of the Sun or Moon; used to denote the extent of an eclipse.

DIGIT (math.). A single figure or numeral; e.g. 325 is a number of 3 digits.

DILATION, dilatation (phys.). Change in volume.

DILATOMETER. Apparatus used for measuring volume changes of substances. Generally consists of a bulb with a graduated stem.

DILUTE. Containing a large amount of solvent, generally water. 'Dilute' laboratory solutions of reagents are generally of twice normal strength, containing 2 gram-equivalents per litre. See *normality*.

DILUTION. 1. Further addition of water or other solvent to a solution.

2. The *reciprocal* (q.v.) of concentration; the volume of solvent in which unit quantity of solute is dissolved.

DIMENSIONS OF UNITS. The dimensions of a physical quantity are the powers to which the *fundamental units* (q.v.) (length l, mass m, time t, etc.) expressing that quantity are raised. E.g. volume, l^3, is of dimensions three in length; velocity, i.e. length per unit time, l/t, is of dimensions one in length and − 1 in time.

DIMORPHISM. Existence of a substance in two different crystalline forms.

DIMORPHOUS. Existing in two different crystalline forms.

DIODE. *Thermionic valve* (q.v.) containing two electrodes, anode and cathode. The diode is used chiefly for *rectification* (q.v.) and demodulation.

DIOPTRE. Unit of power of a lens; the power of a lens in dioptres is the reciprocal of its *focal length* (q.v.) in metres. The power of a converging lens is usually taken to be positive, that of a diverging lens negative.

DIP, magnetic. See *magnetic dip*.

DIP CIRCLE. Instrument for measuring the angle of *magnetic dip* (q.v.). Consists of a magnetized needle mounted to rotate in a vertical plane, the angle being measured on a circular scale, marked in degrees.

DIPOLE. Two equal point electric charges (*electric dipole*) or magnetic poles (*magnetic dipole*) of opposite sign, separated by a small distance. The dipole moment is the product of either charge (or pole) and the distance between the two. May also be expressed as the *couple* (q.v.) which would be required to maintain the dipole at right angles to a field (electric or magnetic) of unit intensity.

DIPOLE MOMENT. See *dipole*.

DIPPEL'S OIL. *Bone oil* (q.v.).

DIRECT CURRENT. An electric current flowing always in the same direction.

DIRECT DYES, cotton dyes, substantive dyes. Group of dyes which dye cotton, viscose rayon and other cellulose fibres direct, without the use of *mordants* (q.v.). Generally used with 'assistants' such as common salt or sodium sulphate, which assist absorption by the fibre.

DIRECT VISION SPECTROSCOPE. Spectroscope designed for compactness and portability. In this instrument, the middle portion of the spectrum (the yellow) remains undeviated. The eye thus looks in the direction of the source when observing the spectrum.

DISACCHARIDES. Group of sugars the molecules of which are derived by the *condensation* (q.v.) of two *monosaccharide* (q.v.) molecules with the elimination of a molecule of water. On *hydrolysis* (q.v.) disaccharides yield the corresponding monosaccharides. E.g. cane-sugar, sucrose, $C_{12}H_{22}O_{11}$, is a disaccharide which, on hydrolysis with dilute acids, gives a mixture of glucose and fructose, both monosaccharides having the formula $C_6H_{12}O_6$. See *inversion of cane-sugar*.

DISCHARGE (elec.). Neutralization or loss of electric charge.

DISCHARGE IN GASES. The passage of electricity through a tube containing a gas at low pressure. Electrons and ions present in the tube are accelerated towards their respective electrodes by the applied potential difference, the net transfer of charge constituting the current. The electrons are accelerated sufficiently to produce ions by collision with the gas molecules. Re-combination of oppositely charged ions gives rise to luminous glows at certain parts of the tube. The study of this phenomenon has led to many important results, including the discovery of the electron and of isotopes.

DISINFECTANT. Substance capable of destroying disease bacteria.

DISPERSE PHASE. The dissolved or suspended substance in a *colloidal solution* or *suspension* (q.v.).

DISPERSION MÉDIUM. Medium in which a substance in the *colloidal state* (q.v.) is dispersed; the *solvent* (q.v.) in a colloidal solution.

DISPERSION OF LIGHT. The splitting of light of mixed wave-lengths into a *spectrum* (q.v.). A beam of ordinary white light, e.g. sunlight, on passing through an optical *prism* (q.v.) or a *diffraction grating* (q.v.), is divided up or dispersed into light of the different wave-lengths of which it is composed; if the beam which emerges after dispersion is allowed to fall upon a screen, a coloured band or spectrum is observed. Dispersion by a prism is due to the fact that light-waves of different wave-lengths are refracted (see *refraction*) or bent through different angles on passing through the prism, and are thus separated.

DISPERSIVE POWER of a medium. A measure of the *dispersion of light* (q.v.) produced by a prism of a particular medium with respect to light of two specified wave-lengths ('1' and '2'); given by the ratio $\frac{\mu_1 - \mu_2}{\mu - 1}$, where μ_1 is the *refractive index* (q.v.) of the medium for wavelength 1, μ_2 that for wave-length 2, and μ is the average of μ_1 and μ_2. When considering the dispersive power of media for ordinary white light, the dispersive power is often defined as $\frac{\mu_b - \mu_r}{\mu_y - 1}$, where μ_b, μ_r and μ_y are the refractive indices for blue, red and yellow light respectively.

DISSOCIATION (chem.). A temporary, reversible decomposition of the molecules of a compound, which occurs under some particular conditions. In electrolytic dissociation, the molecules are split into ions (see *ionic hypothesis*). In *thermal dissociation*, the effect of heat is to decompose a definite fraction of the molecules; e.g. ammonium chloride, NH_4Cl, dissociates into ammonia, NH_3, and hydrogen chloride, HCl, on heating. The products re-combine on cooling, and the degree of dissociation depends on the temperature.

DISTILLATE. Liquid obtained by a condensation of the vapour in *distillation* (q.v.).

DISTILLATION. Process of converting a liquid into vapour, condensing the vapour, and collecting the condensed liquid or *distillate*. Used for separating mixtures of liquids of different boiling points or for separating a pure liquid from a non-volatile constituent.

DIURNAL. Daily; performed or completed once every 24 hours.

DIVALENT, bivalent. Having a *valency* (q.v.) of two.

DIVERGENT. Going away in different directions from a common path or point.

DIVERGING LENS. Lens which causes a parallel beam of light passing through it to diverge or spread out; *concave* (q.v.) lens.

DOLOMITE, pearl spar. Natural double carbonate of magnesium and calcium, $MgCO_3 . CaCO_3$. Whitish solid; occurs naturally in vast amounts, comprising whole mountain ranges.

DOPPLER EFFECT OF SOUND. Change of pitch of sound (i.e. frequency) received by an observer, due to relative motion between the observer and the source, the motions being measured with respect to the air considered at rest. E.g. the whistle of a moving train appears to be higher in pitch when moving towards an observer than when receding from him.

DOPPLER PRINCIPLE. To an observer approaching the source of any wave motion, the frequency appears greater than to an observer moving away; thus light emitted by a receding body would appear more red (red light being of a lower frequency than other colours) than if the body and the observer did not move relatively to each other. This has found important applications in the study of the nature of the Universe.

DOUBLE BOND (chem.). Two *valency* (q.v.) bonds linking two atoms in a chemical compound; characteristic of an *unsaturated* (q.v.) compound.

DOUBLE DECOMPOSITION (chem.). Chemical reaction between two compounds in which each of the original compounds is decomposed and two new compounds are formed. E.g. the action of sodium chloride on silver nitrate in solution to give insoluble silver chloride and sodium nitrate according to the equation $NaCl + AgNO_3 = AgCl + NaNO_3$.

DOUBLE REFRACTION. Formation of two refracted rays of light (see *refraction*) from a single incident ray; property of certain crystals, notably calcite.

DRACHM, FLUID. British unit of volume; 60 minims; 3·55 c.c.

DRUG. Chemical substance used in medicine; term often loosely applied to substances which form a 'habit' by causing a craving for further doses.

DRY CELL, dry battery. Type of small *Leclanché cell* (q.v.) containing no free liquid. The electrolyte of ammonium chloride is in the form of a paste, and the negative zinc pole forms the outer container of the cell. Used for torch batteries, radio batteries, etc.

DRY ICE. Solid carbon dioxide, CO_2, used in refrigeration.

DUCTILITY. Property, especially of metals, of being capable of being drawn out into a wire.

DUCTLESS GLANDS, endocrine glands. Glands or organs producing *hormones* (q.v.) in the body.

DULONG AND PETIT'S LAW. 'For a solid element, the product of the atomic weight and the specific heat, i.e. the *atomic heat* (q.v.), is a constant, approximately equal to 6·4 calories per gram-atom.' For validity of this law, see *atomic heat*.

DURALUMIN. Light hard aluminium alloy containing about 4% copper, and small amounts of magnesium, manganese and silicon.

DUTCH LIQUID, *ethylene dichloride* (q.v.).

DUTCH METAL. Alloy of copper and zinc; variety of *brass* (q.v.).

DWARF STAR. Star of low luminosity.

DYAD (chem.). Element having a *valency* (q.v.) of two.

DYES. Coloured substances which can be fixed firmly to a material to be dyed, so as to be more or less 'fast' to water, light and soap. Usually organic compounds; some which were originally extracted from plants are now made artificially from coal-tar byproducts; most modern dyes are entirely artificial and do not occur in Nature. See *acid dyes, azo dyes, basic dyes, direct dyes, mordants, vat dyes*.

DYNAMIC EQUILIBRIUM. If two opposing processes are going on at the same rate in a system, thus keeping the system unchanged, the system is said to be in *dynamic equilibrium*. E.g. a liquid in equilibrium with its saturated vapour; the rate of evaporation from the liquid surface is equal to the rate of condensation of the vapour.

DYNAMICS. Branch of *mechanics* (q.v.); the mathematical and physical study of the behaviour of bodies under the action of forces which produce changes of motion in them.

DYNAMITE. Explosive consisting of *nitroglycerine* (q.v.) absorbed in *kieselguhr* (q.v.).

DYNAMO. Device for converting mechanical energy into electrical energy. Depends on the fact that if an electrical conductor moves across a magnetic field, an electric current flows in the conductor. (See *induction*.) The simplest form of dynamo consists of a powerful *electromagnet* (q.v.), termed the *field magnet*, between the poles of which a suitable conductor, usually in the form of a coil or coils, termed the *armature*, is rotated. The mechanical energy of the rotation is thus converted into electrical energy in the form of a current in the armature.

DYNAMOMETER. Any instrument designed for the measurement of *power* (q.v.).

DYNATRON OSCILLATOR. Oscillator, using a *tetrode* (q.v.) (screen grid valve) in such a way that the anode current increases as the anode voltage is reduced.

DYNE. Absolute unit of *force* (q.v.); the force which, acting upon a mass of 1 gm., will impart to it an acceleration of 1 cm. per second per second.

DYSPROSIUM. Dy. Element. A.W. 162·46. At. No. 66. See *rare earths*.

E

EARTH, THE. *Planet* (q.v.) having its orbit between those of Venus and Mars. Sphere, slightly flattened towards the poles (i.e. approximating to an oblate *spheroid* (q.v.) in shape). Equatorial radius 3964 miles; polar radius 3950 miles. Mean density 5·53; mass $5·87 \times 10^{21}$ tons.

EARTHING a conductor. Making an electrical connection between the conductor and the Earth; the Earth is assumed to have zero *potential* (q.v.).

EARTH'S CRUST, lithosphere. Consists of an outer layer of surface soil of varying thickness lying upon a mass of hard rock several miles thick.

EARTH'S CRUST, CHEMICAL COMPOSITION OF. The approximate estimated percentages by weight of the chief chemical elements composing the Earth's crust are: oxygen 47%, silicon 28%, aluminium 8%, iron 4·5%, calcium 3·5%, sodium and potassium 2·5% each, magnesium 2·2%, titanium 0·5%, hydrogen 0·2%, carbon 0·2%, phosphorus and sulphur 0·1% each.

EARTH'S MAGNETISM. See *magnetism, terrestrial*.

EAST-WEST ASYMMETRY OF COSMIC RAYS. The observed intensity of *cosmic ray* (q.v.) particles coming from the West is greater than that coming from the East at any given latitude. This asymmetry is due to the deflection of the primary charged cosmic ray particles by the magnetic field of the Earth, and indicates a preponderance of positively charged particles in the incoming radiation.

EAU DE JAVELLE. *Javelle water* (q.v.).

EBONITE, vulcanite. Hard black insulating material made by the action of rubber with high proportions of sulphur. Contains about 30% combined sulphur.

EBULLITION. *Boiling* (q.v.).

ECHELON (phys.). Type of grating which replaces the ordinary *diffraction grating* in spectroscopy when very high resolution is required. Consists essentially of a pile of plates of exactly equal thickness arranged in echelon formation with a constant offset. The echelon can be used either as a transmission or as a reflection grating.

ECHO. Effect produced when sound is reflected or thrown back on meeting a solid obstacle.

ECLIPSE OF THE MOON. Caused by the shadow of the Earth when it falls in line between the Sun and Moon.

ECLIPSE OF THE SUN. Caused by the shadow of the moon when it is in line between the Sun and the Earth. See Fig. 7.

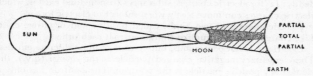

FIG. 7.

ECLIPTIC. The Sun's apparent path in the sky relative to the stars; the circle described by the Sun on the *celestial sphere* (q.v.) in the course of a year.

ECOLOGY. The study of the relation of plants and animals to their environment.

EDDY CURRENTS, electrical, Foucault currents. Induced (see *induction*) electric currents set up in the iron cores of electromagnets and other electrical apparatus. These currents cause considerable waste of energy in the cores of armatures of dynamos and in transformers.

EFFICIENCY OF A MACHINE. The ratio of the output energy to the input energy. The efficiency of a machine can never be greater than unity.

EFFLORESCENCE (chem.). Property of some crystalline salts of losing a part of their *water of crystallization* (q.v.), becoming powdery on the surface. E.g. crystals of washing-soda, $Na_2CO_3 . 10H_2O$.

EFFUSION (chem.) of gases. The passage of gases through small apertures under pressure. The relative rates of effusion of different gases under the same conditions are inversely proportional to the square roots of their densities.

ELASTIC LIMIT of a material. The limit of stress within which the strain in the material completely disappears when the stress is removed.

ELASTIC MODULUS, modulus of elasticity. The ratio of stress to strain in a given material. The strain may be a change in length (see *Young's modulus*); a twist or shear (*rigidity modulus*, q.v.), or a change in volume (see *bulk modulus*); the stress required to produce unit strain being in each case expressed in dynes per sq. cm.

ELASTICITY. The property of a body or material of resuming its original form and dimensions when forces acting upon it are removed.

ELECTRET. *Dielectric* (q.v.) possessing a permanent electric moment.

ELECTRIC ARC. See *arc*.

ELECTRIC BELL. See *bell, electric*.

ELECTRIC BUZZER. See *buzzer, electric*.

ELECTRIC CHARGE. Substances are said to possess electric charge when (a) forces exist between them; (b) they are acted upon by forces when moving in a magnetic field which possesses a component at right angles to their direction of motion. Electric charges differ from magnetic poles in that (1) electric charges of one sign can exist independently; (2) for electric charges, substances (conductors) exist in which electric charges can move freely when subject to electric forces.

Electric charges of two kinds, called positive and negative, exist. Like charges repel and unlike charges attract each other.

Electricity is not continuous, but consists of finite discrete entities. The elementary negative charged particle is the *electron* (q.v.), the elementary positive particle is the positron. The positron has only a transient existence. The amount of electric charge is measured in *electrostatic units* (q.v.) or in *electromagnetic units* (q.v.), the practical unit of which is the *coulomb* (q.v.).

ELECTRIC CURRENT. Flow of electricity along a conductor. Measured as a rate of transfer of electricity. See *ampere*.

ELECTRIC CURRENT, HEATING EFFECT OF. When an electric current flows through a conductor of finite resistance, heat energy is continuously generated at the expense of electrical energy. The quantity of heat produced is proportional to the resistance of the conductor, and is equal to $\dfrac{ei}{4\cdot2}$ or $\dfrac{i^2r}{4\cdot2}$ calories per second, e being the potential difference in volts, i the current in amperes, and r the resistance in ohms.

ELECTRIC DISPLACEMENT. Consider a uniform electric field of strength E in free space; i.e. the electric *flux* (q.v.) through unit area perpendicular to the field is E. Now suppose a *dielectric* (q.v.) medium is introduced into the field. The electric flux at any point in the medium becomes modified owing to the interaction between E and the atoms of the dielectric, and assumes a new value D, called the *electric displacement*.

ELECTRIC FIELD of a charge. The region near an electric charge, in which a force is exerted on a charged particle; completely defined in magnitude and direction at any point by the force upon unit positive charge situated at that point.

ELECTRIC INTENSITY, strength of *electric field* (q.v.).

ELECTRIC LIGHT. Illumination produced by the use of electricity; may be produced by virtue of the heating effect of an electric current on a wire or filament (see *electric-light bulb*), by an electric arc (see *arc lamp*), or by the passage of electricity through a vapour, as in the *mercury vapour lamp* (q.v.) or fluorescent lamps.

ELECTRIC-LIGHT BULB. Glass bulb, often filled with nitrogen or some other chemically inactive gas, containing a wire or filament, usually made of *wolfram* (q.v.). The passage of an electric current through the filament heats it to a white heat.

ELECTRIC MOTOR. Device for converting electrical energy into mechanical energy. Depends on the fact that when an electric current flows through a conductor placed in a magnetic field possessing a component at right angles to the conductor, a mechanical force acts upon the conductor. In its simplest form, consists of a coil or *armature* through which the current flows, placed between the poles of a powerful electromagnet, the *field magnet*; the mechanical force upon the conductor causes the armature to rotate.

ELECTRIC POLARIZATION. When an electric field is applied to an electrically neutral atom, a displacement of the electrons with respect to the positive nucleus occurs. (See *atom, structure of.*) This gives rise to a small electric *dipole* (q.v.) possessing an electric moment in the direction of the field. This effect occurs when a *dielectric* (q.v.) is placed in an electric field, the electric field acting upon each individual atom of the dielectric. The resultant total electric moment per unit volume is called the *electric polarization.*

ELECTRIC POTENTIAL at a point is the work necessary to bring unit positive electric charge from an infinite distance to that point. Analogous to a level; a positive electric charge would be driven from points of higher to lower potential. See *potential difference.*

ELECTRIC POWER, the rate of doing work. Measured in watts; a power of 1 watt does 1 *joule* (q.v.) of work per second. The power in watts is given by the product of the potential difference in volts and the current in amperes.

ELECTRIC SPARK. A discharge of electricity, accompanied by light and sound, through a dielectric or insulator.

ELECTRICAL CAPACITY. See *capacity, electrical.*

ELECTRICAL CONDENSER. See *condenser, electrical.*

ELECTRICAL IMAGE. A set of point charges on one side of a conducting surface which would produce the same electric field on the other side of the surface (in its absence) as the actual electrification of that surface.

ELECTRICAL INDUCTION. See *induction.*

ELECTRICAL LINE OF FORCE. A line in an *electric field* (q.v.) whose direction is everywhere that of the field.

ELECTRICITY. General term used for all phenomena caused by *electric charge* (q.v.) whether static or in motion.

ELECTRICITY, FRICTIONAL, triboelectricity. A separation of *electric charge* (q.v.) which results from the rubbing together of different materials; e.g. on rubbing celluloid with rabbit's fur, the fur is found to possess a positive charge, and the celluloid receives an equal negative charge.

ELECTRICITY, STATIC. Electricity at rest, in contradistinction to dynamic or current electricity. In the static case its effects are due purely to the electrostatic forces produced by the charge, whereas in the case of current electricity other effects, in particular a magnetic force, are added.

ELECTROCHEMICAL EQUIVALENT of an ion. The weight of the ion liberated or deposited by 1 *coulomb* (q.v.) of electricity. Expressed in grams, this is numerically equal to $1/96490$ of the chemical equivalent, which is therefore liberated or deposited by 96490 coulombs, or one *faraday*. See *electrolysis*.

ELECTROCHEMISTRY. Chemical processes making use of *electrolysis* (q.v.).

ELECTRODE. Conductor by which an electric current enters or leaves an electrolyte in *electrolysis* (q.v.); an electric *arc* (q.v.) or a vacuum tube (see *discharge in gases* and *thermionic valve*). The positive electrode is the *anode*, the negative one the *cathode*.

ELECTROLYSIS. Chemical decomposition of certain substances (*electrolytes*, q.v.) by an electric current passed through the substance in a dissolved or molten state. Such substances are ionized (see *ionic hypothesis*) into electrically charged ions, and when an electric current is passed through them by means of conducting *electrodes* (q.v.), the ions move towards the oppositely charged electrodes, there give up their electric charges, become uncharged atoms or groups, and are either liberated or deposited at the electrode, or react chemically with the electrode, the solvent, or each other, according to their chemical nature.

ELECTROLYSIS, FARADAY'S LAWS OF. I. The chemical action of a current of electricity is proportional to the quantity of electricity which passes. 2. The weights of substances liberated or deposited by the same quantity of electricity are proportional to their chemical equivalents. See *electrochemical equivalent*.

ELECTROLYTE. Compound which, in solution or in the molten state, conducts an electric current and is simultaneously decomposed by it. The current is carried not by electrons as in metals, but by ions (see *electrolysis*). Electrolytes may be acids, bases or salts.

ELECTROLYTIC DISSOCIATION, THEORY OF. Explanation of the phenomena of *electrolysis* (q.v.) on the supposition that molecules of *electrolytes* (q.v.) are dissociated into electrically charged ions in solution. See *ionization*.

ELECTROLYTIC GAS, detonating gas. Mixture of hydrogen and oxygen, in a ratio of 2 to 1 by volume, formed by the electrolysis of water.

ELECTROMAGNET. Temporary magnet formed by winding a coil of wire round a piece of soft iron; when an electric current flows through the wire, the iron becomes a magnet.

ELECTROMAGNETIC UNITS. E.M.U. System of electrical units, within the C.G.S. system, based on the unit magnetic pole, which repels a similar pole, placed 1 cm. away, with a force of 1 dyne. The E.M.U. of current is that current which, flowing in an arc of a circle of unit length and radius (i.e. 1 cm.), exerts a force of 1 dyne on a unit magnetic pole placed at the centre. The E.M.U. of resistance is that resistance in which energy is dissipated at the rate of 1 erg per second by the flow of 1 E.M.U. of current. The E.M.U. of electromotive force or potential is that potential which, applied across the ends of a conductor of 1 E.M.U. resistance, causes 1 E.M.U. of current to flow.

ELECTROMAGNETIC WAVES. Wide range of vibrations or wave-motions not requiring any known material medium for their propagation. Travel with a velocity of 2.9978×10^{10} cm. per second (approximately 186,000 miles per second). In order of increasing wave-length, they are gamma rays, X-rays, ultra-violet rays, visible light rays, infra-red (heat) rays, and wireless or Hertzian waves.

ELECTROMETER. Instrument for measuring voltage differences, which draws no current from the source. Essential for measuring electrostatic voltage differences.

ELECTROMOTIVE FORCE, E.M.F. The source of electrical energy required to produce an electric current in a circuit; a measure of its intensity. Defined as the rate at which electrical energy is drawn from the source and dissipated in a circuit when unit current is flowing in the circuit. Practical unit is the *volt* (q.v.). See *potential difference*.

ELECTROMOTIVE SERIES. Potential series of the metals. A list of metals arranged in order of the magnitudes of their *molar electrode potentials*, i.e. the potential difference between the metal and a *normal* (q.v.) solution of one of its salts. Metals with high negative electrode potentials stand at the head of the electromotive series. The list represents the order in which the metals replace one another from their salts, a metal higher in the series replacing one lower down; similarly, metals placed above hydrogen will liberate it from acids. The chief metals in order are sodium, magnesium, aluminium, manganese, zinc, cadmium, iron, cobalt, nickel, tin, lead, *hydrogen*, copper, mercury, silver, platinum, gold.

ELECTRON. Elementary particle having a mass of 9.107×10^{-28} gm., approximately $1/1840$ that of a hydrogen atom, and bearing a negative electric charge of 4.803×10^{-10} electrostatic units. See *atom*, *structure of*.

ELECTRON MICROSCOPE. An instrument similar in purpose to the ordinary light microscope, but with a much greater *resolving power* (q.v.). Instead of a beam of light to illuminate the object, a parallel beam of electrons is used. The object, which must be in the form of a very thin film of the material, allows the electron beam to pass through it; but, owing to differential scattering in the film, an image of the object is carried forward in the electron beam. The latter then passes through a magnetic or electrostatic focusing system which is equivalent to the optical lens system in an ordinary microscope, i.e. it produces a much magnified image. This is received on a fluorescent screen and recorded by using a camera.

ELECTRON MULTIPLIER. *Photo-electric cell* (q.v.) of high sensitivity used for detecting very small quantities of light radiation. Consists of a system of electrodes suitably arranged in an evacuated envelope. Light falling on the first electrode ejects electrons from this surface (see *photo-electric effect*). These electrons are accelerated to the second electrode, where they each produce further electrons by the process of *secondary emission* (q.v.). This process continues until the secondary emission from the final electrode is sufficient to produce a useful current, permitting measurement or the operation of a relay.

ELECTRON-VOLT (*ev*). Unit of energy widely used in nuclear physics. The increase in energy or the work done on an electron when passing through a potential rise of 1 volt. 1 electron-volt = $1 \cdot 6 \times 10^{-12}$ ergs approximately.

ELECTRONEGATIVE elements and groups. *Radicals* (q.v.) which behave as negative ions; radicals taking up electrons, thus acquiring a negative charge, when united with other radicals by electrovalent bonds (see *valency, electronic theory of*). The *halogens* (q.v.) oxygen, sulphur and other non-metals are generally electronegative.

ELECTRONIC CHARGE. The negative electric charge of the *electron* (q.v.), $1 \cdot 602 \times 10^{-19}$ coulombs, $4 \cdot 803 \times 10^{-10}$ electrostatic units.

ELECTRONICS. An applied physical science concerned with the development of electrical circuits using *thermionic valves* (q.v.) and other devices in which the motion of electrons is controlled.

ELECTROPHORESIS, cataphoresis. The migration of the electrically charged solute particles present in a *colloidal solution* (q.v.) towards the oppositely charged electrode, when two electrodes are placed in the solution and connected externally to a source of E.M.F.

ELECTROPHORUS. Laboratory demonstration apparatus for showing electrostatic charging by induction.

ELECTROPLATING. Depositing a layer of metal by *electrolysis* (q.v.), the object to be plated forming the *cathode* (q.v.) in an electrolytic tank or bath containing a solution of a salt of the metal which is to be deposited.

ELECTROPOSITIVE elements and groups. *Radicals* (q.v.) which behave as positive ions; radicals which give up electrons, thus acquiring a positive charge, when united with other radicals by electrovalent bonds (see *valency, electronic theory of*). The metals and acidic hydrogen are generally electropositive.

ELECTROSCOPE. Instrument for detecting the presence of an electric charge. The gold-leaf electroscope consists of two rectangular leaves of gold foil attached to a conducting rod of metal held by an insulating plug; when the rod and leaves acquire an electric charge, the leaves diverge owing to the mutual repulsion of charges of like sign.

ELECTROSTATIC GENERATOR. Machine designed for the continuous separation of electric charge. Examples include the *Wimshurst machine* (q.v.) and the *van der Graaf generator* (q.v.).

ELECTROSTATIC UNIT of electricity. Quantity such that, when placed 1 cm. from an equal quantity in a vacuum, it repels it with a force of 1 *dyne* (q.v.).

ELECTROSTATIC UNITS, E.S.U. System of electrical units based upon the *electrostatic unit* (q.v.) of charge.

ELECTROSTATICS. The study of static electricity.

ELECTROSTRICTION. The change in the dimensions of a *dielectric* (q.v.) when placed in an electric field.

ELECTROTYPING. Production of copies of plates of type, etc., by the electrolytic deposition of a layer of metal on a previously prepared mould. This is a cast of the object to be copied, made of plastic material and coated with a layer of graphite which acts as a conductor of electricity. It is then suspended to act as a cathode in an electrolytic bath (see *electroplating*) containing a solution of a salt of the metal required, usually copper. The passage of an electric current will deposit a layer of any required thickness of metal upon the cathode, the layer being a replica of the original type.

ELECTROVALENCY. See *valency, electronic theory of*.

ELECTRUM. Natural alloy of gold (55%–85%) and silver.

ELEMENT (chem.). Substance consisting entirely of atoms of the same *atomic number* (q.v.).

ELEMENTS, MAGNETIC. See *magnetic elements*.

ELEVATION, ANGLE OF. If C is a point above the level of another point A, the angle of elevation of C from A is the angle which C makes with the horizontal plane AX through A. See Fig. 5.

ELEVATION OF BOILING POINT. Rise in the boiling point of a solution produced by a non-volatile substance dissolved in a solvent. For a dilute solution the elevation is proportional to the number of molecules or ions present, and the elevation produced by the same *molecular concentration* (q.v.) or ionic concentration in the case of an *electrolyte* (q.v.) is a constant for a particular solvent. This forms the principle of the boiling-point method (ebulliscopic method) for the determination of molecular weights.

ELEVEN-YEAR PERIOD. A periodic change in occurrence of sunspots, the cycle being complete in approximately eleven years; associated with this is a cyclic variation in the magnitude of the *daily variation* (q.v.).

ELINVAR. Variety of steel containing 36% nickel and 12% chromium. The elasticity is almost unaffected by changes of temperature; used for hair-springs of watches.

ELLIPSE. Closed plane figure formed by cutting all elements of a circular cone by a plane.

ELLIPSOID. Solid figure traced out by an ellipse rotating about one of its axes.

ELLIPTICALLY POLARIZED LIGHT. Light which can be resolved into two vibrations lying in planes at right angles, and of equal frequency. The electric vector at any point in the path of the wave describes an ellipse about the direction of propagation of the light. The form of this ellipse is determined by the amplitudes of these two vibrations and by the difference of *phase* (q.v.) between them. (See also *polarization of light*.)

EMANATION, radium emanation. See *radon*.

EMERY. Mixture of *corundum* (q.v.) and iron oxide, usually magnetite, Fe_3O_4. Used as an abrasive.

EMISSION OF RADIATION. The net rate at which a body emits heat radiation to its surroundings depends on the temperature of the body, the temperature of its surroundings and the nature of the surface of the body. Dull black surfaces have the greatest *emissive power* (q.v.) while brightly polished reflecting surfaces have least. See *Stefan's law*.

EMISSION SPECTRUM. *Spectrum* (q.v.) observed when light coming directly from a source is examined with a spectrometer.

EMISSIVE POWER, total. The total energy emitted from unit area of a surface of a body per second. The total emissive power depends upon the temperature of the body and the nature of its surface.

EMISSIVITY. The ratio of the total emissive power of a body to the total emissive power of a perfect black body at the same temperature (see *black body radiation*). The emissivity is a pure numeric, equal to the *absorptivity* (q.v.).

EMPIRICAL. Based upon the results of experiment and observation only.

EMULSION. A two-phase system in which the *disperse phase* (q.v.) consists of minute droplets of liquid.

EMULSOID SOL. See *colloidal solutions*.

ENAMEL. Class of substances having similar composition to *glass* (q.v.) with the addition of tin dioxide, SnO_2, or other infusible substances to render the enamel opaque.

ENANTIOMORPHISM. Occurrence of substances in two crystalline forms, one being a mirror image of the other.

ENANTIOTROPIC substances. Substances which exist in two different physical forms, one being stable below a certain temperature (the transition point), the other above it. E.g. sulphur exists as alpha-sulphur at all temperatures below 96° C.; above this, the stable form is beta-sulphur.

ENDOCRINE GLANDS, ductless glands. Glands or organs producing *hormones* (q.v.) in the animal body.

ENDOSMOSIS. Inward flow of water into a cell containing an aqueous solution, through a semi-permeable membrane, due to *osmosis* (q.v.).

ENDOTHERMIC PROCESS. A process accompanied by the absorption of heat.

ENERGY. Capacity for doing *work* (q.v.). Various forms of energy, interconvertible by suitable means, include potential, kinetic, electrical, heat, chemical, atomic, and radiant energy.

ENERGY LEVELS. An atom as a whole, or an individual nucleus, can exist only in certain definite states characterized by the energy of the state. Thus, for each different atom or nucleus, there exists a series of energy levels corresponding to these permissible states.

ENERGY VALUE of a food. Measure of the heat energy available by the complete burning of a stated weight of the food; often given in large

Calories per lb. Takes no account of the value of the food from any other point of view, or sometimes even of the suitability of the food for use by the human organism.

ENGINE. A device for converting one form of energy into another, especially for converting other forms of energy into mechanical (i.e. kinetic) energy.

ENTHALPY. Heat content per unit mass.

ENTROPY. A quantity introduced in the first place to facilitate the calculations, and to give clear expression to the results of *thermodynamics* (q.v.). Changes of entropy can be calculated only for a *reversible process* (q.v.), and may then be defined as the ratio of the amount of heat taken up to the *absolute temperature* (q.v.) at which the heat is absorbed. Entropy changes for actual irreversible processes are calculated by postulating equivalent theoretical reversible changes. The entropy of a system is a measure of its degree of disorder. The total entropy of any isolated system can never decrease in any change; it must either increase (irreversible process) or remain constant (reversible process). The total entropy of the Universe therefore is increasing, tending towards a maximum, corresponding to complete disorder of the particles in it.

ENZYMES. Organic substances produced by living cells, which act as *catalysts* (q.v.) in chemical changes. Enzymes are specific in their action; i.e. each enzyme affects only one type of chemical reaction. E.g. *diastase* (q.v.).

EPSOM SALTS, magnesium sulphate. $MgSO_4.7H_2O$. White crystalline soluble salt.

EQUATION, CHEMICAL. Representation of a chemical reaction, using the symbols of the elements to represent the actual atoms and molecules taking part in the reaction; the re-arrangement of the various atoms of the substances taking part is thus shown. E.g. the chemical equation $H_2 + Cl_2 = 2HCl$ represents the reaction between hydrogen and chlorine to form hydrogen chloride, and states that a hydrogen molecule, consisting of two atoms of hydrogen (H_2), reacts with a similarly constituted chlorine molecule, to give two molecules of hydrogen chloride, each consisting of one hydrogen and one chlorine atom ($2HCl$). From a knowledge of the equation for any chemical reaction, and of the *atomic weights* (q.v.) of all the elements taking part, it is thus possible to calculate the proportions by weight in which the substances react, since the whole bulk of the reaction consists merely of the repetition, a vast number of times, of the process depicted by the equation.

EQUATION, MATHEMATICAL. A statement of equality between known and unknown quantities, true only for certain values of the unknown quantities. Thus the equation $3x = 15$ is true only when $x = 5$.

EQUATION OF STATE of a substance. Any equation connecting the pressure p, volume v and temperature t of the substance. Some equations of state attempt to cover more than one phase of the substance, e.g. *van der Waals' equation of state* (q.v.), and are approximate. Others are intended to be applied to one particular phase of the substance, e.g. the gaseous phase, and then only within certain limits of p, v and t. With these limitations, these latter equations can represent the actual behaviour of the substance with greater accuracy.

EQUATION OF TIME. The difference between mean solar time, as given by a clock, and apparent solar time, i.e. sundial time. The time of rotation of the Earth upon its axis is not exactly equal to the time from noon to noon, the difference being caused by the motion of the Earth relative to the Sun to complete a circuit in one year, and also by the inclination of the *ecliptic* (q.v.) to the Equator.

EQUATOR, CELESTIAL. See *celestial equator*.

EQUATOR, MAGNETIC. See *magnetic equator*.

EQUATOR, TERRESTRIAL; the Earth's equator. *Great circle* (q.v.) of the Earth, lying in a plane perpendicular to the axis of the Earth, equidistant from the two Poles.

EQUILATERAL figure. Figure having all its sides equal in length. E.g. equilateral triangle.

EQUILIBRIUM. State of balance between opposing forces or effects.

EQUILIBRIUM, CHEMICAL. See *chemical equilibrium*.

EQUIMOLECULAR MIXTURE. Mixture containing substances in equal molecular proportions; i.e. in the ratio of their molecular weights. E.g. invert sugar, formed by the *hydrolysis* (q.v.) of cane-sugar. Each molecule of the cane-sugar is split into a molecule of glucose and a molecule of laevulose, thus forming an equimolecular mixture of the two latter.

EQUINOX. The moment (or, astronomically, the point) at which the Sun apparently crosses the *celestial equator* (q.v.); the point of intersection of the *ecliptic* (q.v.) and the celestial equator.

EQUIPARTITION OF ENERGY. In any physical system in thermal equilibrium the average energy per degree of freedom is the same, and equals $KT/2$, where $K = $ *Boltzmann's constant* (q.v.) and $T = $ the absolute temperature of the system. This provides a means of calculating the total thermal energy of a system. Thus, in 1 gram-atom of a monatomic gas, each atom possesses three degrees of freedom (due to its translatory motion), and the total number of atoms is N (*Avogadro's number*, q.v.). Hence the total energy per gram-atom of the gas is $3NKT/2$ or $= 3RT/2$, since $K = R/N$, where R is the *gas constant* (q.v.).

EQUIPOTENTIAL LINES AND SURFACES. Lines and surfaces having the same *electric potential* (q.v.).

EQUIVALENT, CHEMICAL. See *chemical equivalent*.

EQUIVALENT, ELECTROCHEMICAL. See *electrochemical equivalent*.

ERBIUM. Er. Element. A.W. 167·2. At. No. 68. See *rare earths*.

ERECTING PRISM. Right-angled optical *prism* (q.v.) used in optical instruments to render an inverted image upright.

ERG. Unit of *work* (q.v.) in the C.G.S. system of units; the work done by a force of 1 dyne acting through a distance of 1 cm.

ERGOSTEROL. $C_{28}H_{43}OH$. White solid, m.p. 163° C. Member of the *sterol* (q.v.) group of organic compounds; occurs in small amounts in the fats of animals; converted into vitamin D_2 (*calciferol*, q.v.) by the action of ultra-violet radiation.

ERINOID. Plastic material prepared from *casein* (q.v.) and *formaldehyde* (q.v.).

ESTERIFICATION. Formation of an *ester* (q.v.) by the chemical reaction of an acid with an alcohol; e.g. the action of ethyl alcohol on acetic acid to form ethyl acetate and water.

ESTERS. Organic compounds corresponding to inorganic salts, derived by replacing hydrogen of an acid by an organic radical or group. E.g. ethyl acetate, $CH_3COOC_2H_5$, is the ethyl ester of acetic acid, CH_3COOH. Many esters are pleasant-smelling liquids used for flavouring essences. Many vegetable and animal fats and oils also belong to this class.

ESTRON. Term proposed in the United States of America for *rayon* (q.v.) made from cellulose esters, e.g. *cellulose acetate* (q.v.).

ETHANE. C_2H_6. Second member of the *paraffin series* (q.v.) of hydrocarbons. Colourless odourless invisible gas.

ETHANOL. *Ethyl alcohol* (q.v.).

ETHER, diethyl ether, sulphuric ether. $(C_2H_5)_2O$. Colourless inflammable liquid with a characteristic sweetish smell. B.p. 34·5° C. Powerful anaesthetic. Made by the *dehydration* (q.v.) of ethyl alcohol, C_2H_5OH, by means of concentrated sulphuric acid, H_2SO_4. Used in medicine and as a solvent.

ETHER, THE; Aether, the. Hypothetical medium, which has been supposed to fill all space; the medium in which *electromagnetic waves* (q.v.), i.e. light, wireless waves, etc., are transmitted through space. Once the subject of controversy, now regarded as an unnecessary assumption.

ETHYL ACETATE, 'acetic ether'. $CH_3COOC_2H_5$. Colourless liquid with a pleasant fruity smell, b.p. 77° C. Used as a solvent and in medicine.

ETHYL ALCOHOL, alcohol, ethanol, spirits of wine. Colourless inflammable liquid with a characteristic vinous odour and burning taste. B.p. 78·5° C. Prepared by the *fermentation* (q.v.) of sugars. Constituent of alcoholic beverages; used as a fuel and in the manufacture of other organic compounds.

ETHYL FLUID. Solution of tetraethyl lead, $Pb(C_2H_5)_4$, and ethylene dibromide, $C_2H_4Br_2$, used as an anti-knock compound in motor fuel.

ETHYL GROUP. The univalent *alkyl radical* (q.v.) —C_2H_5.

ETHYL NITRITE, nitrous ether. $C_2H_5NO_2$. Volatile liquid with a sweet smell, b.p. 17° C. Used in medicine.

ETHYLENE. C_2H_4. First member of the *olefine* (q.v.) *series* of hydrocarbons. Colourless inflammable gas with a sweetish smell.

ETHYLENE DICHLORIDE, 'Dutch liquid'. $C_2H_4Cl_2$. Colourless oily liquid, b.p. 83·5° C. Used as a solvent and fumigant.

ETHYLENE GLYCOL, glycol. $(CH_2OH)_2$. Colourless viscous liquid with a sweet taste. B.p. 197° C. Used as an anti-freeze compound for radiators of petrol engines, and in the manufacture of certain *plasticizers* (q.v.).

ETHYNE. *Acetylene* (q.v.).

EUCHLORINE. Gaseous mixture of chlorine, Cl_2, and explosive chlorine peroxide, ClO_2.

EUDIOMETER. Glass tube for measuring volume changes in chemical reactions between gases.

EUROPIUM. Eu. Element. A.W. 152·0. At. No. 63. See *rare earths*.

EUTECTIC MIXTURE. A solid solution of two or more substances, having the lowest freezing point of all the possible mixtures of the components. This is taken advantage of in alloys of low melting point, which are generally eutectic mixtures.

EUTECTIC POINT. Two or more substances capable of forming solid solutions with each other have the property of lowering each other's freezing point; the minimum freezing point attainable, corresponding to the *eutectic mixture* (q.v.), is termed the *eutectic point*.

EVAPORATION. Conversion of a liquid into vapour, without necessarily reaching the boiling point; used in concentrating solutions by evaporating off the solvent.

EWING'S MOLECULAR THEORY. See *magnetization, molecular theory of*.

EXCESS (chem.). Greater quantity of one substance or reagent than is necessary to react exactly with a given quantity of another.

EXCHANGES, PREVOST'S THEORY OF. Bodies at all temperatures are constantly radiating energy to each other, those at constant temperature receiving in a given time as much energy as they emit.

EXOSMOSIS. Outward osmotic flow. See *osmosis*.

EXOTHERMIC PROCESS. Process in which energy in the form of heat is released.

EXPANSION, COEFFICIENT OF. 1. *Linear*. The increase in length per unit length, caused by a rise in temperature of 1° C. 2. *Area (superficial expansion)*. Increase in area per unit area caused by a rise in temperature of 1° C. 3. *Volume*. Increase in volume per unit volume caused by a rise in temperature of 1° C. For *isotropic* (q.v.) media, the area and volume coefficients are approximately double and treble the linear coefficient respectively, for the same substance.

EXPANSION OF GASES. A *perfect gas* (q.v.) expands by 1/273 of its volume at 0° C. for each degree rise in temperature, the pressure being constant. Real gases obey this law only approximately at ordinary pressures, but the approximation becomes more and more valid as the pressure is reduced, i.e. as the gas tends towards a perfect gas.

EXPANSION OF LIQUIDS. The directly observed expansion is the *apparent* expansion, since the vessel containing the liquid also expands. The coefficient of true expansion is the sum of the coefficient of apparent expansion, and the coefficient of volume expansion of the containing vessel.

EXPLOSION. Violent and rapid chemical reaction, generally accompanied by sound, in which a quantity of gas at a high temperature is produced.

EXPLOSIVES. Substances which undergo a rapid chemical change, with production of gas, on being heated or struck. The volume of gas produced being very great relatively to the bulk of the solid explosive, great pressures are set up when the action takes place in a confined space.

EXPONENT (math.). The number indicating the *power* (q.v.) of a quantity. Thus the exponent of x in x^4 is 4.

EXTENDER. A substance, usually a white pigment such as *blanc fixe* (q.v.) which is added to paint.

EXTENSOMETER. Instrument for measuring the extension produced in a body under an applied stress.

EXTRAORDINARY RAY. See *ordinary ray*.

EXTRAPOLATION. Filling in values or terms of a series on either side of the known values, thus extending the range of values.

EYE-PIECE. In optical instruments, the lens or system of lenses nearest the observer's eye; generally used to view the image formed by the *objective* (q.v.).

F

FACTOR (math.). A number or quantity is exactly divisible by its factors; thus the factors of 12 (i.e. the integral or whole-number factors) are 1, 2, 3, 4, 6, 12.

FACTOR, PRIME. Prime factors of a quantity are the prime numbers (i.e. numbers themselves possessing no factors other than themselves and unity) which, when multiplied together, give the quantity. Thus, the prime factors of 165 are 3, 5 and 11.

FACTORIAL NUMBER is the product of a number and all the consecutive positive whole numbers below it down to 1. Thus, factorial 5, written $\underline{|5}$ or $5! = 5 \times 4 \times 3 \times 2 \times 1 = 120$.

FAHRENHEIT DEGREE. $\frac{1}{180}$ of the difference between the temperature of melting ice and that of water boiling under standard atmospheric pressure (760 mm.).

FAHRENHEIT SCALE of temperature. Temperature scale in which the melting point of ice is taken as 32° F. and the boiling point of water under standard atmospheric pressure (760 mm.) as 212° F. 9 Fahrenheit degrees = 5 Centigrade degrees. To convert degrees F. to degrees C., subtract 32 from the F. value, multiply by 5 and divide by 9; to convert degrees C. to degrees F., multiply by 9, divide by 5, then add 32 to the result.

FARAD. Unit of electrostatic *capacity* (q.v.). A capacity of 1 farad requires 1 *coulomb* (q.v.) of electricity to raise its potential 1 volt. 1 farad = 9×10^{11} electrostatic units. The usual practical unit of capacity is the *microfarad*, $1/1,000,000$ farad.

FARADAY, THE. Quantity of electricity required to liberate or deposit 1 gram-equivalent of an ion. 96,490 coulombs. See *electrochemical equivalent*.

FARADAY EFFECT. The rotation of the plane of vibration (see *polarization of light*) of polarized light on traversing an *isotropic* (q.v.) transparent medium placed in a magnetic field possessing a component in the direction of the light ray.

FARADAY'S LAWS OF ELECTROLYSIS. See *electrolysis, Faraday's laws of*.

FATHOM. 6 feet; used as a unit of marine depth.

FATHOMETER. Depth-sounding instrument. The depth of water is measured by noting the time the echo of a sound takes to return from the sea bed.

FATIGUE OF METALS. Deterioration of metals owing to repeated stresses above a certain critical value; accompanied by changes in the crystalline structure of the metal.

FATS AND OILS. Mixtures of various *glycerides* (q.v.) of *fatty acids* (q.v.) Natural organic compounds which occur in plants and animals and serve as storage materials. The distinction between fats and oils (as distinct from *mineral oils* (q.v.), which are hydrocarbons) is one of melting point; the term *oil* is usually applied to glycerides liquid at 20° C., the others being termed *fats*.

FATTY ACIDS. Organic *monobasic* (q.v.) acids having the general formula $R.COOH$, where R is hydrogen or a group of carbon and hydrogen atoms. The *saturated* fatty acids have the general formula $C_nH_{2n+1}COOH$. Many fatty acids occur in living things, usually in the form of *glycerides* (q.v.) in fats and oils.

FEBRIFUGE. See *antipyretic*.

FEHLING'S SOLUTION. Solution of copper sulphate, $CuSO_4$, caustic soda, NaOH, and *Rochelle salt* (q.v.). Used for the detection and estimation of certain sugars and other reducing agents, which act upon the solution with the formation of a red precipitate of cuprous oxide, Cu_2O.

FELDSPAR. See *felspar*.

FELSPAR, feldspar. Name of a large group of rock-forming minerals consisting chiefly of alumino-silicates of potassium and sodium. Constituents of granite and other primary rocks.

FERMAT'S PRINCIPLE OF LEAST TIME. The path taken by a ray of light or other wave motion in traversing the distance between any two points is such that the time taken is a minimum or a maximum.

FERMENT. *Enzyme* (q.v.); any substance which will produce *fermentation* (q.v.).

FERMENTATION. Chemical change brought about in organic substances by living organisms (yeast, bacteria, etc.) by enzyme action. Usually applied to the alcoholic fermentation produced by the action of *zymase* (q.v.) on certain sugars, giving alcohol and carbon dioxide according to the equation $C_6H_{12}O_6 = 2C_2H_5OH + 2CO_2$.

FERRIC. Term denoting a compound of tervalent (trivalent) iron. Ferric salts are usually yellow or brown in colour.

FERRIC ALUM, iron alum. Crystalline ferric potassium sulphate, $Fe_2(SO_4)_3 . K_2SO_4 . 24H_2O$. Violet soluble crystals.

FERRIC CHLORIDE. $FeCl_3.6H_2O$. Brown-yellow deliquescent crystalline salt.

FERRIC OXIDE. Fe_2O_3. Red insoluble solid, occurs naturally as haematite.

FERRITE. 1. Name applied to several types of iron ore. 2. Salt of the hypothetical 'ferrous acid', derived from ferric oxide, Fe_2O_3.

FERRO-. Prefix denoting iron, especially in names of alloys; e.g. *ferromanganese* (q.v.).

FERROCHROME. Alloy of chromium with 30%–40% iron, obtained by the reduction of *chromite* (q.v.) with carbon in the electric furnace.

FERROMAGNETIC SUBSTANCES. The metals iron, cobalt, nickel, and certain alloys, vastly more magnetic than any other known substance. Ferromagnetism is due to unbalanced electron *spin* (q.v.) in the inner electron orbits of the elements concerned (see *atom, structure of*) which give the atom a resultant magnetic moment. The ionic spacing in ferromagnetic crystals is such that very large forces, called *exchange forces*, cause the alignment of all the individual magnetic moments of large groups of atoms to give highly magnetized domains. In an unmagnetized piece of iron, these domains are oriented at random, their magnetic axes pointing in all directions. The application of an external field serves to line up the domain axes, giving rise to the observed magnetism. Ferromagnetic substances have very large *magnetic permeabilities* (q.v.) which vary with the strength of the applied field. A given ferromagnetic substance loses its ferromagnetic properties at a certain critical temperature, the *Curie temperature* (q.v.), for that substance.

FERROMANGANESE. Alloy of manganese (70%–80%) and iron.

FERROUS. Term denoting a compound of bivalent (divalent) iron; more loosely, pertaining to iron. Ferrous salts are generally pale green in colour.

FERROUS SULPHATE, green vitriol, copperas. $FeSO_4.7H_2O$. Pale green crystalline soluble salt. Made by dissolving scrap iron in dilute sulphuric acid. Used in dyeing, tanning and ink manufacture.

FERTILIZERS. Materials put into the soil to provide compounds of elements essential to plant life; more particularly nitrogen, phosphorus and potassium. Nitrogen is provided in the form of nitrates, ammonium salts, *Nitrolime* (q.v.), etc. (see *fixation of atmospheric nitrogen*); phosphorus is added in the form of *superphosphate* (q.v.), *basic slag* (q.v.), various phosphates, etc. Potassium is obtained from natural potassium salts. Products of organic decomposition and waste, manure, etc., contain these and other necessary elements and form valuable fertilizers.

FIELD, ELECTRIC. See *electric field*.

FIELD LENS. The lens in the eye-piece system of optical instruments farthest from the eye.

FIELD MAGNET. Magnet which provides a magnetic field in the *dynamo* (q.v.), *electric motor* (q.v.), or other electrical machine.

FIELD, MAGNETIC. See *magnetic field*.

FILAMENT. Thin thread. In incandescent electric lamps and radio valves, a wire of tungsten or other metal of high melting point, which is made hot by the passage of an electric current.

FILTER. Device for separating solids or suspended particles from liquids. Consists of a porous material (e.g. filter-paper) through the pores of which only liquids and dissolved substances can penetrate.

FILTRATE. Clear liquid after *filtration* (q.v.); substance which has been filtered, containing no suspended matter.

FILTRATION. The process of separating solids from liquids by passing through a *filter* (q.v.).

FINENESS OF GOLD. Amount of gold in an alloy expressed as parts per thousand. Thus gold with a fineness of 900 is an alloy containing 90% gold. See also *carat*.

FIRE. Chemical action accompanied by evolution of heat, light and flame (i.e. a glowing mass of gas). Generally applied to the chemical combination with oxygen of carbon and other elements constituting the substance which is being burnt.

FIRE-DAMP. Explosive mixture of methane (CH_4) and air, formed in coal mines.

FIRE EXTINGUISHERS. Devices for putting out fires by cutting off the supply of air necessary for burning. Two main types are used. The *acid-carbonate* type contains sodium carbonate, Na_2CO_3, and sulphuric acid, H_2SO_4. On pressing the knob, the tube containing the acid is broken, and the acid acts upon the sodium carbonate giving a froth of liquid and carbon dioxide, which covers the burning material. The *pyrene* type contains carbon tetrachloride, CCl_4. These should not be used on burning metal, e.g. incendiary bombs.

FISCHER-TROPSCH PROCESS. A process for the manufacture of hydrocarbon oils from coal, lignite or natural gas. The process essentially consists of the *hydrogenation* (q.v.) of carbon monoxide, CO, in the presence of *catalysts* (q.v.); this results in the formation of *hydrocarbons* (q.v.) and steam.

FITZGERALD-LORENTZ CONTRACTION. Explanation put forward

independently by Fitzgerald (1893) and Lorentz (1895) to explain the result of the *Michelson-Morley* experiment (q.v.) on the supposition that a body moving with high velocity through the 'ether' would experience a contraction in length in the direction of the motion. This contraction was later shown to be a direct consequence of the *relativity* (q.v.) theory.

FIXATION OF ATMOSPHERIC NITROGEN. Manufacture of compounds of nitrogen for use as *fertilizers* (q.v.), from the free nitrogen in the air; made necessary by the increasing shortage of natural nitrogen compounds in the *nitrogen cycle* (q.v.). This shortage is caused partly by increased cultivation of the soil due to increase of populations, and partly by the loss of nitrogen compounds from animal waste products by sewage disposal into the sea. The first practical process was the *Birkeland and Eyde process* (q.v.); the *cyanamide*, *Haber* and *Serpek* processes are now the main ones used. In addition, certain bacteria in the soil fix atmospheric nitrogen.

FIXED AIR. Former name for carbon dioxide, CO_2.

FIXED ALKALI. Former name for potassium or sodium carbonate, to distinguish them from volatile alkali, ammonium carbonate.

FIXED POINT. Any accurately reproducible equilibrium temperature. Examples include the *ice point* (q.v.), the *steam point* (q.v.) and the *sulphur point* (q.v.).

FIXED STARS. True *stars* (q.v.); heavenly bodies termed fixed because they do not appear to alter their relative positions on the *celestial sphere* (q.v.).

FIXING, PHOTOGRAPHIC. Rendering that portion of the sensitive film, plate or paper which has not been affected by light, insensitive to exposure, after *developing* (q.v.). Usually carried out by the action of sodium thiosulphate, $Na_2S_2O_3$ ('hypo'), which reacts with the unaffected silver bromide to give a soluble double salt, silver sodium thiosulphate, which is then washed away. See *photography*.

FLAME. Glowing mass of gas produced during *combustion* (q.v.).

FLASH POINT. The lowest temperature at which a substance gives off sufficient inflammable vapour to produce a momentary flash when a small flame is applied.

FLINT. Natural variety of impure silica, SiO_2. 'Flints' of automatic lighters are composed of *pyrophoric alloys* (q.v.) of metals such as cerium and iron.

FLINT GLASS. Variety of *glass* (q.v.) containing lead silicate; used for optical purposes.

FLOTATION, PRINCIPLE OF. The weight of liquid displaced by a floating body is equal to the weight of the body. A particular case of *Archimedes' principle* (q.v.).

FLOTATION PROCESS. Separation of a mixture, e.g. of zinc blende. ZnS, and galena, PbS, making use of the surface tension of water. Zinc blende is not easily wetted by water and floats, supported by the surface film of water, while galena sinks. In modern practice, special materials are added to the water which cause one of the constituents to float in the froth produced by aerating and agitating the water.

FLOWERS OF SULPHUR. Fine powder, consisting of very small crystals of *sulphur* (q.v.) obtained by the condensation of sulphur vapour during distillation of crude sulphur.

FLUID. Substance taking the shape of the vessel containing it; liquid or gas.

FLUID DRACHM. See *drachm*.

FLUID MEASURE. See *apothecaries' fluid measure*.

FLUID OUNCE. British measure of volume of liquids. 28.41 c.c. See *apothecaries' fluid measure*.

FLUORENE, *ortho*-diphenylene methane. $C_{13}H_{10}$. Aromatic *hydrocarbon* (q.v.); white crystalline solid, m.p. 81° C.

FLUORESCEIN. $C_{20}H_{12}O_5$. Dark red crystalline organic compound, m.p. 314° C. Dissolves in alkaline solutions to give a liquid of intense green *fluorescence* (q.v.).

FLUORESCENCE. Property of many substances (e.g. quinine sulphate solutions, paraffin oil, fluorescein solutions) of absorbing light of one wave-length (i.e. colour, when in the visible region of the spectrum) and in its place emitting light of another wave-length or colour. Unlike *phosphorescence* (q.v.), the phenomenon ceases immediately the source of light is cut off.

FLUORINE. F. Element. A.W. 19.00. At. No. 9. Pale yellowish-green gas, resembling chlorine but more reactive. Occurs combined as *fluorspar* (q.v.) and as *cryolite* (q.v.). Made by the *electrolysis* (q.v.) of a solution of potassium hydrogen fluoride in anhydrous hydrogen fluoride. The fluorine organic compounds, made by replacing hydrogen in organic compounds by fluorine, are assuming considerable industrial importance.

FLUORITE. See *fluorspar*.

FLUORSPAR. Natural calcium fluoride, CaF_2. Colourless crystals, often coloured by impurities. Used as a source of fluorine and its compounds.

FLUX (chem.). Substance added to assist fusion.

FLUX (phys.). The flux of any *vector* (q.v.) quantity (*electric intensity, magnetic intensity*, etc.) through an area is the product of the area and the component of the vector at right angles to the area.

FLUX, LUMINOUS. The luminous flux through any area is the amount of light passing through that area per second. Measured in *lumens* (q.v.).

FLUXMETER. Instrument for the measurement of *magnetic flux* (q.v.). Essentially a moving coil galvanometer so designed that the coil experiences negligible restoring torque from its suspension system. A change in the magnetic flux through a flux coil connected to the galvanometer induces a current in the coil, thus causing a deflection of the galvanometer.

FOCAL LENGTH. Distance from the optical centre or pole to the principal focus of a lens or spherical mirror. See *lens; spherical mirrors.*

FOCUS. Point at which converging rays, usually of light, meet; or a point from which diverging rays are considered to be directed (virtual focus).

FOG. Effect caused by the condensation of water vapour upon particles of dust, soot, etc.

FOOD PRESERVATION. Prevention of chemical decomposition and of the development of harmful bacteria in foods. Generally effected by the sterilization of the food (i.e. by the destruction of bacteria in it) by heating in sealed vessels, i.e. canning; or by making the conditions unfavourable for the development of bacteria, by pickling, drying, smoking, etc.

FOOT. British unit of length; one-third of a yard; 30·48 cm.

FOOT-CANDLE. Unit of *illumination* (q.v.). One *lumen* (q.v.) per square foot.

FOOT-POUND. Practical unit of work. Work done by a force of 1 pound weight acting through a distance of 1 foot.

FOOT-POUNDAL. Unit of work in the foot-pound-second system (see *F.P.S. system*); the work done by a force of 1 *poundal* (q.v.) acting through a distance of 1 foot.

FORCE. External agency capable of altering the state of rest or motion in a body; measured in *dynes* (q.v.) or *poundals* (q.v.).

FORCES, PARALLELOGRAM OF. See *parallelogram of forces.*

FORCES, TRIANGLE OF. See *triangle of forces.*

FORMALDEHYDE. HCHO. Gas with an irritating smell, very soluble in water. 40% solution is known as *formalin.* Made by the oxidation of *methyl alcohol* (q.v.). Used in the manufacture of plastics and dyestuffs, in the textile industry, in medicine and as a disinfectant.

FORMALIN. 40% solution of *formaldehyde* (q.v.), used as a disinfectant.

FORMIC ACID. HCOOH. Colourless, corrosive fuming liquid with a pungent smell. M.p. 8·4°, b.p. 100·5° C. Occurs in various plants and in ants. Made industrially from sodium formate, HCOONa, which is produced by the action of carbon monoxide, CO, on sodium hydroxide, NaOH. Used in dyeing, tanning and electroplating.

FORMULA (chem.). The representation of a *molecule* (q.v.) or smallest portion of a compound, using symbols for the atoms of the elements which go to make up the molecule. E.g. the formula of water, H_2O, implies that the smallest portion of water that can exist independently consists of 2 hydrogen atoms chemically united with 1 oxygen atom. *Structural formula* represents the way in which the atoms in a molecule are actually believed to be joined by *valency* (q.v.) bonds. E.g. the structural formula of water is written H—O—H, indicating that 2 hydrogen atoms, having 1 valency each, are both attached to the bivalent oxygen atom. The *empirical formula* of a compound is its simplest formula, indicating only the numerical ratio of the atoms present in a molecule, but not necessarily their actual number. Thus the empirical formula of hydrogen peroxide is HO while its actual or molecular formula is H_2O_2.

FORMULA (math. and phys.). A statement of facts in a symbolical or general form, by substitution in which a result applicable to particular data may be obtained. Thus the time of swing of a pendulum is given by the formula $T = 2\pi\sqrt{\dfrac{l}{g}}$, showing the connection between length and time of swing.

FORTIN BAROMETER. Mercury *barometer* (q.v.) which, used in conjunction with various correction tables, enables accurate measurements of atmospheric pressure to be made.

FOURIER ANALYSIS. The expansion of a mathematical function or of an experimentally obtained curve in the form of a trigonometric series.

FOURTH DIMENSION. Ordinary space has three dimensions, i.e. length, breadth and thickness, each one at right angles to both the others. Mathematically it is possible to write down equations, similar to those governing relations between points in ordinary three-dimensional space, but connecting any number of imaginary dimensions. These are sometimes said to refer to a 'hyperspace' of many dimensions. In dealing with a material particle, it is necessary to state not only where it is, but when it is there. Thus time is somewhat analogous to a dimension of space. Relativity has shown in particular in what manner time may be regarded as a fourth dimension of a kind of blend of time and space, the 'space-time continuum' in which all events take place.

FOWLER'S SOLUTION. A solution containing potassium arsenite; used in medicine.

F.P.S. SYSTEM, the foot-pound-second system of units. The British system of physical units derived from the three fundamental units of length, mass and time, i.e. the foot, pound mass, and the second.

FRACTIONAL CRYSTALLIZATION. Separation of a mixture of dissolved substances by making use of their different solubilities.

FRACTIONAL DISTILLATION, fractionation. Separation of a mixture of several liquids which have different boiling points, by collecting separately 'fractions' boiling at different temperatures.

FRACTIONATION. Separation of a mixture, usually of chemically related or otherwise similar components, into fractions of different properties. Term is usually applied to *fractional distillation* (q.v.).

FRANCIUM. The element of At. No. 87.

FRASCH PROCESS for the extraction of sulphur. Used to extract sulphur from deposits deep down under sand. A series of concentric pipes is sunk down to the level of the sulphur deposit, superheated steam is forced down to melt the sulphur, which is then forced to the surface by compressed air blown down the centre pipe.

FRAUNHOFER DIFFRACTION. The class of *diffraction* (q.v.) phenomena in which both the light source and the receiving screen are effectively at an infinite distance from the diffracting system. Compare *Fresnel diffraction*.

FRAUNHOFER LINES. Dark lines in the continuous *spectrum* (q.v.) of the Sun, caused by the absorption of certain wave-lengths of the white light from the hotter regions of the Sun, by chemical elements present in the cooler *chromosphere* (q.v.) surrounding the Sun.

FREE (chem.). Uncombined; applied to elements which occur as such.

FREEZING. Change of state from liquid to solid; takes place at a constant temperature (freezing point) for any given substance under a given pressure. The freezing point normally quoted is that for standard atmospheric pressure.

FREEZING MIXTURES. Certain salts which, when dissolved in water or mixed with crushed ice, produce a considerable lowering of temperature. The action depends upon absorption of *heat of solution* (q.v.) by the dissolving salt; in the case of mixtures in contact with ice, the melting point of ice is lowered in the presence of a dissolved substance; latent heat of fusion of ice is absorbed, and the salt dissolves in the melting ice.

FREEZING POINT. The temperature of equilibrium between solid and liquid substance at a pressure of one standard atmosphere (760 mm. mercury).

FREEZING-POINT DEPRESSION. See *depression of freezing point*.

FRENCH CHALK. Powdered *talc* (q.v.).

FREQUENCY of a vibratory motion (wave motion) is the number of vibrations per second. Numerically equal to the velocity divided by the wave-length.

FRESNEL DIFFRACTION. Class of *diffraction* (q.v.) phenomena in which the light source or the receiving screen, or both, are at a finite distance from the diffracting system. Compare *Fraunhofer diffraction*.

FRIABLE. Easily crumbled.

FRICTION. Name given to forces offering resistance to relative motion between surfaces in contact.

FRICTION, COEFFICIENTS OF. If F_s = the frictional resistance when a body is on the point of sliding along a specified surface, F_k = the frictional resistance when steady sliding has been attained, and R = the perpendicular force between the surfaces in contact, the *static coefficient of friction* = F_s/R; the *kinetic coefficient* = F_k/R.

FRUCTOSE, fruit sugar, laevulose. $C_6H_{12}O_6$. Sweet soluble crystalline sugar, m.p. 102–104° C. Occurs in sweet ripe fruits, in the nectar of flowers and in honey.

FRUSTUM. Any part of a solid figure cut off by a plane parallel to the base, or lying between two parallel planes.

FUEL. A substance which is used for producing heat energy by burning it.

FULLER'S EARTH. Name of a variety of clay-like materials which absorb oil and grease. Chemical composition varies; consists of hydrated silicates of magnesium, calcium, aluminium and sometimes other metals. Used in scouring textiles and in refining fats and oils.

FULMINATE OF MERCURY, mercuric *iso*cyanate, $Hg(ONC)_2$. Substance which explodes violently on being struck; used for detonators to initiate explosions.

FUMIGATION. Destruction of bacteria, insects and other pests by exposure to poisonous gas or smoke.

FUNCTION (math.). One quantity y is said to be a function of another quantity x, written $y = f(x)$, if a change in one produces a change in the other. Thus, in the statement $y = 3x^2 + 5x$ (i.e. $f(x) \equiv 3x^2 + 5x$), y is a function of x, and a change in the value of x produces a change in the value of y.

FUNDAMENTAL NOTE (phys.). See *quality of sound*.

FUNDAMENTAL UNITS. The units in which physical quantities (e.g. viscosity, surface tension, etc.) are measured, are not all independent; many of them are derived from a small number of *fundamental units*. In the C.G.S. system, the fundamental units chosen are the centimetre, gram mass and second.

FUNGICIDE. Substance capable of destroying harmful fungi, such as moulds and mildews.

FUR IN KETTLES. Insoluble gritty deposit, consisting mainly of the carbonates of calcium, magnesium and iron; formed by the decomposition of the soluble bicarbonates of these metals when *hard water* (q.v.) is boiled.

FUSE (elec.). Device to prevent an unduly high current from passing through a circuit. Consists of a piece of wire made of metal of low melting point, e.g. tin, placed in series in the circuit. A high current will raise the temperature of the fuse wire sufficiently to melt it and thus break the circuit.

FUSED (chem.). In the molten state, usually applied to solids of relatively high melting point; or, having previously been melted and allowed to solidify.

FUSEL OIL. Mixture of butyl and *iso*-amyl alcohols (C_4H_9OH, $C_5H_{11}OH$) together with other organic substances; a liquid of unpleasant smell and taste; by-product of the distillation of alcohol produced by *fermentation* (q.v.).

FUSIBLE ALLOYS. Alloys of low melting point; generally *eutectic mixtures* (q.v.) of metals of low melting point such as bismuth, lead, tin and cadmium. *Wood's metal* (q.v.) and *Lipowitz alloy* both contain all four and melt below the boiling point of water. Fusible alloys having a melting point a little above the boiling point of water are used in the construction of automatic sprinklers, heat from a fire melting the metal and releasing a spray of water.

FUSION. Melting; melting together.

FUSION, LATENT HEAT OF. See *latent heat*.

FUSION MIXTURE. Mixture of anhydrous sodium and potassium carbonates, Na_2CO_3 and K_2CO_3.

G

g. Symbol for the value of the *acceleration due to gravity* (q.v.).

GADOLINIUM. Gd. Element. A.W. 156·9. At. No. 64. See *rare earths*.

GALAXIES, extra-galactic nebulae. Gigantic star-clusters or 'island universes', separated by even vaster stretches of space. E.g. the *Galaxy* (q.v.).

GALAXY, THE. Enormous cluster of stars and other heavenly bodies, of which the *Solar System* (q.v.) and all visible stars form a part.

GALENA. Natural lead sulphide, PbS. Heavy crystalline mineral of metallic appearance; principal ore of *lead* (q.v.).

GALLIUM. Ga. Element. A.W. 69·72. At. No. 31. Silvery-white metal, S.G. 5·9, m.p. 29·78° C. Compounds very rare; the metal is used in high-temperature thermometers.

GALVANIZED IRON. Sheet iron coated with a layer of zinc, usually made by dipping into the molten metal.

GALVANOMETER. Instrument for detecting, comparing, or measuring small electric currents, but not usually calibrated in amperes; requires calibration when an actual current measurement is needed. Usually depends upon the magnetic effect produced by an electric current. See *ammeter*.

GAMBOGE. Yellow substance obtained from the hardened gum-resin of the tree Garcinia Hanburii.

GAMMA-IRON. *Allotropic form* (q.v.) of iron, stable at high temperatures. See *austenite*.

GAMMA-RAYS, γ-rays. *Electromagnetic waves* (q.v.) of very short wavelengths, shorter than those of X-rays. Produced during the disintegration of radioactive elements. See *radioactivity*.

GARNET. Group of minerals of varying composition, mainly double silicates of calcium or aluminium with other metals. Several varieties are red in colour, and are used as gems.

GAS. Substance in the gaseous state, always occupying the whole of the available space in the containing vessel, and consisting of *molecules* (q.v.) moving freely in space. See *kinetic theory of gases*.

GAS CARBON, retort carbon. Hard deposit consisting of fairly pure carbon, found on the walls of the retorts used for the destructive distillation of coal in the manufacture of coal-gas. Good conductor of electricity, used for making carbon electrodes.

GAS CONSTANT, *R*. In the gas equation, $pv = RT$ (see *gas equation*); $R = 8\cdot314 \times 10^7$ ergs (or $1\cdot987$ calories) per degree Centigrade.

GAS EQUATION. An equation connecting the pressure and volume of a quantity of gas with the *absolute temperature* (q.v.). For a *gram-molecule* (q.v.) of a *perfect gas* (q.v.), $pv = RT$, where $p =$ pressure, $v =$ volume $T =$ absolute temperature, and $R =$ the *gas constant* (q.v.).

GAS LAWS, THE. Statements as to the volume changes of gases under the effect of alterations of pressure and temperature. *Boyle's law* states that at constant temperature the volume of a given mass of gas is inversely proportional to the pressure; i.e. $pv =$ constant. *Charles' law* states that at constant pressure all gases expand by $1/273$ of their volume at $0°$ C. for a rise in temperature of $1°$ C.; i.e. the volume of a given mass of gas at constant pressure is directly proportional to the *absolute temperature* (q.v.). The two laws may be combined in the expression $pv \propto T$, where T is the absolute temperature; or, for a gram-molecule of a gas, $pv = RT$ (see *gas equation*). This gives the behaviour of a gas when both temperature and pressure are altered. The gas laws are not perfectly obeyed by ordinary gases, being strictly true only for the *perfect gas* (q.v.). See *gas laws, deviations from*.

GAS LAWS, DEVIATIONS FROM. Gases do not strictly obey the gas laws, but follow them more and more closely as the pressure of the gas is reduced. Various equations have been derived which attempt to give a better approximation to the behaviour of actual gases. The best known of these is *van der Waals' equation* (q.v.).

GAS MANTLE. Structure composed of the oxides of thorium (99%) and cerium (1%), made by impregnating a combustible fabric with a solution of the nitrates of the metals, and decomposing the nitrates by heat.

GAS MASK, RESPIRATOR. Device for protecting the face and breathing organs against poisonous 'gases'. (These include poisonous smokes, etc., used in chemical warfare.) The air is drawn through a layer of *activated carbon* (q.v.) which adsorbs vapours, and also through a filter-pad which retains solid particles of 'smokes'. Such an arrangement is effective against war 'gases' and smokes, but not against gases of low molecular weight such as carbon monoxide or coal-gas.

GAS THERMOMETER. Apparatus for measuring temperature by the alteration in pressure produced by temperature changes in a gas kept at constant volume, or by the alteration in volume in a gas kept at constant pressure. For practical purposes, other more convenient forms of thermometer are used whenever possible. However, the gas thermometer, operated at low pressure, gives the only direct means of determining *absolute thermodynamic temperatures* (q.v.).

GASEOUS COMBINATION, law of. See *Gay-Lussac's law*.

GASEOUS PRESSURE, pressure of a gas exerted on the walls of the containing vessel; is caused by the bombardment of the molecules of the gas upon the walls of the vessel.

GASOLINE, gasolene, petrol. Mixture of *hydrocarbons* (q.v.) obtained from *petroleum* (q.v.). See *petrol*.

GAUSS. Unit of magnetic induction. If a magnetic field of 1 oersted intensity exists in a medium of unit permeability, e.g. air, then the induction will be 1 gauss.

GAY-LUSSAC'S LAW OF GASEOUS COMBINATION. When gases combine, they do so in a simple ratio by volume to each other, and to the gaseous product, measured under the same conditions of temperature and pressure. Explained by *Avogadro's law* (q.v.).

GEIGER COUNTER. Instrument for the detection of ionizing radiations (chiefly *alpha*, *beta* and *gamma rays*, q.v.), capable of registering individual particles or *photons* (q.v.). Consists normally of a fine wire anode surrounded by a coaxial cylindrical metal cathode, mounted in a glass envelope containing gas at low pressure. A large potential difference, usually about 1000 volts, is maintained between the anode and the cathode. The ions produced in the counter by an incoming ionizing particle are accelerated by the applied potential difference towards their appropriate electrodes, causing a momentary drop in the potential between the latter. This voltage pulse is then passed on to various electronic circuits by means of which it can, if desired, be made to work a mechanical counter.

GEISSLER TUBE. Tube for showing the luminous effects of a discharge of electricity through various rarefied gases.

GEL. *Colloidal solution* (q.v.) which has set to a jelly, the viscosity being so great that the solution has the elasticity of a solid. Formation attributed to a mesh-like structure of the *disperse phase* (q.v.) or colloid, with the *dispersion medium* (q.v.) circulating through the meshwork.

GELATIN, gelatine. Complex *protein* (q.v.) formed by the *hydrolysis* (q.v.) of *collagen* (q.v.) in animal cartilages and bones, by boiling with water. Soluble in water; solution has the property of setting to a jelly. Used in foods, photography, as an adhesive, textile size, and in a variety of other arts and industries.

GELIGNITE. Explosive consisting of a mixture of *nitroglycerin* (q.v.), *nitrocellulose* (q.v.), saltpetre (potassium nitrate, KNO_3) and wood pulp.

GEODESIC. Shortest distance between two points on a spherical surface; arc of a *great circle* (q.v.).

GEODESY. Surveying on a scale which involves making allowance for the curvature of the Earth.

GEOLOGY. Scientific study of the Earth's crust.

GEOMETRICAL PROGRESSION. A series of quantities in which each term is obtained by multiplying the preceding term by some constant factor, termed the *common ratio*. E.g. 1, 3, 9, 27, 81 . . ., each term being three times the preceding. For a series of n terms, having common ratio r and the first term a, the sum, $S = a(r^n - 1)/(r - 1)$; or, if r is less than 1, a more convenient expression is $S = a(1 - r^n)/(1 - r)$.

GEOMETRY. Mathematical study of the properties and relations of lines, surfaces and solids in space.

GERMAN SILVER. Alloy of copper, zinc and nickel in varying proportions, approximating to 5 parts Cu, 2 of Zn and 2 of Ni.

GERMANIUM. Ge. Element. A.W. 72·60. At. No. 32. Brittle white metal. S.G. 5·35, m.p. 958·5° C. Compounds rare. Used in the *transistor* (q.v.).

GERMICIDE. Substance capable of destroying bacteria.

GETTER, vacuum getter. Substance used for getting rid of the last traces of air or other gases in attaining a high vacuum. E.g. magnesium metal is used in radio valves; after exhausting and sealing the valve a small amount of magnesium which is left in the valve is vaporized by heat and combines chemically with any remaining oxygen and nitrogen.

GHOSTS (phys.). False lines appearing in a *line spectrum* (q.v.) due to imperfections in the ruling of the *diffraction grating* (q.v.) used.

GIANT STAR. Star possessing high luminosity.

GILDING. Covering with a thin layer of metallic gold, often by electrolysis (see *electroplating*).

GLACIAL ACETIC ACID. Pure *acetic acid* (q.v.); solid crystalline acetic acid, below its freezing point (16·6° C.).

GLASS. Hard brittle mixture, usually transparent or translucent, of the silicates of calcium, sodium or other metals. Ordinary soda glass is made by melting together sand (*silica*, q.v.), sodium carbonate and lime. Glass for special purposes may contain lead, potassium, barium or other metals in place of the sodium, and boron oxide in place of the silica. See *crown glass*, *flint glass*.

GLASS WOOL. Material consisting of very fine glass threads, resembling cotton wool. Used for filtering and absorbing corrosive liquids.

GLAUBER'S SALT. Crystalline sodium sulphate, $Na_2SO_4 . 10H_2O$.

GLAZE. Vitreous (glass-like) covering for pottery. Chemically related to *glass* (q.v.).

GLOBULINS. Groups of *proteins* (q.v.) soluble in dilute solutions of mineral salts, such as common salt, NaCl; Epsom salts, $MgSO_4$, etc. Occur in many animal and vegetable tissues and fluids; e.g. *lactoglobulin* in milk, *serum globulin* in blood, *vegetable globulins* in seeds.

GLUCINUM. See *beryllium*.

GLUCOSE, dextrose, grape-sugar. $C_6H_{12}O_6$. Colourless crystalline soluble sugar. M.p. 146° C. Occurs in honey and sweet fruits. Other sugars and *carbohydrates* (q.v.) are converted into glucose in the human body before being utilized to provide energy. Commercially prepared from starch and other carbohydrates by *hydrolysis* (q.v.); used in brewing, jam-making, confectionery, etc.

GLUCOSIDES. Derivatives of *glucose* (q.v.) in which one hydrogen atom in the molecule is replaced by an organic radical. The term *glycoside* is applied generally to such compounds of all sugars.

GLUE. General name for *adhesives* (q.v.), particularly those made by extracting hides, bones, cartilages, etc., of animals with water.

GLUTEN. *Protein* (q.v.). Contained in wheat flour (8%–15%).

GLYCERIDES. *Esters* (q.v.) of glycerol, *glycerin* (q.v.) with organic acids. Animal and vegetable fats are mainly composed of *triglycerides* of *fatty acids* (q.v.), such as stearic, palmitic and oleic, a molecule of such a triglyceride being derived by the combination of one molecule of glycerol with three fatty acid molecules.

GLYCERIN, glycerol. $CH_2OH.CHOH.CH_2OH$. Thick syrupy sweetish liquid, soluble in water. B.p. 290° C. Occurs combined with fatty acids in *fats and oils* (q.v.); obtained by the *saponification* (q.v.) of fats in the manufacture of soap. Used in the manufacture of explosives (see *nitroglycerin*), plastics, in pharmacy, and as an 'anti-freeze'.

GLYCEROL, *glycerin* (q.v.).

GLYCOGEN, animal starch. Complex *carbohydrate* (q.v.) formed from glucose and starch in the liver and other organs of animals, serving as a sugar reserve.

GLYCOL. See *ethylene glycol*.

GLYCOLS, dihydric alcohols. Organic compounds derived from aliphatic hydrocarbons by the substitution of hydroxyl groups for two of the hydrogen atoms in the molecule. See also *ethylene glycol*.

GLYCOSIDES. See *glucosides*.

GLYOXAL, diformyl. $(CHO)_2$. Yellow crystals, m.p. 15° C., b.p. 51° C. Used in the manufacture of plastics, and in textile finishing.

GLYPTAL RESINS, alkyd resins. Class of synthetic resins obtained by the reaction of *polyhydric alcohols* (alcohols containing two or more hydroxyl groups in the molecule) with *polybasic* (q.v.) organic acids or their anhydrides; e.g. glycerol and phthalic anhydride. Used chiefly for surface coatings.

GOLD. Au. Element. A.W. 197·2. At. No. 79. Bright yellow rather soft metal; m.p. 1063° C. S.G. 19·4. Extremely malleable and ductile. Not corroded by air or water; unattacked by most acids. Occurs mainly as the free metal; most compounds are unstable and easily reduced to gold. Extracted from ore and sand by the *amalgamation process* (q.v.) and the *cyanide process* (q.v.). Alloys with copper or silver to give hardness are used for coinage, jewellery and dentistry. Compounds are used in photography and medicine.

GOLD LEAF. Gold is the most malleable of metals, and can be beaten into leaves ·0001 mm. thick (i.e. 254,000 thicknesses to the inch). The leaf has the appearance of metallic gold, but transmits green light; i.e. appears green when held up to the light.

GOLD-LEAF ELECTROSCOPE. See *electroscope*.

GOLDSCHMIDT PROCESS. Preparation of metals from their oxides by the *thermit* (q.v.) *process*.

GONIOMETER. Instrument for the measurement of angles (of crystals).

GRADIENT. Usually expressed as unit rise in height per number of units covered along the slope; i.e. the sine of the angle of rise (see *trigonometrical ratios*). Mathematically, the gradient is the ratio of the vertical distance to horizontal distance, i.e. the tangent of the angle. For small gradients the difference between the sine and the tangent is small.

GRADUATION. Marking the scale of an instrument, e.g. the stem of a thermometer is graduated in degrees.

GRAHAM'S LAW of gaseous diffusion. The velocity of diffusion of a gas is inversely proportional to the square root of its density.

GRAIN. British unit of weight. 1/7000 of a pound; ·0648 gm.

GRAM, GRAMME. One of the *fundamental units* (q.v.) of measurement in the C.G.S. system of units. Unit of mass, 1/1000 of the mass of the International Prototype Kilogram, a platinum-iridium standard preserved in Paris.

GRAM WEIGHT, a unit of force, the pull of the Earth on the gram mass, varies slightly in different localities, depending on the value of g, the *acceleration due to gravity* (q.v.) at the given place. Force expressed in grams weight = force in *dynes* (q.v.) divided by the appropriate value of g at the place under consideration. A force of 1 gram weight = approx. 981 dynes. 1 gm. = 0·0353 oz.; 453·6 gms. = 1 lb.

GRAM-ATOM. The atomic weight of an element expressed in grams; e.g. 32 gms. of sulphur.

GRAM-EQUIVALENT. The equivalent weight in grams. See *chemical equivalents*.

GRAM-ION. The sum of the atomic weights of the atoms in an ion (see *electrolysis*) expressed in grams.

GRAM-MOLECULAR VOLUME. The volume occupied by one grammolecule of a gas. Approximately the same for all gases under the same conditions of temperature and pressure; at a pressure of 760 mm. and 0° C., equal to 22·415 litres for a *perfect gas* (q.v.).

GRAM-MOLECULE, gram-molecular weight, mole, mol. The molecular weight of a compound expressed in grams. E.g. 18 gms. of water.

GRANITE. Heterogeneous mixture of felspar, quartz and mica.

GRAPE SUGAR. See *glucose*.

GRAPH. Diagram, generally plotted between axes at right angles to each other, showing the relation of one variable quantity to another. E.g. the variation of rainfall with time, or the variation in the value of a mathematical *function* (q.v.) as different values are assigned to one of the variables in the function.

=GRAPH. Suffix applied to instruments which automatically record or write down observations; e.g. *barograph* (q.v.).

GRAPHITE, blacklead, plumbago. Natural *allotropic form* (q.v.) of carbon. Used for pencil leads, in electrical apparatus, and as a lubricant for heavy machinery.

GRAVIMETRIC ANALYSIS. Branch of chemical quantitative analysis. The amount of a substance present is determined by converting it, by a suitable chemical reaction, into some other substance of known chemical composition, which can be readily isolated, purified and weighed.

GRAVITATION, Newton's law of. Every particle in the Universe attracts every other particle with a force which is directly proportional to the product of the masses of the particles and inversely proportional to the square of the distance between them. Thus, the force of attraction between two masses M_1 and M_2, in grams, separated by a distance of d centimetres, is given by $F = \dfrac{G.M_1M_2}{d^2}$ dynes, where G is the gravitational constant, $6 \cdot 659 \times 10^{-8}$ C.G.S. units.

GREAT CIRCLE. Circle obtained by cutting a sphere by a plane passing through the centre. E.g. regarding the Earth as a sphere, the Equator is a great circle, as are all the meridians of longitude. On the Earth's surface, an apparent straight line joining any two points is an arc of a great circle, i.e. a *geodesic*.

GREEK FIRE. Mixture of materials which caught fire when wetted; used by the ancient Greeks in naval warfare. Probably composed of sulphur, naphtha and quicklime or similar materials.

GREEN VITRIOL, copperas. Ferrous sulphate crystals, $FeSO_4 . 7H_2O$.

GR-N. See *Buna-N*.

GR-S. See *Buna-S*.

GROUND STATE. The most stable state of an atom. The normal state of an atom when its circum-nuclear electrons move in orbits such that the energy of the atom is a minimum. See *atom, structure of*.

GRÜNEISEN'S LAW. The ratio of the coefficient of expansion of a metal to its specific heat at constant pressure is a constant at all temperatures.

GUANO. Large deposits formed from the excrement and bodies of seabirds. Found on islands off the coast of Peru. Very rich in nitrogen and phosphorus compounds; valuable *fertilizer* (q.v.).

GUMS. General name applied to a large class of substances of vegetable origin, usually exuded from plants.

GUN-COTTON, *cellulose nitrate* (q.v.), nitrocellulose. Powerful explosive formed by the action of nitric acid on cellulose.

GUN-METAL. Variety of bronze containing about 90% copper, 8%–10% tin, and up to 4% zinc.

GUNPOWDER. Mixture of potassium nitrate, KNO_3, powdered charcoal and sulphur. When ignited, a number of chemical reactions take place, evolving gases, thus producing an explosion in a confined space.

GUTTA-PERCHA. Material very similar to *rubber* (q.v.), obtained from the latex of certain Malayan trees; chemically, the *trans*- form of polyisoprene. A horny substance at ordinary temperatures; thermoplastic; at about 70° C. resembles unvulcanized rubber. Used for golf ball covers.

GYPSUM. Natural hydrated calcium sulphate, $CaSO_4.2H_2O$. Loses three-quarters of its *water of crystallization* (q.v.) when heated to 120° C., becoming *Plaster of Paris* (q.v.).

GYRATION. Motion round a fixed axis or centre.

GYRO-COMPASS, gyroscopic compass. Compass which does not make use of magnetism, and is therefore not affected by magnetic storms, etc.; consists of a universally-mounted spinning wheel which has a rigidity of direction of axis and plane of rotation relative to space; the rotation being electrically maintained. See *gyroscope*.

GYROSCOPE. Spinning wheel which is mounted in such a way that it is free to rotate about any axis; i.e. 'universally mounted'. Such a wheel has two properties upon which applications of the gyroscope depend – namely, 1. Rigidity in space (gyroscopic inertia); the support of the wheel may be turned in any direction without altering the direction of the wheel relative to space. 2. Precession. When a gyroscope is subjected to a force tending to alter the direction of its axis, the wheel will turn about an axis at right angles to the axis about which the force was applied.

H

HABER PROCESS. Industrial preparation of ammonia, for use in fertilizers, from atmospheric nitrogen. See *fixation of atmospheric nitrogen*. A heated mixture of nitrogen and hydrogen is passed over a *catalyst* (q.v.) under pressure; the gases combine to form ammonia gas according to the equation $N_2 + 3H_2 = 2NH_3$.

HAEMATITE. Natural ferric oxide, Fe_2O_3. Valuable ore of iron.

HAEMOGLOBIN. Red colouring matter (respiratory pigment) present in the red corpuscles of blood; consists of a *protein* (q.v.), *globin*, combined with a pigment, *haem*, the latter being a highly complex organic compound containing iron, nitrogen, carbon, hydrogen and oxygen. Serves to carry oxygen, which is breathed in, round the body in the form of an easily decomposed compound, oxyhaemoglobin.

HAFNIUM, celtium. Hf. Element. A.W. 178·6. At. No. 72. Rare metal, S.G. 13·3, m.p. 1700° C. Used in the manufacture of tungsten filaments.

HAIR SALT. Natural aluminium sulphate, $Al_2(SO_4)_3.18H_2O$. White soluble crystalline salt.

HALF-PERIOD ZONES. Division of a wave front into elements of area or zones such that secondary wavelets (see *Huygens' construction*) reaching a given point ahead of the wave from adjacent zones differ in phase by half a period, or π. This construction is used in theoretical investigations of *Fresnel diffraction* (q.v.) in simple cases.

HALF-VALUE PERIOD, half-life period, period of decay. The time taken for the activity of a radioactive element to decay to one-half of its original value. $T = \dfrac{\log_e 2}{\lambda}$ where $T =$ half-value period, and $\lambda =$ *transformation constant* (q.v.).

HALF-WAVE PLATE. Plate of double refracting material (see *double refraction*) cut parallel to the *optic axis* (q.v.) and of such a thickness that a phase difference of π or $180°$ is introduced between the *ordinary ray* (q.v.) and the extraordinary ray for light of a particular wavelength (usually sodium light). The half-wave plate is chiefly used to alter the plane of vibration of plane-polarized light.

HALIDE. *Binary* (q.v.) compound of one of the halogen elements (fluorine, chlorine, bromine or iodine); salt of the hydride of one of these.

HALL EFFECT. If a current flows in a wire placed in a strong transverse magnetic field, a potential difference is developed across the wire, at right angles to both the magnetic field and the wire.

HALO. A luminous ring sometimes observed surrounding the Sun or the Moon. Caused by the *refraction* (q.v.) of light by ice crystals in the atmosphere.

HALOGENS. The four elements fluorine, chlorine, bromine and iodine, having closely related and graded properties.

HARCOURT PENTANE LAMP. Lamp burning pentane, C_5H_{12}, under certain specified conditions. The lamp has been used as a standard source of light; the former unit of luminous intensity, the *international candle* (q.v.) was defined in terms of it.

HARD WATER. Water which does not form an immediate lather with soap, owing to the presence of calcium, magnesium and iron compounds dissolved in the water. The addition of soap produces an insoluble scum consisting of salts of these metals with the fatty acids of the soap (see *soap*), until no more is left in solution. Removal of these salts from solution renders the water soft. Hardness is divided into two types: 1. Temporary hardness, due to bicarbonates of the metals. These enter the water by the passage of the water, containing dissolved carbon dioxide, over solid carbonates (chalk or limestone deposits, etc.). Such hardness is removed by boiling, the soluble bicarbonates being decomposed into the insoluble carbonates (see *fur in kettles*), carbon dioxide and water. 2. Permanent hardness, due to sulphates of the metals. This is destroyed by the addition of washing-soda, sodium carbonate, which precipitates the insoluble carbonates. All hardness may be destroyed by the use of *zeolites* (q.v.).

HARDENING OF FATS. Conversion of liquid fats (oils) consisting mainly of *triolein* (q.v.) into hard fats by the action of hydrogen in the presence of a *catalyst* (q.v.). See *hydrogenation of oils*.

HARMONIC MOTION. See *simple harmonic motion*.

HARMONICS of a *wave motion* (q.v.). Waves superimposed on a fundamental wave, having a frequency which is a whole multiple of the fundamental frequency.

HARTSHORN, SPIRITS OF. Solution of *ammonia* (q.v.) in water.

HEAT. Energy possessed by a substance in the form of kinetic energy of molecular translation, rotation and vibration. Usually measured in *calories* (q.v.). Transmitted by *conduction, convection* and *radiation* (q.v.). The chief observable physical effects of a change in the heat content of a body may include rise in temperature (see *temperature*); change of state from solid to liquid (melting), solid to gas (sublimation) and liquid to gas (evaporation and boiling); *expansion* (q.v.); and electrical effects such as the *Peltier* and *Seebeck* effects (q.v.).

HEAT CAPACITY. The quantity of heat required to raise the temperature of a body through 1° C. Numerically equal to the product of the mass of the body and its specific heat (see *heat, specific*).

HEAT, LATENT. Quantity of heat required to effect a change of state of 1 gm. of a substance from solid to liquid (latent heat of fusion) or from liquid to vapour (latent heat of vaporization) without change of temperature. At the freezing and boiling points of a substance, addition of heat produces no rise in temperature until the change of state is complete. Energy required to bring about the change of state is absorbed in the form of latent heat, and an equal amount of heat is liberated in reversing the process.

HEAT OF FORMATION. The quantity of heat (usually expressed in calories) liberated or absorbed when 1 *gram-molecule* (q.v.) of a compound is formed from its elements in their normal state. The heat of formation of elements is, for the purpose of thermochemical calculations, taken as zero. See *Hess's law*.

HEAT OF NEUTRALIZATION. The quantity of heat evolved when 1 *gram-equivalent* (q.v.) of an acid or base is exactly neutralized. For all strong acids or bases, its value is approximately 13,700 calories.

HEAT OF REACTION. See *thermal value of a chemical reaction*.

HEAT OF SOLUTION. The quantity of heat evolved or absorbed when 1 *gram-molecule* (q.v.) of a substance is dissolved in a large volume of water.

HEAT RADIATION. *Electromagnetic waves* (q.v.) of wave-lengths intermediate between those of visible red light and the shortest wireless waves.

HEAT, SPECIFIC, of a substance. The quantity of heat required to raise the temperature of 1 gm. of the substance through 1° C.

HEAT, SPECIFIC, OF GASES. The two most important specific heats of a gas are (1) that measured at constant pressure, and (2) that measured at constant volume. The specific heat at constant pressure, C_p, is greater than that at constant volume, C_v; this is explained by the fact that a gas heated at constant pressure expands, and heat energy must be supplied equivalent to the work done in the expansion. The ratio C_p/C_v, denoted by γ (gamma), varies from 1·66 for *monatomic* (q.v.) gases to a little over 1 for gases with complex molecules. The value of gamma thus gives an indication of the number of atoms in the molecule of a gas.

HEAVISIDE-KENNELLY LAYER, ionosphere. Ionized region of the upper atmosphere, which reflects the longer wireless waves, thus permitting their reception round the curved surface of the Earth.

HEAVY SPAR. *Barytes* (q.v.).

HEAVY WATER. *Deuterium* (q.v.) oxide, D_2O. Liquid similar to ordinary water and occurring in it in small amounts. S.G. 1·1. F.p. 3·82° C. B.p. 101·42° C. Used as a *moderator* (q.v.) in some types of *atomic pile* (q.v.).

HECTARE. Metric unit of area; 10,000 square metres, 2·4711 acres.

HECTO-. Prefix denoting one hundred times.

HELIUM. He. Element. A.W. 4·003. At. No. 2. *Inert gas* (q.v.) occurs in certain natural gases in the U.S.A., occluded in *monazite* and *cleveite* (q.v.) and in the atmosphere (1 part in 200,000). Non-inflammable, very light, valuable for filling airships and balloons.

HELIX. Spiral.

HENRY, THE. Unit of self- and mutual inductance (see *self-induction, mutual induction*). An inductance such that a rate of change of current of 1 ampere per second produces an induced E.M.F. of 1 volt.

HENRY'S LAW. The weight of a gas dissolved by a definite volume of liquid at constant temperature is directly proportional to the pressure. From this it follows that the volume of a gas absorbed by a given volume of liquid at constant temperature is independent of the pressure. The law holds only for sparingly soluble gases at low pressures.

HEPTA-. Prefix meaning seven.

HERTZIAN WAVES, wireless waves, radio waves. *Electromagnetic waves* (q.v.) covering a range of frequency from above 3×10^{10} cycles per second, corresponding to the shortest *radar* (q.v.) waves of 1 cm., to below $1·5 \times 10^5$ cycles (150 kilocycles) per second, corresponding to long waves of 2000 metres. Used in *radio* (q.v.) transmission.

HESS'S LAW. If a chemical reaction is carried out in stages, the algebraic sum of the amounts of heat evolved in the separate stages is equal to the total amount of heat evolved when the reaction occurs directly. A consequence of the law of *conservation of energy* (q.v.) as applied to thermochemistry.

HETERO-. Prefix denoting other, different.

HETEROCYCLIC COMPOUNDS. Organic chemical compounds containing a ring structure of atoms in the molecule, the ring including atoms of elements other than carbon. E.g. pyridine, C_5H_5N, having a molecule consisting of 5 carbon atoms and 1 nitrogen atom in a closed ring, with a hydrogen atom attached to each carbon atom.

HETERODYNE. A beat effect (see *beats*) produced by superimposing two waves of different frequency. Used extensively in radio communications to alter the frequency of an alternating current.

HETEROGENEOUS. Not of a uniform composition; showing different properties in different portions.

HEUSLER'S ALLOYS. Strongly *ferromagnetic* (q.v.) alloys containing neither iron, nickel, nor cobalt. Composed of copper, manganese and aluminium.

HEXA-. Prefix denoting six ; six times.

HEXAMETHYLENE TETRAMINE, hexamine, urotropine. $(CH_2)_6N_4$. White crystalline substance obtained by the *condensation* (q.v.) of ammonia with formaldehyde. Used in medicine and in the manufacture of *cyclonite* (q.v.).

HEXAMINE. *Hexamethylene tetramine* (q.v.).

HEXOGEN. *Cyclonite* (q.v.).

HIGH-SPEED STEEL. Very hard steel containing 12%–22% tungsten, with chromium, vanadium, molybdenum and small amounts of other elements; used for tools which remain hard even at red heat.

HOLMIUM. Ho. Element. A.W. 164·94. At. No. 67. See *rare earths*.

HOLO-. Prefix denoting whole-; e.g. holohedral crystal, a crystal having the full number of faces for perfect symmetry.

HOMO-. Prefix denoting same-; e.g. *homogeneous* (q.v.).

HOMOCYCLIC COMPOUNDS. Organic chemical compounds the molecules of which contain a ring structure of atoms of the same kind (usually carbon). E.g. benzene, C_6H_6.

HOMOGENEOUS. Of uniform composition throughout.

HOMOLOGOUS SERIES. Series of chemical compounds of uniform chemical type, showing a regular gradation in physical properties, and capable of being represented by a general molecular formula, the molecule of each member of the series differing from the preceding one by a definite constant group of atoms. E.g. the *paraffin series* (q.v.).

HOMOLOGUES. Members of the same *homologous series* (q.v.); e.g methane, CH_4, and ethane, C_2H_6.

HOOKE'S LAW. Within the elastic limit, a strain is proportional to the stress producing it. '*Ut tensio, sic vis.*' See *elasticity, elastic modulus.*

HORIZONTAL INTENSITY of the Earth's magnetic field. The total *magnetic intensity* (q.v.) of the Earth's field may be resolved into two components, the horizontal and the vertical. If I = total intensity and ϕ the angle of dip (see *magnetic dip*) the horizontal intensity, $H = I \cos \phi$.

HORMONES. Specific substances produced by the endocrine glands of the body, regulating many functions of the organism. Organic compounds of a very complex nature. E.g. *insulin* (q.v.) maintains the concentration of sugar in the blood at a constant level.

HORN SILVER, cerargyrite, chlorargyrite. Natural silver chloride, AgCl. Important ore of silver.

HORNBLENDE. Rock-forming mineral consisting mainly of silicates of calcium, magnesium and iron.

HORSE-POWER. H.P. British unit of power; work done at the rate of 550 *foot-pounds* (q.v.) per second. 1 H.P. = 746 *watts* (q.v.).

HUMIDITY OF THE ATMOSPHERE. A measure of the water vapour present in the air. May be given in terms of *relative humidity* (q.v.), or as *absolute humidity*, the mass of water present in a cubic metre of the air.

HUMUS. Vegetable matter decomposed by the action of bacteria and other living organisms.

HUYGENS' CONSTRUCTION. Each point of a wave front may be regarded as a new source of secondary wavelets. Knowing the position of the wave front at any given time, the construction enables its position to be determined at any subsequent time.

HUYGENS' PRINCIPLE OF SUPERPOSITION. The resultant displacement at any point due to the superposition of any system of waves is equal to the sum of the displacements of the individual waves at that point. This principle forms the basis of the theory of light *interference* (q.v.).

HYDRARGYRUM. *Mercury* (q.v.).

HYDRATE. A compound containing combined water. Generally applied to salts containing *water of crystallization* (q.v.).

HYDRATED. Opposite of *anhydrous* (q.v.); containing chemically combined water; (salt) containing *water of crystallization* (q.v.).

HYDRAULIC CEMENT. Cement which hardens in contact with water.

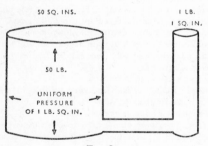

FIG. 8.

HYDRAULIC PRESS. Application of *Pascal's law* (q.v.); a device whereby a force applied by a piston over a small area is transmitted through water to another piston having a large area; by this means very great forces may be obtained. See Fig. 8.

HYDRAULICS. The practical application of *hydrodynamics* (q.v.) to engineering.

HYDRIDE. *Binary compound* (q.v.) with hydrogen.

HYDRO-. Prefix denoting water-; e.g. *hydrogen*, water producer. In chemical nomenclature, often denotes a compound of hydrogen; e.g. hydrochloric acid.

HYDROCARBON. Chemical compound of carbon and hydrogen only. Mineral oils are mainly a mixture of various hydrocarbons.

HYDROCHLORIC ACID, muriatic acid, spirits of salts. A solution of hydrogen chloride, HCl, in water. The concentrated acid contains 35%–40% HCl by weight, and is a colourless, fuming, corrosive liquid. Manufactured by the action of sulphuric acid, H_2SO_4, on common salt, or by the direct chemical combination of hydrogen and chlorine obtained by the *electrolysis* (q.v.) of brine. Used in chemical industry.

HYDROCYANIC ACID, prussic acid, hydrogen cyanide. HCN. Colourless, intensely poisonous liquid with a smell of bitter almonds. B.p. 26·5° C.

HYDRODYNAMICS. Mathematical study of the motion, energy and pressure of liquids in motion.

HYDROELECTRIC POWER. Electrical energy obtained from waterpower, the latter being used to drive a *dynamo* (q.v.).

HYDROFLUORIC ACID. Solution of hydrogen fluoride, HF, in water. Term also applied to the compound HF itself, a colourless, corrosive fuming liquid, b.p. 19·5° C. Attacks glass; used for etching glass.

HYDROGEL. Colloidal *gel* (q.v.) in which water is the solvent.

HYDROGEN. H. Element. A.W. 1·0080. At. No. 1. Colourless, odourless, tasteless gas. Lightest substance known. Inflammable, combines with oxygen to form water. Molecule is diatomic; i.e. contains two atoms, written H_2. Occurs as water, H_2O; in organic compounds, and in all living things. Manufactured by the *Bosch process* (q.v.) and by electrolysis. Used in the oxy-hydrogen blowpipe, as a reducing agent, in the manufacture of synthetic ammonia (see *fixation of atmospheric nitrogen*) and of synthetic oil (see *Fischer-Tropsch process*) and for *hydrogenation of oils* (q.v.).

HYDROGEN ARSENIDE. See *arsine*.

HYDROGEN CHLORIDE. HCl. Gas, very soluble in water, giving a solution of *hydrochloric acid* (q.v.).

HYDROGEN FLUORIDE. See *hydrofluoric acid*.

HYDROGEN ION. Positively charged hydrogen atom; proton. General properties of *acids* (q.v.) in solution are due to the presence of hydrogen ions.

HYDROGEN-ION CONCENTRATION. Number of grams of hydrogen ions per litre of solution. A measure of the acidity of a solution. Often conveniently expressed in terms of $p_H = \log_{10} \dfrac{1}{[H^\cdot]}$, where $[H^\cdot] =$ hydrogen-ion concentration. On this scale a strictly neutral solution has $p_H = 7$, while as a solution changes from extreme acidity to extreme alkalinity, as represented by a decrease of hydrogen-ion concentration, the p_H value increases from 0 to 14, each unit of p_H representing a tenfold decrease in hydrogen-ion concentration.

HYDROGEN PEROXIDE, peroxide of hydrogen. H_2O_2. Thick, syrupy liquid; as usually sold, a solution of the pure compound in water. Gives off oxygen readily, used as a disinfectant and bleaching agent. Strength of solution usually given in terms of 'volume strength'; thus, 10 volume hydrogen peroxide will evolve 10 times its own volume of oxygen gas.

HYDROGEN PHOSPHIDE. See *phosphine*.

HYDROGEN SULPHIDE, sulphuretted hydrogen. H_2S. Colourless poisonous gas with a smell of bad eggs. Formed by the decomposition of organic matter containing sulphur; occurs naturally in some mineral waters. Prepared by the action of dilute acids on sulphides of metals; used in chemical analysis.

HYDROGENATION. Subjecting to the chemical action of, or causing to combine with, hydrogen.

HYDROGENATION OF COAL. The manufacture of artificial mineral oil from coal by the action of hydrogen; causing the carbon in coal to combine with hydrogen to form *hydrocarbons* (q.v.). See *Bergius process*, *Fischer-Tropsch process*.

HYDROGENATION OF OILS. Artificial hardening of liquid animal and vegetable oils by the action of hydrogen. Liquid fats and oils contain a high percentage of liquid *triolein* (q.v.), $C_{57}H_{104}O_6$, which may be converted into a solid *tristearin* (q.v.), $C_{57}H_{110}O_6$, by the action of hydrogen in the presence of finely divided nickel which acts as a *catalyst* (q.v.); the result being a hard fat of higher melting point.

HYDROLITH. Calcium hydride, CaH_2. Decomposed by water, used for the production of hydrogen, according to the equation $CaH_2 + 2H_2O = Ca(OH)_2 + 2H_2$.

HYDROLYSIS. Chemical decomposition of a substance by water, the water itself being also decomposed; reaction of the type $AB + H_2O = A(OH) + HB$. Salts of weak acids, weak bases, or both, are partially hydrolyzed in solution; *esters* (q.v.) may be hydrolyzed to form an alcohol and acid. See *saponification*.

HYDROMETER. Instrument for measuring the *density* (q.v.) or *specific gravity* (q.v.) of liquids. The common type consists of a weighted bulb with a graduated, slender stem; the apparatus floats vertically in the liquid being tested. In liquids of high density a greater length of stem is exposed than in liquids of low density.

HYDROPONICS. Cultivation of plants without the use of soil, by the use of solutions of those mineral salts which a plant normally extracts from the soil.

HYDROSOL. *Colloidal solution* (q.v.), as distinct from a *hydrogel* (q.v.), water being the solvent.

HYDROSPHERE. Watery portion of the Earth's crust, comprising the oceans, seas and all other waters. Composition by weight is given as oxygen 85.8%, hydrogen 10.7%, chlorine 2.1%, sodium 1.1%, magnesium 0.14%, not more than 0.05% of any other element being present. The chief constituents are water, H_2O, sodium chloride, NaCl, and magnesium chloride, $MgCl_2$.

HYDROSTATICS. The mathematical study of forces and pressures in liquids or at rest.

HYDROXIDE. Compound derived from water, H_2O, by the replacement of one of the hydrogen atoms in the molecule by some other atom or group; compound containing the hydroxyl group. E.g. sodium hydroxide, NaOH.

HYDROXYL GROUP. The univalent radical or group consisting of one hydrogen and one oxygen atom, forming a part of a molecule of a compound. The —OH group.

HYDROXYL ION. Negatively charged *ion* (q.v.); free *hydroxy group* (q.v.) bearing a negative electric charge. The presence of hydroxyl ions is the cause of the characteristic properties of alkaline solutions.

HYGRO-. Prefix denoting moisture, humidity. E.g. *hygrometer* (q.v.).

HYGRODEIK. *Wet and dry bulb hygrometer* (q.v.) with a chart attached which enables the *relative humidity* (q.v.) to be obtained directly from the readings of the two thermometers.

HYGROMETER. Any instrument designed to measure the *relative humidity* (q.v.) of the atmosphere.

HYGROMETRIC STATE of the atmosphere. See *relative humidity*.

HYGROSCOPE. Instrument for showing variations of *relative humidity* (q.v.) of the air.

HYGROSCOPIC. Having a tendency to absorb moisture.

HYPER-. Prefix denoting over, above, beyond.

HYPERBOLA. Curve traced out by a point which moves so that its distance from a fixed point, the *focus*, always bears a constant ratio greater than unity to its distance from a fixed straight line, the *directrix*.

HYPERFINE STRUCTURE OF SPECTRUM LINES. Very fine structure of certain *spectrum* (q.v.) lines observed when they are examined under very high resolution. The lines are caused either (a) by the presence of different *isotopes* (q.v.) of the element emitting the spectrum, or (b) if the atomic nuclei of the element possess a *spin* (q.v.), and therefore a resultant magnetic moment.

HYPERMETROPIA. Long sight. Defect of vision; the subject is unable to see near objects distinctly. Corrected by the use of convex spectacle lenses.

HYPEROL. Trade name of a crystalline compound of urea and hydrogen peroxide; $CO(NH_2)_2.H_2O_2$. Evolves hydrogen peroxide by the action of water.

HYPERTONIC. A solution is said to be hypertonic with respect to another if it has a greater *osmotic pressure* (q.v.).

HYPNOTIC (chem.). Substance producing sleep.

HYPO-. Prefix denoting under, below.

HYPO (phot.). Sodium thiosulphate, $Na_2S_2O_3.5H_2O$. Formerly incorrectly called 'sodium hyposulphite'. Used in photography. See *fixing*.

HYPOCHLORITE. Salt of hypochlorous acid, HClO. Hypochlorites of sodium, potassium and calcium are used as disinfectants and for bleaching, by virtue of their oxidizing properties.

HYPOTENUSE. The side opposite the right angle (i.e. the longest side) in a right-angled triangle.

HYPOTHESIS. Supposition put forward in explanation of observed facts.

HYPOTONIC. A solution is said to be hypotonic with respect to another if it has a smaller *osmotic pressure* (q.v.).

HYPSOMETER. 'Height-measurer.' Apparatus for the determination of the boiling point of a liquid. Since the boiling point of liquids depends upon the pressure, and the atmospheric pressure varies with the altitude, the apparatus may be used for the determination of altitude above sea-level.

HYSTERESIS. A physical phenomenon chiefly met in the elastic and magnetic behaviour of materials. When a body is stressed, the strain produced is a function of the stress. On releasing the stress, the strain lags behind; i.e. the strain for a given value of stress is greater when the stress is decreasing than when it is increasing. On removing the stress completely, a residual strain remains. This lagging of effect behind cause is called *hysteresis*. It also occurs in induced magnetism. See *hysteresis cycle*.

HYSTERESIS CYCLE. Cycle of magnetizing field variations to which an initially demagnetized ferromagnetic substance is subjected. The magnetizing field is periodically reversed in direction until a steady state is reached in which the *magnetic induction* (q.v.) in the specimen at any instant is a function only of the magnitude of the magnetizing field and the sign of its rate of change at that instant. When this condition has been reached, a plot of induction against magnetizing field gives a *hysteresis loop* or curve. Important magnetic properties of the substance, e.g. *coercive force* (q.v.), *remanence* (q.v.), the energy dissipated as heat during one cycle, etc, can be obtained from this curve.

HYSTERESIS LOOP. See *hysteresis cycle*.

I

IATROCHEMISTRY. Mediaeval medical chemistry; early attempts at the application of drugs to medicine.

ICE. Water, H_2O, in the solid state. Formed at the freezing point of water, 0° C. Less dense than water; thus water expands on freezing, and ice floats on water.

ICE POINT. The temperature of equilibrium between ice and water under normal atmospheric pressure (see *atmosphere, standard*); i.e. the melting point of ice. The ice point is assigned the value of 0° C. in the Centigrade scale.

-IDE. Chemical suffix denoting a *binary compound* (q.v.) of the two named elements or radicals; e.g. hydrogen sulphide, a compound of hydrogen and sulphur only.

IDEAL GAS. See *perfect gas*.

IDENTITY (math). A statement of equality between known or unknown quantities, which holds true for all values of the unknown quantities. E.g. $3x = 2x + x$ irrespective of what value is assigned to x.

IGNIS FATUUS. Will-o'-the-wisp. Pale flame sometimes seen over marshy ground, probably caused by the spontaneous combustion of methane, CH_4, or other inflammable gases.

IGNITION. 1. Setting on fire. 2. Strong heating.

IGNITION POINT of a substance is the temperature to which it must be heated before *combustion* (q.v.) can take place.

ILLUMINATION of a surface. The amount of light falling on unit area of the surface per second. Measured in *lumens* (q.v.) per unit area.

ILMENITE. Natural ferrous titanite, $FeTiO_3$. Ore of *titanium* (q.v.).

IMAGE, REAL (phys.). An image formed by a mirror or lens at a point through which the rays of light entering the observer's eye actually pass. Such an image can be obtained on a screen.

IMAGE, VIRTUAL (phys.). An image seen at a point from which the rays of light appear to come to the observer, but do not actually do so; e.g. the image seen in a plane mirror. Such an image cannot be obtained on a screen placed at its apparent position, since the rays of light do not pass through that point.

IMAGINARY NUMBERS. Numbers with negative squares; thus $\sqrt{-1}$ is an imaginary number, denoted by i; $i^2 = -1$.

IMMERSION OBJECTIVE, oil-immersion lens. Type of *objective* (q.v.) used in high-power microscopes, the lowest lens of the objective lens system being immersed in a drop of cedar-wood oil placed upon the slide to be examined. Such an arrangement causes more light to enter the system than if the oil were absent.

IMMISCIBLE. Incapable of being mixed to form a homogeneous substance; usually applied to liquids; e.g. oil and water are immiscible.

IMPACT. Collision of bodies. See *conservation of momentum*.

IMPEDANCE of an alternating-current circuit. The quantity which determines the amplitude of the current for a given voltage. For a circuit containing resistance R, self-inductance L, and a capacity C connected in series, the impedance of the circuit is given by the expression $\mathcal{Z} = \left[R^2 + \left(Lw - \frac{1}{Cw} \right)^2 \right]^{\frac{1}{2}}$, where w is a constant, the *angular velocity*, equal to $2\pi n$, n being the frequency of the alternating current.

IMPFING. 'Seeding' a liquid with a small crystal in order to induce crystallization.

IMPULSE (phys.). Concept of a force acting during a very short time; given (for a constant force) by the product of the magnitude of the force and the time during which the force acts; equal to the total change of *momentum* (q.v.) produced by it.

INCANDESCENCE. State of glowing at high temperatures; white or bright-red heat.

INCIDENCE, ANGLE OF. The angle between a *ray* (q.v.) of light meeting a surface, and the *normal* (q.v.) to the surface at that point.

INCUBATOR. Box designed to maintain a constant internal temperature by the use of a *thermostat* (q.v.); used for rearing chickens and pre-maturely-born infants, and in bacteriology.

INDEX (math.). The *exponent* (q.v.) of a quantity raised to a power; number indicating the power to which the quantity is raised. E.g. the index of a in $4a^5$ is 5.

INDIAN INK, Chinese ink. Black ink containing a suspension of carbon.

INDICATOR (chem.). Substance which, by a sharp colour change, indicates the completion of a chemical reaction. Frequently used in *volumetric analysis* (q.v.). Indicators for titrations of acids and alkalies are usually weak organic acids or bases, yielding ions of a different colour from the un-ionized molecules. (See *ionization*.) E.g. *litmus* (q.v.) is red with acids and blue with alkalies, a change in colour indicating that neutralization is complete.

INDIGO. $C_6H_{10}N_2O_2$. Important blue *vat dye* (q.v.), formerly extracted from plants of the genus *Indigofera*, in which it occurs as indican, a *glucoside* (q.v.). Now manufactured artificially on a large scale.

INDIUM. In. Element. A.W. 114·76. At. No. 49. Soft silvery-white metal, S.G. 7·31, m.p. 155° C. Compounds rare. Used in electroplating.

INDUCED CURRENT. See *induction*.

INDUCTANCE. See *self-induction; mutual induction*.

INDUCTION, CHARGING BY. A process of electrically charging an insulated conductor, using the force due to another nearby charge to separate the positive and negative charges existing on the conductor.

INDUCTION COIL. Instrument for producing a high electromotive force from a supply of low E.M.F. Essentially consists of a cylindrical soft-iron core, usually laminated to prevent losses due to *eddy currents* (q.v.), round which are wound two coils, the primary and the secondary. The primary coil consists of a few hundred turns; rapid variation of an electric current in this coil, produced by a repeated interruption or break in the circuit by a mechanism similar to that in the electric *bell* (q.v.) produces an induced E.M.F. (see *induction, electromagnetic*) in the secondary coil, which contains a very large number of turns of thin wire.

INDUCTION, ELECTROMAGNETIC. When the *magnetic flux* (q.v.) through a circuit changes, an electromotive force is induced in the circuit. This phenomenon is called *electromagnetic induction*. The induced E.M.F. is equal to the rate of decrease of magnetic flux through the circuit (*Faraday's Law*). If the circuit is closed, this E.M.F. gives rise to an induced current, and the phenomenon forms the basis of the *dynamo, transformer* (q.v.), etc. The induced current is in such a direction that its magnetic field tends to neutralize the change in magnetic flux producing it (*Lenz's Law*).

INDUCTION, MAGNETIC. See *magnetic induction*.

INDUCTIVITY. See *specific inductive capacity*.

INDUCTOMETER. A variable inductance.

INERT GASES, noble gases, rare gases. The elements *helium, neon, argon, krypton, xenon, radon* (q.v.). Chemically inactive, although some compounds have been reported. Argon occurs in appreciable amounts (0·8%) in the air; the others, with the exception of radon, occur in the air in very minute amounts.

INERTIA (phys.). Tendency of a body to preserve its state of rest or uniform motion in a straight line.

INFINITESIMAL. A quantity smaller than any assignable quantity; the concept is obtained by imagining a quantity decreasing indefinitely without actually becoming zero.

INFINITY. ∞. That quantity which is greater than any assignable quantity.

INFRA-RED RAYS, invisible heat radiation, radiant heat. *Electromagnetic waves* (q.v.) possessing wave-lengths between those of visible light and those of wireless waves, i.e. from approximately 7500 *Ångström units* (q.v.) to 1 mm. Infra-red radiation has the power of penetrating fog or haze which would scatter ordinary visible light; thus photographs taken on a plate made sensitive to infra-red radiation may often disclose detail invisible on an ordinary plate or to the naked eye.

INFUSIBLE. Difficult to melt; having a very high melting point.

INFUSORIAL EARTH. See *kieselguhr*.

INKS. Deeply coloured liquids of varied composition; many black and blue-black inks owe their colour to organic compounds of iron.

INORGANIC (chem.). Of mineral origin; not belonging to the large class of carbon compounds which are termed *organic* (q.v.).

INSECTICIDE. Substance used for killing insect pests.

INSOLATION. Exposure to the rays of the Sun.

INSOLUBLE. Not capable of forming a solution (in water, unless some other solvent is specified). Relative term, since most substances have been shown to dissolve in water to some extent.

INSULATION. Prevention of the passage of electricity, or heat, by conduction.

INSULATOR. Non-conductor of electricity or heat.

INSULIN. *Hormone* (q.v.) produced in the pancreas; controls the sugar *metabolism* (q.v.) in the body. When injected, lowers the blood sugar content and so relieves the symptoms of *diabetes mellitus*.

INTEGER. Whole number.

INTEGRAL. Denotes whole numbers or integers.

INTEGRAL CALCULUS. Branch of the calculus making use of the processes of *integration* (q.v.).

INTEGRATION. Mathematical process used in the calculus; the inverse process to differentiation. Gives a method of finding the areas enclosed by curves, and of finding solutions to other problems involving the summation of infinitesimals.

INTENSITY, ELECTRICAL. See *electric intensity*.

INTENSITY, MAGNETIC. See *magnetic intensity*.

INTENSITY OF ILLUMINATION. See *illumination*.

INTER-. Prefix denoting between, among.

INTERFERENCE OF WAVE MOTIONS (phys.). The addition or combination of waves; if the crest of one wave meets the trough of another of equal *amplitude* (q.v.), the wave is destroyed at that point; conversely, the super-position of one crest upon another leads to an increased effect (see also *Huygens' principle of superposition*). The colour effects of thin films are due to interference of light waves; *beats* (q.v.) produced by two notes of similar frequency are the result of the interference of sound waves.

INTERFEROMETER. Any instrument which divides a beam of light into a number of beams and re-unites them to produce *interference* (q.v.). Uses include the accurate determination of wave-lengths of light, the testing of prisms and lenses, the examination of the *hyperfine structure of spectrum lines* (q.v.), measurement of the diameters of stars and the determination of the number of light waves of a certain wavelength in the standard metre.

INTERMEDIATE FREQUENCY. In 'superhet' wireless receivers, the carrier wave frequency of the incoming radio wave is changed to a fixed *intermediate frequency* (q.v.) by *heterodyne* (q.v.) action, for ease of amplification before detection.

INTERNAL-COMBUSTION ENGINE. An engine in which energy supplied by a burning fuel is directly transformed into mechanical energy by the controlled burning of the fuel in an enclosed cylinder behind a piston. Usually applied to the petrol-burning engine.

INTERNATIONAL CANDLE. Former unit of *luminous intensity* (q.v.). A point source emitting light uniformly in all directions at one-tenth of the rate of the *Harcourt pentane lamp* (q.v.) burning under specified conditions. Now replaced by the *candela* (q.v.).

INTERNATIONAL TEMPERATURE SCALE. See *temperature scale, international*.

INTERPOLATION. Filling in intermediate values or terms of a series between known values or terms.

INTRA-. Prefix denoting within; e.g. intra-molecular forces are forces within the molecule, while inter-molecular forces are forces between molecules.

INTRINSIC ENERGY. It is assumed in calculations in *thermochemistry* (q.v.) that every substance possesses a definite quantity of intrinsic energy, i.e. energy which is inherent in the substance, and which may be in part released in the form of heat if the substance takes part in a chemical reaction. In a chemical action, no energy is gained or lost, and the sum of the intrinsic energies of the reacting substances is equal to the sum of the intrinsic energies of the final products plus or minus the energy given out or absorbed as heat during the reaction. See *Hess's law*.

INVAR. Alloy containing 63·8% iron, 36% nickel, 0·2% carbon. Has a very low coefficient of *expansion* (q.v.). Used for balance wheels of watches and in other accurate instruments which would otherwise be affected by temperature changes.

INVERSE SQUARE LAW. A law which states that the intensity of an effect at a point B due to a source at A varies inversely as the square of the distance AB. Examples include the illumination of a surface, gravitational force, field due to an electric charge, etc. Thus, the illumination of a surface 1 foot away from a source will be 9 times as great as that of a surface 3 feet away.

INVERSE VARIATION. One quantity is said to vary inversely as another, or to be inversely proportional to another, if the product of the two is a constant.

INVERSION OF CANE-SUGAR. The conversion of cane-sugar (sucrose, $C_{12}H_{22}O_{11}$) into a mixture of equal amounts of *glucose* (q.v.) and *laevulose* (q.v.), two isomeric sugars (see *isomerism*) having the formula $C_6H_{12}O_6$. The action is one of *hydrolysis* (q.v.) and may be carried out by the action of the *enzyme* (q.v.) invertase, or by boiling with dilute acids. The resulting mixture is laevorotatory, while a solution of cane-sugar is dextrorotatory, *inversion* of the optical rotation being thus obtained.

INVERSION TEMPERATURE. See *Joule-Thomson effect*.

INVERT SUGAR. Mixture of glucose and laevulose in equal proportions, obtained by the *inversion of cane-sugar* (q.v.).

INVERTASE, sucrase. *Enzyme* (q.v.) contained in yeast; converts cane sugar into glucose and laevulose. See *inversion of cane-sugar*.

IODIDE. Binary compound with iodine; salt of hydriodic acid, HI.

IODINE. I. Element. A.W. 126·92. At. No. 53. Blackish-grey, crystalline solid. S.G. 4·95. M.p. 114° C. B.p. 184° C. Very volatile, gives rise to a violet vapour. Very slightly soluble in water, readily soluble in alcohol (giving 'tincture of iodine') and in potassium iodide solution, KI. Compounds occur in seaweed; sodium iodate, $NaIO_3$, occurs in crude Chile saltpetre. Essential to the functioning of the thyroid gland; lack of iodine in the diet is a cause of goitre. Used in medicine, chemical analysis and photography.

IODINE VALUE OF FATS. A measure of the amount of *unsaturated* (q.v.) fats present in a sample of fat or oil. The weight of iodine absorbed by 100 gm. of the fat.

IODOFORM. CHI_3. Yellow, crystalline solid with a peculiar odour. M.p. 120° C. Used as an antiseptic.

ION. Electrically charged atom or group of atoms. Positively charged ions have fewer *electrons* (q.v.) than is necessary for the atom or group to be electrically neutral; negative ions have more. Thus, the *proton* (q.v.), the hydrogen atom without its circum-nuclear electron, is a hydrogen ion; the *alpha-particle* (q.v.) is a helium ion. Gaseous ions can be produced in gases by electric sparks, the passage of energetic charged particles, *X-rays, gamma-rays* (q.v.), ultra-violet rays, etc. Ions in solution are due to the ionization of the dissolved substance (see *ionic hypothesis*).

ION EXCHANGE. Certain substances have the power of acting on solutions containing *ions* (q.v.), such as solutions of salts, and replacing some of the ions by others; e.g. in a typical *cation exchange* ('base exchange') action, when hard water is passed through a suitable ion exchange resin or a *zeolite* (q.v.), the calcium ions in the water are replaced by sodium ions. In *anion exchange* acid radicals or anions are exchanged similarly. Ion exchange has many important industrial uses in addition to water softening.

IONIC HYPOTHESIS. Originally introduced to explain the phenomena of *electrolysis* (q.v.), etc. Ionic compounds consist of oppositely charged atoms or groups of atoms termed *ions* (q.v.). When an electric current is passed through such a compound in the dissolved or molten state, the ions are attracted to the oppositely charged electrodes.

IONIZATION. The formation of ions.

IONIZATION POTENTIAL. The work which must be done, measured in electron-volts, to remove an electron from an atom. See *atom, structure of*.

IONOSPHERE. See *Heaviside-Kennelly layer*.

IRIDIUM. Ir. Element. A.W. 193·1. At. No. 77. Rare metal resembling, and occurring together with, platinum. S.G. 22·42, m.p. 2440° C. Extremely hard and resistant to chemical action. Alloys of platinum and iridium are used for fountain-pen nib-tips, crucibles for fine analytical work, and numerous other purposes where extreme hardness and a high melting point are required.

IRON. Fe. (Ferrum.) Element. A.W. 55·85. At. No. 26. White, magnetic metal, S.G. 7·86, m.p. 1535° C. Physical properties are greatly modified by the presence of small amounts of other metals and of carbon. Occurs as magnetite, Fe_3O_4; haematite, Fe_2O_3; siderite, $FeCO_3$; limonite, hydrated, Fe_2O_3; and as *pyrites* (q.v.) in combination with sulphur. Extracted by the *blast furnace* (q.v.) process. According to the method and conditions of working and cooling, the carbon in iron and *steel* (q.v.) may be present in various forms, upon which the particular properties of the metal depend. Compounds of iron are essential to the higher forms of life.

IRON ALUM. See *ferric alum*.

IRON, COMPOUNDS OF. See under the required *ferric* or *ferrous* compound.

IRRADIATION. 1. The phenomenon of the appearance of white or brightly coloured objects on a dark background, when the objects appear brighter than they really are. 2. Exposure to radioactive radiations, light, or other forms of radiation.

IRREVERSIBLE PROCESS. Term of considerable importance in *thermodynamics* (q.v.). Any but a completely *reversible process* (q.v.)

IRREVERSIBLE REACTION. A chemical reaction which proceeds to completion, and in which the resulting products do not react to form the original substances. See *chemical equilibrium*.

ISINGLASS. Product containing about 90% *gelatin* (q.v.). Made from the swimming bladders of fish. Used for clarifying alcoholic beverages.

ISLAND UNIVERSES. See *galaxies*.

ISO-. Prefix denoting equal.

ISOBAR. Line connecting points having equal (atmospheric) pressure.

ISOBARIC SURFACE. Surface of equal (atmospheric) pressure. An altimeter will record constant height when moving along such a surface. The intersection of an isobaric surface with the ground is along an isobar (q.v.).

ISOBARS. *Isotopes* (q.v.) of different elements, and hence having different *atomic numbers* (q.v.), but possessing identical mass numbers (see *isotopic weight*). E.g. the tin isotope, $_{50}Sn^{115}$, and the indium isotope, $_{49}In^{115}$, are isobars, 115 being the mass number and 50 and 49 the atomic numbers.

ISOCHORE. A line which graphically represents the relationship between the pressure and the temperature of a liquid or gas, the volume of the system being kept constant.

ISOCHROMATIC FILM. See *orthochromatic*.

ISOCLINAL. Line connecting points of equal angle of *magnetic dip* (q.v.).

ISODIMORPHISM. The phenomenon of a *dimorphous* (q.v.) substance being *isomorphous* (q.v.) with another dimorphous substance in both its forms.

ISODYNAMIC LINE. Line passing through points of equal *horizontal intensity* (q.v.) of the Earth's magnetic field.

ISOELECTRIC POINT. The *pH value* (q.v.) at which a substance or system (e.g. a protein solution) is electrically neutral; at this value *electrophoresis* (q.v.) does not occur when a direct electric current is applied.

ISOGONAL LINE. Line passing through points of equal *magnetic declination* (q.v.).

ISOGONISM (chem.). Type of *isomorphism* (q.v.) where two substances having little or no chemical resemblance have the same crystalline form.

ISOMERISM. Existence of two or more chemical compounds with the same molecular formula but having different properties owing to a different arrangement of atoms within the molecule. E.g. ammonium cyanate, NH_4CNO, is isomeric with urea, $CO(NH_2)_2$.

ISOMERS. Compounds having the same molecular formula. See *isomerism*.

ISOMORPHISM. Similarity or identity of crystalline form, usually indicating similar or analogous chemical composition; e.g. the *alums* (q.v.) are isomorphous.

ISOPRENE. $CH_2 : CH . C(CH_3) : CH_2$. Colourless liquid, b.p. 34° C. Natural *rubber* (q.v.) consists mainly of a polymer of isoprene. See *polymerization*.

ISOSCELES TRIANGLE. Triangle having two of its sides equal.

ISOSTERISM. Phenomenon of substances having molecules with the same number of atoms and the same total number of electrons; this leads to similarity in physical properties. E.g. carbon dioxide, CO_2, and nitrous oxide, N_2O.

ISOTHERM, isothermal line. Line connecting points at an equal temperature.

ISOTHERMAL CHANGE. Change taking place at constant temperature. E.g. the isothermal expansion of a gas. See *adiabatic*.

ISOTONIC SOLUTIONS. Solutions having the same osmotic pressure, being of the same molecular concentration.

ISOTOPES. Atoms of the same element, i.e. having the same *atomic number* (q.v.) but differing in atomic weight, are called *isotopes* of that element. The isotopes of an element are identical in chemical properties, and in all physical properties except those determined by the mass of the atom. The different isotopes of an element contain different numbers of neutrons in their nuclei. Nearly all elements found in nature are mixtures of several isotopes. See *atom, structure of*.

ISOTOPIC WEIGHT. The *atomic weight* (q.v.) of an individual isotope expressed on a scale on which the most abundant isotope of oxygen has a weight exactly equal to 16. Isotopic weights are very nearly integral (whole numbers), the integer being called the *mass number* of the isotope concerned.

ISOTROPIC. Substances exhibiting uniform properties throughout, in all directions.

-ITE. Suffix denoting, in chemical nomenclature, a salt of the corresponding -ous acid; e.g. sulphite from sulphurous acid.

IVORY BLACK. Form of carbon obtained from *animal charcoal* (q.v.), by dissolving out inorganic compounds, such as calcium phosphate, by means of hydrochloric acid.

J

JASPER. Coloured impure form of natural silica, SiO_2.

JAVELLE WATER, eau de Javelle. Solution containing potassium hypochlorite, $KOCl$; made by the action of chlorine on a cold solution of potassium hydroxide, KOH. Used for bleaching and as a disinfectant.

JET. Very hard, lustrous form of natural carbon, allied to coal.

JOULE, THE. Unit of work. 1 joule = 10^7 ergs. The work done in 1 second by a current of 1 ampere flowing through a resistance of 1 ohm.

JOULE'S EQUIVALENT. See *mechanical equivalent of heat.*

JOULE'S LAW. The internal energy of a gas at constant temperature is independent of the volume. Joule's law is obeyed strictly only by a *perfect gas* (q.v.), and real gases show deviations from it.

JOULE-THOMSON EFFECT, Joule-Kelvin effect. When a gas expands through a porous plug, a change of temperature occurs, proportional to the pressure difference across the plug. The temperature change is due partly to a departure of the gas from *Joule's law* (q.v.), the gas performing internal work in overcoming the mutual attractions of its molecules and thus cooling itself; and partly to deviation of the gas from *Boyle's law* (q.v.). The latter effect can give rise either to a cooling or to a heating effect, depending upon the initial temperature and pressure difference used. For a given mean pressure, the temperature at which the two effects balance, resulting in no alteration of temperature, is called the *inversion temperature.* Gases expanding through a porous plug below their inversion temperature are cooled, otherwise they are heated.

JUPITER (Astr.). Planet, having nine small satellites, with its orbit between those of Mars and Saturn. Largest of the planets. Mean distance from the Sun = 483 million miles. Sidereal period ('year') = 11·86 years. Mass approximately 318 times that of the Earth. Surface temperature probably about −150° C.

K

KAINITE. Double salt of magnesium sulphate and potassium chloride, $MgSO_4.KCl.3H_2O$. Occurs naturally in Poland and in the *Stassfurt Deposits* (q.v.). Valuable source of potassium salts.

KALIUM. *Potassium* (q.v.).

KAOLIN. *China clay* (q.v.).

KATABOLISM, catabolism. Part of *metabolism* (q.v.) concerned with the decomposition of complex substances into simpler ones, with the evolution of energy.

KATHODE. Negative electrode. See *cathode.*

KATHODE RAYS. See *cathode rays.*

KATION. See *cation.*

KEEPERS OF MAGNETS. Short bars of soft iron used to prevent permanent magnets from losing their magnetism.

KELP. Sea-weed or its ash, used as a source of iodine.

KELVIN EFFECT. See *Thomson effect.*

KELVIN SCALE OF TEMPERATURE. See *absolute thermodynamic temperature.*

KEPLER'S LAWS. I. The planets move about the Sun in ellipses, at one focus of which the Sun is situated. 2. The *radius vector* (q.v.) joining each planet with the Sun describes equal areas in equal times. 3. The ratio of the square of the planet's year to the cube of the planet's mean distance from the Sun is the same for all planets.

KERATIN. *Protein* (q.v.) forming the principal constituent of wool, hair, horns and hoofs.

KEROSENE, kerosine. See *paraffin oil.*

KERR CELL. In its simplest form, consists of a small glass cell into which are sealed two metal electrodes. The cell is filled with pure nitrobenzene, a transparent liquid which exhibits *double refraction* (q.v.) when a high potential difference is applied across the electrodes.

KETEN, ketene. $CH_2:CO$. Colourless gas, first member of the keten series of the general formula $CR_2:CO$.

KETONES, THE. Series of organic chemical compounds having the general formula RR' C:O, where R and R' are univalent hydrocarbon radicals. E.g. *acetone* (q.v.), dimethyl ketone, $(CH_3)_2CO$.

KIESELGUHR, infusorial earth. Mass of hydrated silica (SiO_2) formed from skeletons of minute plants known as diatoms. Very porous and absorbent. Used for filtering and absorbing various liquids, in the manufacture of *dynamite* (q.v.) and in other industries.

KILLED SPIRITS OF SALTS. Solution of zinc chloride, $ZnCl_2$, made by acting with zinc on hydrochloric acid. Used in soldering.

KILO-. Prefix denoting a thousand, thousandfold, in metric units.

KILOCYCLE. Measure of frequency. 1000 cycles.

KILOGRAM, kilogramme. 1000 *grams* (q.v.). Practical continental unit of mass and weight. 2·2046 lb.

KILOMETRE. 1000 metres. Practical continental unit of distance. 1094 yards, ·6214 mile.

KILOWATT. Unit of power. 1000 *watts* (q.v.).

KILOWATT-HOUR, Board of Trade unit. Practical unit of work. Work done when a rate of work of 1000 watts is maintained for 1 hour.

KINETIC ENERGY. *Energy* (q.v.) which a body possesses by virtue of its motion.

KINETIC THEORY OF GASES. Mathematical explanation of the behaviour of gases on the assumption that gases consist of molecules which are in ceaseless motion in space, the kinetic energy of the molecules depending upon the temperature of the gas; the molecules are considered to be perfectly elastic particles which collide with each other and with the walls of the containing vessel. The pressure exerted by a gas on the walls of the vessel is due to the collisions of the molecules with it. The *gas laws* (q.v.) may be shown to be in full agreement with this theory.

KIPP'S APPARATUS. Device used in laboratories for the production of a supply of any gas which can be evolved by the action of a liquid on a solid without heating.

KIRCHHOFF'S LAWS. 1. In any network of wires the algebraic sum of the electric currents which meet at a point is zero. 2. The algebraic sum of the electromotive forces in any closed circuit or mesh is equal to the algebraic sum of the products of the resistances of each portion of the circuit and the currents flowing through them.

KISH. Variety of *graphite* (q.v.) occasionally formed in iron-smelting furnaces.

KNOCKING in the internal-combustion (petrol) engine. Violent explosions in the cylinder, often due to over-compression of the mixture of air and petrol vapour before sparking.

KNOT. Unit of speed; 1 *nautical mile* (q.v.) per hour.

KRYPTOL. Mixture of graphite, carborundum and clay, used as an electrical resistance in electric furnaces.

KRYPTON. Kr. Element. A.W. 83·80. At. No. 36. *Inert gas* (q.v.), occurs in the atmosphere (1 part in 670,000).

KUPFER-NICKEL. Natural nickel arsenide, NiAs. Important ore of nickel.

L

LABILE. Prone to undergo change or displacement; unstable.

LACHRYMATOR. See *tear-gas*.

LACTIC ACID. $CH_3CH(OH)COOH$. Organic acid, occurring in three stereoisomeric forms (see *stereoisomerism*). Colourless, crystalline solid, m.p. 18° C. *dl*-lactic acid, a mixture of equal amounts of (dextrorotatory) *d*-acid and (laevorotatory) *l*-acid, is formed by the action of certain bacteria on the *lactose* (q.v.) of milk during souring. The *d*-form, sarcolactic acid, occurs in muscle tissue. The optically inactive *dl*-form is used in dyeing and tanning.

LACTOSE, milk sugar. $C_{12}H_{22}O_{11}$. Hard, gritty, crystalline soluble sugar, m.p. 203° C., less sweet than cane-sugar. Occurs in the milk of all mammals. *Hydrolysis* (q.v.) gives a mixture of glucose and galactose. In the action of certain bacteria on milk ('lactic acid fermentation') lactose is converted into *lactic acid* (q.v.).

LAEVOROTATORY. Rotating or deviating the plane of vibration of polarized light to the left (observer looking against the oncoming light). See *optical activity*.

LAEVULOSE, fructose, fruit sugar. $C_6H_{12}O_6$. See *fructose*.

LAKE. In dyeing, a coloured insoluble substance formed by the chemical combination of a soluble dye with a *mordant* (q.v.).

LAMBERT. A unit of *brightness* (q.v.) used especially when considering a perfectly diffusing surface; i.e. a surface the brightness of which is independent of the direction in which it is observed. The lambert is the brightness of such a surface emitting or reflecting 1 *lumen* (q.v.) per square centimetre.

LAMINA. A thin sheet.

LAMINATED IRON. Thin sheets of iron (or, more frequently, *stalloy*, q.v.) used for cores of *transformers* (q.v.) instead of solid iron cores, in order to reduce losses due to *eddy currents* (q.v.).

LAMP-BLACK. Soot; allotropic form of *carbon* (q.v.).

LANOLINE. Wax-like material obtained from wool-grease. Contains cholesterol, $C_{27}H_{45}OH$, and other complex organic substances. Readily absorbed by the skin; used in ointments and cosmetics.

LANTHANUM. La. Element. A.W. 138·92. At. No. 57. See *rare earths*.

LAPIS LAZULI. Sodium aluminium silicate containing sulphur. Rare mineral of beautiful blue colour.

LARGE CALORIE, kilogram-calorie, Calorie. 1000 calories. See *calorie*.

LARMOR PRECESSION. The orbital motion of the electrons about the nucleus of an atom is usually such as to give the atom a resultant angular momentum and a magnetic moment. These two properties cause the atom to precess (see *precessional motion*) about the direction of any applied magnetic field. This is *Larmor precession*, and its frequency is the *Larmor frequency*.

LATENT HEAT. See *heat, latent*.

LATERAL. In a sideways direction.

LATERAL INVERSION. The inversion produced by a plane mirror. Seen when the image of a printed page is observed in a mirror.

LATITUDE of a point of the Earth's surface is its angular distance from the equator measured upon the curved surface of the Earth.

LATITUDE, LINES OF; parallels of latitude. Circles parallel to the equator, joining points of equal latitude; the equator itself is latitude 0°, while the poles are latitude 90°.

LAUDANUM. Alcoholic tincture of *opium* (q.v.).

LAUGHING GAS, nitrous oxide. N_2O. Colourless gas with a sweetish taste, used as a mild anaesthetic in dentistry, etc.

LEACHING. Washing out of a soluble constituent.

LEAD. Pb. (Plumbum.) Element. A.W. 207·21. At. No. 82. Soft, bluish-white metal, S.G. 11·34, m.p. 327·4° C. Occurs chiefly as galena, PbS. Extracted by roasting the ore in a reverberatory furnace. Compounds are poisonous. Metal is used in alloys and in plumbing; compounds are used in paint manufacture.

LEAD ACCUMULATOR. See *accumulator*.

LEAD ACETATE, sugar of lead. $(CH_3COO)_2Pb.3H_2O$. White crystalline soluble salt, with a sweet taste.

LEAD-CHAMBER PROCESS. Manufacture of sulphuric acid by the action of nitrogen dioxide, NO_2, on sulphur dioxide, SO_2, to give nitric oxide, NO, and sulphur trioxide, SO_3. The former reacts with oxygen from the air to give NO_2 again; the SO_3 combines with water to give sulphuric acid, the process being carried out in large lead chambers.

LEAD DIOXIDE, lead peroxide. PbO_2. Amorphous, dark brown powder.

LEAD MONOXIDE. See *litharge*.

LEAD PEROXIDE. See *lead dioxide*.

LEAD, RED. See *red lead*.

LEAD, WHITE. See *white lead*.

LEBLANC PROCESS, salt-cake process. Almost obsolete process for the manufacture of sodium carbonate, Na_2CO_3. Common salt is converted into sodium sulphate, Na_2SO_4 ('salt-cake') by heating with sulphuric acid. This is heated with coal and limestone; the sodium sulphate is reduced by the carbon to sodium sulphide, which then reacts with the limestone to give sodium carbonate and calcium sulphide.

LE CHATELIER PRINCIPLE. If a system in equilibrium is subjected to a stress, the system tends to react in such a way as to oppose the effect of the stress.

LECITHINS. Class of organic compounds occurring in living organisms. Chemically very similar to fats, but the molecule contains the elements nitrogen and phosphorus in addition to carbon, hydrogen and oxygen.

LECLANCHÉ CELL. Primary cell with a positive electrode or pole of carbon surrounded by a mixture of manganese dioxide and powdered carbon in a porous pot. This stands in a solution of ammonium chloride, the *electrolyte* (q.v.), in a jar which also contains the negative electrode of zinc. When the external circuit is completed, a current flows, chlorine ions in the electrolyte moving towards the zinc and ammonium ions towards the carbon electrode. The chlorine ions react with the zinc to form zinc chloride, and the ammonium ions decompose at the positive electrode to give ammonia and hydrogen. The hydrogen liberated tends to cause *polarization* (q.v.) of the cell. This tendency is partly counteracted by the manganese dioxide, which oxidizes the hydrogen. The E.M.F. is approximately 1·5 volts. Leclanché cells are widely used for many purposes which require an intermittent current. The common *dry cell* is a special form of Leclanché cell.

LENGTH, BRITISH UNITS OF.

12 lines	= 1 inch	= 2·5400 cm.
12 ins	= 1 foot.	
3 ft	= 1 yard	= 0·9144 metre.
22 yds	= 1 chain.	
10 chains	= 1 furlong	= 201·17 metres.
8 fur.	= 1 mile	= 1609·3 metres.

LENGTH, METRIC UNITS OF.

10 millimetres	= 1 centimetre	= 0·3937 inch.
100 cm.	= 1 metre	= 1·0936 yard.
1000 m.	= 1 kilometre	= 0·62137 mile.

LENS. Any device which causes a beam of rays to converge or diverge on passing through it. The *optical lens* is a portion of a transparent refracting medium (see *refraction of light*), usually glass, bounded by two surfaces, generally curved. Such lenses are classified according to the nature of the surfaces into bi-concave, bi-convex, plano-convex, etc. The centres of the spheres of which the lens surfaces are considered to form a part, are termed the *centres of curvature;* the line joining these is the *axis;* the *optical centre* is a point on the axis within the lens; all rays passing through this point emerge without deviation. A parallel beam of light incident on a lens is made to converge (convex lens) or diverge (concave lens). The point of divergence or convergence is called a *principal focus*. Regarding all distances as being measured from the optical centre, and taking all distances as positive when measured in a direction opposite to that of the incident light, the distances of the object and image from the lens are given by the formula $1/v - 1/u = 1/f$, where u and v are the distances from the lens of object and image respectively, and f is the *focal length*, i.e. the distance of the focus from the lens. Electrostatic and electromagnetic lenses, for converging beams of electrons and other elementary charged particles, are also of importance, e.g. in the *electron microscope* (q.v.).

LENZ'S LAW. When a circuit and a magnetic field move relatively to each other, the current induced in the circuit will have a magnetic field opposing the motion. See *induction, electromagnetic*.

LEVER. Rigid bar which may be turned freely about a fixed point of support, the *fulcrum*. The *mechanical advantage* (q.v.) of a lever is given by the ratio of the perpendicular distance of the line of action of the effort from the fulcrum, to the perpendicular distance of the line of action of the resistance from the fulcrum.

LEWISITE, chlorovinyl dichlorarsine. $ClCH:CHAsCl_2$. Oily liquid; war 'gas' with lethal vesicant properties. Destroyed by oxidizing agents, e.g. bleaching powder.

LEYDEN JAR. Form of electrostatic *condenser* (q.v.) of historical interest.

LIEBIG CONDENSER. See *condenser* (chem.).

LIGHT. Name given to the agency by means of which a viewed object influences the observer's eye. Consists of *electromagnetic waves* (q.v.) within the wave-length range 4×10^{-5} cm. to 7×10^{-5} cm. approximately; variations in the wave-length produce different sensations in the eye, corresponding to different colours. See *colour, colour vision*.

LIGHT, VELOCITY OF. Mean value is 2.9978×10^{10} cm./sec. = 186,326 miles/sec.

LIGHT-YEAR. Astronomical measure of distance; the distance travelled by light (see *light, velocity of*) in one year. Approximately 6×10^{12} miles (6 million million miles).

LIGHTNING. Electric discharge in the form of a spark or flash between two charged clouds, or between a cloud and the Earth.

LIGHTNING CONDUCTOR. A conductor of electricity connected to earth and ending in one or more sharp points attached to a high part of a building. The effect of a passing electric charge, such as an electrically charged cloud, is to produce a discharge of electricity of opposite charge from the conductor ; since the density of charge is greatest at the more pointed parts of the conductor, the strength of the electric field in the air near the sharp points will become so great as to make the air a conductor of electricity. Thus a stream of electricity of opposite charge to that of the cloud will proceed from the sharp points, causing a quiet neutralization of charges instead of an accumulation which may become great enough to break down the insulation of the air and thus cause a lightning discharge.

LIGNIN. Complex organic material which occurs in the woody tissues of plants, often combined with *cellulose* (q.v.). The preparation of pure cellulose by removing the lignin is an important step in the manufacture of pulp for the paper and rayon industries.

LIGNITE, brown coal. Brownish-black, natural deposit resembling coal. Contains a higher percentage of *hydrocarbons* (q.v.) than ordinary coal; probably of more recent origin.

LIGROIN. Mixture of *hydrocarbons* (q.v.) of the *paraffin series* (q.v.); generally applied to a mixture having b.p. 70° C.–120° C.

LIME. *Quicklime*, calcium oxide, CaO. White solid made by heating *limestone* (q.v.) in lime-kilns. *Slaked lime*, calcium hydroxide, $Ca(OH)_2$, is a white solid formed by the action of water ('slaking') on quicklime. Term sometimes loosely applied to calcium salts in general.

LIMESTONE. Natural calcium carbonate, $CaCO_3$.

LIME-WATER. Solution of calcium hydroxide, $Ca(OH)_2$, in water. Turns milky by the action of carbon dioxide, CO_2, owing to the formation of insoluble calcium carbonate, $CaCO_3$.

LIMIT, limiting value (math.). Mathematical concept. A *function* (q.v.) of a variable quantity x, written $f(x)$, approaches a limiting value k as x approaches a value a, if the difference $k - f(a + \delta)$ may be made smaller than any assignable value by making δ sufficiently small.

LIMIT OF SPECTRAL SERIES. The lines appearing in the *line spectrum* (q.v.) of any element can be grouped into definite series. The shortest wave-length of any such series is called the limit of the series. At this series limit, the lines crowd closer and closer together from the long wave-length side.

LIMONITE. Natural hydrated form of ferric oxide, Fe_2O_3. Ore of iron.

LINE SPECTRUM. *Spectrum* (q.v.) (emission or absorption) consisting of definite single lines, each corresponding to a particular wave-length; characteristic of an element in the atomic state.

LINEAR ACCELERATOR. Apparatus for accelerating ions to high energies. Consists of a row of cylindrical electrodes separated by small gaps and having a common axis. Alternate electrodes are connected to each other and a high-frequency potential is applied between the two sets of electrodes. The frequency, and the lengths of the different electrodes, are such that the ions are accelerated each time they cross a gap between two electrodes.

LINES OF FORCE. See *electrical lines of force; magnetic lines of force*.

LINKAGE between atoms. See *valency*.

LIPASE. *Enzyme* (q.v.) with the power of hydrolyzing fats.

LIPOCLASTIC, lipolytic. Fat-splitting; applied to enzymes having the power of hydrolyzing fats into the fatty acid and glycerin; e.g. lipase.

LIPOWITZ' ALLOY. Fusible alloy, m.p. 65° C. to 70° C.; consists of 50% bismuth, 27% lead, 13% tin, 10% cadmium.

LIQUATION. Separation of a solid mixture by heating till one of the constituents melts and can be drained away.

LIQUEFACTION OF GASES. A gas possessing a *critical temperature* (q.v.) above room temperature may be liquefied merely by increasing the pressure on it. Otherwise, the gas must first be cooled to below its critical temperature and then compressed; or, if desired, cooled directly to its boiling point under normal pressure. The methods of cooling are (1) by evaporation under reduced pressure, as in the *cascade liquefier* (q.v.); (2) by using the principle of the *Joule-Thomson effect* (q.v.) (the Linde process); (3) by causing the gas to expand against an external pressure; in so doing the gas does work, thereby cooling itself. This principle is used in the Claude process.

LIQUID. State of matter intermediate between solid and gas; has a definite volume, but assumes the shape of the vessel in which it is contained.

LIQUID AIR. Pale blue liquid, containing mainly liquid oxygen, b.p. − 182·9° C., and liquid nitrogen, b.p. − 195·7° C.

LISSAJOUS FIGURE. The locus of the resultant displacement of a point on which two or more simple periodic motions are impressed. In the common case, two periodic motions are at right angles and are of the same frequency. The Lissajous figures then become, in general, a series of ellipses corresponding to the possible differences of *phase* (q.v.) between the two motions.

LITHARGE, lead monoxide. PbO. Reddish-yellow crystalline solid, m.p. 888° C. Used in the manufacture of glass, paints, varnishes and glazes.

LITHIUM. Li. Element. A.W. 6·94. At. No. 3. Light, silvery-white metal, m.p. 186° C. S.G. 0·534; lightest solid known. Chemically resembles sodium, but is less active. Used in alloys.

LITHOPONE. Mixture of zinc sulphide, ZnS, and barium sulphate, BaSO₄. Used in paints as a non-poisonous substitute for white lead.

LITHOSPHERE. See *earth's crust*.

LITMUS. Soluble, purple substance of vegetable origin; turned red by acids and blue by alkalies. Used as an *indicator* (q.v.).

LITRE. Unit of volume in the metric system. The volume of 1 kilogram of pure air-free water at 4° C. and 760 mm. pressure. Often taken to be equal in volume to 1000 c.c.; actually = 1000·027 c.c. Subdivided into 1000 millilitres, ml., used synonymously with c.c.

LIVER OF SULPHUR. Mixture of sulphides and other sulphur compounds of potassium, obtained by fusing potassium carbonate, K₂CO₃, with sulphur. Used as an insecticide and fungicide in gardening.

LIXIVIATION. Extraction of soluble material from a mixture by washing with water.

LOCUS (math.). The locus of a point is the line which can be drawn through adjacent positions of the point, thus tracing out the path of the point in space.

LODESTONE. Magnetic variety of natural iron oxide, Fe_3O_4, *magnetite* (q.v.).

LOGARITHMIC SCALE. A scale of measurement in which an increase of one unit represents a tenfold increase in the quantity measured (for common logarithms).

LOGARITHMS. If a number, *a*, is expressed as a power of another number, *b*, i.e. if $a = b^n$, then *n* is said to be the logarithm of *a* to base *b*, written $\log_b a$. *Common logarithms* are to base 10. Multiplication, division, and other computations are shortened by the use of common logarithms; the addition of logarithms of numbers gives the logarithm of the product of the numbers; similarly division can be performed by subtraction of the logarithms. Logarithms corresponding to ordinary numbers have been tabulated, and calculations are carried out by the use of such tables.

LONG SIGHT. See *hypermetropia, presbyopia*.

LONGITUDE. The angle which the terrestrial meridian through the geographical poles and a point on the Earth's surface makes with a standard meridian (usually through Greenwich) is the longitude of the point.

LONGITUDE, LINES OF. Imaginary meridians on the Earth's surface, referred to a standard meridian; *great circles* (q.v.) of the Earth intersecting at the poles.

LONGITUDINAL. Lengthwise; in a line with the length of the object under consideration.

LONGITUDINAL WAVES. Waves in which the vibration or displacement takes place in the direction of propagation of the waves; e.g. sound waves. See also *transverse waves*.

LOUDNESS OF SOUND. See *decibel; phon*.

LUMEN. Unit of luminous flux (see *flux, luminous*). The amount of light emitted per second in unit solid angle by a uniform point source of one *candela* (q.v.) intensity; i.e. the amount of light falling per second on unit area placed at unit distance from such a source.

LUMINESCENCE. Emission of light from a body from any cause other than high temperature. *Fluorescence* (q.v.) and *phosphorescence* (q.v.) are particular cases of luminescence.

LUMINOSITY. The property of emitting *light* (q.v.).

LUMINOUS INTENSITY. The amount of light emitted per second in unit solid angle by a point source, in a given direction. The unit of luminous intensity is the *candela* (q.v.). The term is restricted to point sources.

LUMINOUS PAINT. Paint prepared from phosphorescent compounds such as calcium sulphide, etc., which glows after exposure to light. See *phosphorescence*.

LUNAR CAUSTIC. *Silver nitrate* (q.v.), AgNO₃, usually fused and cast into sticks.

LUTETIUM, cassiopeium. Lu. Element. A.W. 174·99. At. No. 71. See *rare earths*.

LUX, metre candle. Unit of *illumination* (q.v.); one *lumen* (q.v.) per square metre.

LYDDITE. Explosive consisting of picric acid (trinitrophenol, $C_6H_2OH(NO_2)_3$), mixed with 10% nitrobenzene and 3% vaseline.

LYOPHILIC COLLOID. 'Solvent-loving colloid.' See *colloidal solutions*.

LYOPHOBIC COLLOID. 'Solvent-hating colloid.' See *colloidal solutions*.

LYSOL. A mixture of the *cresols* (q.v.) with a solution of soft soap. Used as a disinfectant.

M

MACHINE. Defined mathematically as a device for overcoming resistance at one point by the application of a force, usually at some other point. Generally understood to be any arrangement for the purpose of taking in some definite form of energy, modifying it and delivering it in a form more suitable for the desired purpose.

MACRO-. Prefix denoting large, in contrast to *micro-*, small.

MACROMOLECULE. Very large molecule, generally of a polymer. See *polymerization*.

MAGENTA, fuchsine. $C_{20}H_{22}N_3OCl$. Red dye, prepared from *aniline* and *toluidine* (q.v.).

MAGNALIUM. Light alloy, S.G. 2 to 2·5; aluminium with from 5% to 30% magnesium.

MAGNESIA. Magnesium oxide, MgO; *magnesia alba* of pharmacy is basic magnesium carbonate; *fluid magnesia* is a solution of magnesium bicarbonate.

MAGNESIUM. Mg. Element. A.W. 24·32. At. No. 12. Light, silvery-white metal, S.G. 1·74, m.p. 651° C., tarnishes easily in air. Burns with an intense white flame to form magnesium oxide, MgO. Occurs as magnesite, $MgCO_3$; dolomite, $MgCO_3.CaCO_3$; carnallite, $KCl.MgCl_2.6H_2O$, and in many other compounds. Essential to life; see *chlorophyll*. Prepared by electrolysis (q.v.) of fused carnallite. Used in light-weight alloys, and in photography, signalling and incendiary bombs. Compounds used in medicine.

MAGNESIUM SULPHATE. See *Epsom salts*.

MAGNET, permanent. *Ferromagnetic substance* (q.v.) which has a permanent magnetic field and magnetic moment associated with it.

MAGNETIC AMPLIFIER. A device for the amplification of small direct currents and of low frequency alternating currents. Depends upon the fact that the output from the secondary coil of a *transformer* (q.v.)

due to an alternating current in the primary coil is also a function of a direct current (the signal to be amplified) in a third winding on the transformer core.

MAGNETIC DECLINATION, magnetic variation, variation of the compass. The angle between the planes of the geographic and magnetic meridian.

MAGNETIC DIP, angle of dip. The angle between the direction of the Earth's magnetic field and the horizontal; i.e. the angle through which a magnetic needle will 'dip' from the horizontal when suspended free to swing in a vertical plane in the magnetic meridian. See *dip circle*.

MAGNETIC ELEMENTS. The three quantities, magnetic declination, angle of dip (see *magnetic dip*) and the *horizontal intensity* (q.v.), which define completely the Earth's magnetic field at any point.

MAGNETIC EQUATOR. Line of zero *magnetic dip* (q.v.) lying fairly near the geographical equator, but passing North of it in Africa and the Indian Ocean, and South of it in America and the Eastern Pacific.

MAGNETIC FIELD. A field of force which is said to exist at any point if a small coil of wire carrying an electric current experiences a *couple* (q.v.) when placed at that point. A magnetic field may exist at a point as a result of the presence of either a permanent magnet or of an electrical circuit carrying a current, in the neighbourhood of the point.

MAGNETIC FIELD OF ELECTRIC CURRENT. A wire or coil carrying an electric current is surrounded by a magnetic field. The direction of the field relative to the current may be determined by the following corkscrew rule: If a corkscrew, held in the right hand, is turned along the conductor in the direction of the current, the movement of the thumb indicates the direction of the magnetic field produced.

MAGNETIC FIELD, STRENGTH OF. See *magnetic intensity*.

MAGNETIC FLUX through any area is the product of the area and of the component of the *magnetic intensity* (q.v.) at right angles to that area.

MAGNETIC INDUCTION. Consider a uniform magnetic field of strength H in free space; i.e. the magnetic flux through unit area perpendicular to the field is H. Now suppose a material medium to be introduced into the field. The magnetic flux at any point in the medium becomes modified owing to the interaction between H and the atoms of the medium, and assumes a new value B, which is called the magnetic induction of the medium.

MAGNETIC INTENSITY, strength of magnetic field at a point. The force which would be exerted on unit north *magnetic pole* (q.v.) situated at that point. Measured in *oersteds* (q.v.).

MAGNETIC IRON ORE. *Magnetite* (q.v.).

MAGNETIC LINE OF FORCE, line of magnetic force. A line whose direction at each point is that of the magnetic field at that point; the path along which a free magnetic pole would travel.

MAGNETIC MERIDIAN. See *magnetism, terrestrial.*

MAGNETIC MOMENT, moment of a magnet. The *couple* (q.v.) required to hold a magnet at right angles to a field of unit *magnetic intensity* (q.v.); the product of the *magnetic pole strength* (q.v.) and the length of the magnet.

MAGNETIC PERMEABILITY, μ. The ratio of the *magnetic induction* (q.v.) to the external magnetic field H causing the induction. For most substances μ has a constant small value. When μ is less than 1, the material is said to be *diamagnetic;* if μ is greater than 1, it is *paramagnetic.* A few substances, notably iron, have very large values of μ, which tend to fall as H increases so that the magnetic induction tends to a limiting value called the *saturation value.* Such substances are said to be *ferromagnetic.*

MAGNETIC POLE. A magnet appears to have its magnetism concentrated at two points termed the poles. If a bar magnet is suspended to swing freely, one of these, the North-seeking, North, or positive pole, will point North, and the other South. Unlike poles attract and like poles repel each other. The force of attraction or repulsion between two poles varies inversely as the square of the distance between them (see *inverse square law*). The force in dynes between two poles of strength m_1 and m_2 (see *magnetic pole strength*) situated d centimetres apart in vacuum is $m_1 m_2/d^2$ dynes.

MAGNETIC POLE STRENGTH. The strength of a magnetic pole measured in terms of the unit magnetic pole; see *magnetic pole, unit.*

MAGNETIC POLE, UNIT. Unit magnetic pole is one of such a strength that when situated 1 centimetre from an equal pole in vacuum, the force between the poles will be 1 *dyne* (q.v.).

MAGNETIC POTENTIAL. Concept analogous to electrical potential; the difference of magnetic potential between two points is measured by the work done in carrying unit magnetic pole from one point to the other.

MAGNETIC STORM. Sudden magnetic disturbance affecting compass needles over considerable areas. Associated with sun-spots and the Aurora Borealis.

MAGNETIC SUSCEPTIBILITY. Ratio of the intensity of magnetization produced in a substance to the intensity of the magnetic field to which it is subjected.

MAGNETIC VARIATION. See *magnetic declination.*

MAGNETISM, TERRESTRIAL, the Earth's magnetism. The Earth possesses a magnetic field, the intensity of which varies with time and locality. The field is similar to that which would be produced by a powerful magnet situated at the centre of the Earth and pointing approximately North and South. A magnetized needle suspended to swing freely in all planes will set itself pointing to the Earth's magnetic North and South poles, at an angle to the horizontal (see *magnetic dip*). The vertical plane through the axis of such a needle is termed the *magnetic meridian,* defined as the vertical plane which contains the direction of the Earth's magnetic field. The cause of the Earth's magnetism is not definitely known.

MAGNETITE, magnetic iron ore. Natural black oxide of iron, Fe_3O_4.

MAGNETIZATION, INTENSITY OF. The *magnetic moment* (q.v.) per unit volume of a magnetized body.

MAGNETO. Small *dynamo* (q.v.) provided with a spark-coil, for ignition of petrol vapour in petrol *internal-combustion engines* (q.v.).

MAGNETOMETER. Instrument for comparing strengths of magnetic fields, and magnetic moments. Consists of a short magnet with a long, non-magnetic pointer at right angles across it, pivoted at the junction. The pointer swings along a circular scale, thus enabling deflections of the short magnet to be measured.

MAGNETOSTRICTION. A change in the dimensions of ferromagnetic substances on magnetization.

MAGNETRON. Generator of very short wireless waves, in the centimetre region. Used extensively in *radar* (q.v.).

MAGNIFICATION produced by microscope (or other optical instrument). The ratio of the linear dimensions of the final image to the linear dimensions of the object.

MAGNIFYING GLASS. A convex lens. See *microscope, simple.*

MAGNIFYING POWER OF A COMPOUND MICROSCOPE. The ratio of the angle subtended at the eye by the final image to the angle subtended by the object placed at the *least distance of distinct vision* (i.e. the shortest distance from the eye at which the object can be seen distinctly).

MAGNIFYING POWER OF A LENS. Ratio of the angle subtended at the eye by the virtual image to the angle subtended by the object when placed at the least distance of distinct vision; this latter is generally taken to be 25 cm.

MAGNITUDE OF STARS. Measure of the relative apparent brightness of stars. A star of any one magnitude is approximately 2·51 times brighter than a star of the next magnitude. E.g. a star of the first magnitude is $(2·51)^3$ times as bright as a star of the fourth magnitude.

MALACHITE. Natural basic copper carbonate, $CuCO_3.Cu(OH)_2$. Bright green mineral.

MALIC ACID, hydroxysuccinic acid. $COOH.CH_2.CH(OH).COOH$. White crystalline organic acid, m.p. 98° C. –99° C. Occurs in unripe apples and other fruits.

MALLEABILITY. Capacity of being hammered out into thin sheets.

MALONYL UREA. See *barbiturates.*

MALT. Grain (usually barley) which has been allowed to germinate and then heated and dried. See *brewing.*

MALT SUGAR. See *maltose.*

MALTASE. *Enzyme* (q.v.) occurring in yeast and other organisms. Hydrolyzes (see *hydrolysis*) *maltose,* malt sugar (q.v.), into glucose.

MALTOBIOSE. See *maltose*.

MALTOSE, malt sugar, maltobiose. $C_{12}H_{22}O_{11}$. Hard crystalline soluble sugar, less sweet than cane-sugar. Formed in *malt* (q.v.) by the action of the enzyme *diastase* (q.v.) on starch.

MANGANESE. Mn. Element. A.W. 54·93. At. No. 25. Reddish-white, hard brittle metal. S.G. 7·20, m.p. 1260° C. Occurs as *pyrolusite* (q.v.), MnO_2, from which it is extracted by reduction with carbon or aluminium. Used in numerous alloys.

MANGANESE BRONZE, manganese brass. A copper-zinc alloy containing up to 4% manganese.

MANGANESE DIOXIDE, manganese peroxide, MnO_2. Heavy, black powder; occurs naturally as pyrolusite. Used as a source of manganese metal, as an oxidizing agent, in glass manufacture, in Leclanché cells, as a catalyst in the laboratory preparation of oxygen, etc.

MANGANESE STEEL. Very hard variety of steel containing up to 13% manganese.

MANGANIN. Alloy containing 83% copper, 13% manganese, 4% nickel. Electrical resistance affected only slightly by change in temperature; used for resistance coils.

MANOMETER. Any instrument used for measuring gaseous pressure.

MANTISSA. The decimal, always positive, portion of a common logarithm.

MANURE, ARTIFICIAL. See *fertilizers*.

MARBLE. Form of natural calcium carbonate, $CaCO_3$.

MARGARINE. Butter substitute prepared from purified vegetable and animal fats and oils. Milk is added to a suitable blend of fats; bacterial action in the milk produces a butter-like flavour; vitamins A and D (see *vitamins*) and suitable colouring materials are added.

MARS (astr.). Planet, with two small satellites, having its orbit between those of the Earth and Jupiter. Mean distance from the Sun = 141·5 million miles. Sidereal period ('year') = 687 days. Mass approximately one-ninth that of the Earth. Probably possesses an atmosphere containing oxygen. Surface temperature about 0° C. No evidence of conscious life on the planet is available.

MARSH GAS. *Methane*, CH_4 (q.v.).

MARSH'S TEST. Sensitive test for arsenic. Depends upon the formation of *arsine* (q.v.) when arsenic or its compounds are present in a solution evolving hydrogen. When the arsine is passed through a narrow, heated tube, it is decomposed and leaves a deposit of metallic arsenic.

MASS. It is a matter of observation that a force applied to a body produces an acceleration proportional to the force. The constant of proportionality is the *mass* of the body.

MASS ACTION LAW. The velocity of a chemical change is proportional to the active masses (molecular concentrations) of the reacting substances.

MASS DEFECT. The difference between the *isotopic weight* (q.v.) of any atom and its *mass number*. The mass defect is normally taken as positive when the isotopic weight is greater than the mass number.

MASS-ENERGY EQUATION. Mass and energy are mutually convertible under certain conditions. The equation connecting the two quantities in any such transformation is $E = mc^2$, where c is the velocity of light in cms./sec. and E is the energy, in ergs, released when a mass of m grams is completely converted into energy. See *annihilation radiation*, *cosmic ray showers*.

MASS NUMBER. See *isotopic weight*.

MASS SPECTROGRAPH. Apparatus for the determination of the exact masses of individual atoms, i.e. isotopic weights, by using the technique of *positive ray analysis* (q.v.).

MASS SPECTRUM. See *positive ray analysis*.

MASSICOT. Yellow powder form of unfused lead monoxide, PbO.

MASURIUM. Former name of element of At. No. 43; replaced in 1949 by the name *technetium* (q.v.).

MATCHES. The heads of safety matches usually contain antimony sulphide, oxidizing agents such as potassium chlorate, and some sulphur or charcoal; while the striking surface contains red phosphorus. Ordinary non-safety match-heads contain phosphorus sulphide, P_4S_3; very rarely red phosphorus.

MATTE. Mixture of the sulphides of iron and copper obtained as an intermediate stage in the smelting of copper.

MAUVE, mauveine, aniline violet. Reddish-violet dye; complex organic compound, the first organic dye to be prepared artificially.

MAXIMUM (math.). A function $y = f(x)$ has a maximum value at $x = a$ if $f(a)$ is greater than the values of the function immediately preceding and immediately following $x = a$. The function has a minimum value at $x = b$ if $f(b)$ is less than the value of the function immediately preceding and immediately following $x = b$.

MAXIMUM AND MINIMUM THERMOMETER. See *thermometer*.

MAXWELL, THE. Unit of *magnetic flux* (q.v.). The flux through 1 square centimetre normal to a field of intensity of 1 gauss.

MEAN (math.). Generally understood to be the *arithmetic mean*, i.e. the average. The *geometric mean*, M, between two quantities A and B is such a quantity that A, M and B are in *geometrical progression* (q.v.); thus $M/A = B/M$, $AB = M^2$, and $M = \sqrt{AB}$.

MEAN FREE PATH. Average or mean distance traversed by a molecule of a gas before collision with another. Increased at low pressures, since in a rarefied gas the number of molecules per unit volume is less than in the same gas at higher pressure. See *kinetic theory of gases*.

MECHANICAL ADVANTAGE. In a machine, the ratio of the actual load raised to the force required to maintain the machine at constant speed.

MECHANICAL EQUIVALENT OF HEAT. If H units of heat are completely converted into W units of work then $W = JH$, where J is a constant called the *mechanical equivalent of heat*, or *Joule's equivalent*. J represents the amount of work obtainable by the complete conversion of unit quantity of heat into mechanical work. 1 calorie (15°) $\equiv$ $4 \cdot 185 \times 10^7$ ergs; 1 British Thermal Unit $\equiv$ 778 ft-lb.; i.e. J has the values of $4 \cdot 185 \times 10^7$ ergs/calorie and 778 ft-lb./B.Th.U. respectively for these two sets of units.

MECHANICS. Branch of physical science dealing with the behaviour of matter under the action of force. See *dynamics; statics*.

MECHANISTIC THEORY. The view that all biological phenomena may be explained in mechanical, physical and chemical terms; in opposition to the *vitalistic theory* (q.v.).

MEDIAN. Line joining a vertex of a triangle to the mid-point of the opposite side.

MEERSCHAUM. Natural hydrated magnesium silicate, $Mg_2Si_3O_8 . 2H_2O$. White solid used for tobacco pipes.

MEGA-. Prefix denoting one million times, in metric units; e.g. megohm, one million ohms; more loosely, denoting 'very large.'

MEGACYCLE. Measure of frequency of high-frequency electric alternating current or oscillatory discharge. One million cycles. Unit used in high-frequency alternating current measurement.

MEGOHM. One million *ohms* (q.v.).

MELTING POINT. The constant temperature at which the solid and liquid phase of a substance are in equilibrium at a given pressure. Melting points are normally quoted for standard atmospheric pressure, 760 mm. of mercury.

MENISCUS. The curved surface of a liquid in a vessel. If the *contact angle* (q.v.) between the liquid and the wall of the vessel is less than 90°, the meniscus is concave; if greater, the meniscus is convex.

MENSURATION. Measurement of lengths, areas and volumes.

MENTHOL. $C_{10}H_{20}O$. One of a series of organic compounds of the camphor group. Occurs in natural oils. White crystals, m.p. 42° C., with a characteristic smell. Used in medicine.

MERCURIC. Compound of *bivalent* (q.v.) mercury.

MERCURIC CHLORIDE. *Corrosive sublimate* (q.v.).

MERCUROUS. Compound of *univalent* (q.v.) mercury.

MERCUROUS CHLORIDE. See *calomel*.

MERCURY (astr.). Planet with its orbit nearest the Sun. Mean distance from the Sun = 36 million miles. Sidereal period ('year') = 88 days. Mass approximately one twenty-ninth that of the Earth. Probably at a high temperature, and without an atmosphere.

MERCURY. Hg. Element. A.W. 200·61. At. No. 80. Liquid, silvery-white metal, S.G. 13·6, m.p. − 39° C., b.p. 357° C. Occurs as cinnabar, HgS. Extracted by roasting the ore in a current of air. Used in thermometers, barometers, manometers and other scientific apparatus; alloys (amalgams) used in dentistry. Compounds are poisonous; some are used in medicine.

MERCURY VAPOUR LAMP. Lamp emitting a strong bluish light by the passage of an electric current through mercury vapour in a bulb. The light is rich in *ultra-violet* radiations (q.v.); used in artificial sun-ray treatment and in street lighting.

MERIDIAN, CELESTIAL. The *great circle* (q.v.) of the *celestial sphere* (q.v.) passing through the zenith and the celestial poles, meeting the horizon at points called the North and South points.

MERIDIAN, MAGNETIC. See *magnetic meridian*.

MESONS. Particles found in *cosmic rays* (q.v.), having a *rest mass* (q.v.) intermediate between those of the electron and the proton; positive, negative, and possibly also neutral mesons exist, the charge being the same in magnitude as that of the electron. Two types, the π and the μ, are known, of rest mass approximately 283 and 215 times that of the electron; there is evidence of further types.

METABOLISM. The sum total of all the chemical processes in a living organism.

METAL. Substance having a 'metallic' lustre, malleable, ductile, of high specific gravity, and a good conductor of heat and electricity. Elements having such physical properties to a greater or less degree are generally *electropositive* (q.v.), combine with oxygen to give *bases* (q.v.); their chlorides are stable towards water. A number of elements normally regarded as metals have only some of the above properties. See *metalloid*.

METALDEHYDE, Meta. Solid *polymer* (q.v.) of acetaldehyde, CH_3CHO. Used as fuel in small heaters. White, volatile, inflammable, poisonous solid.

METALLOID. Element having some properties characteristic of metals, others of non-metals. Element giving rise to an *amphoteric oxide* (q.v.). E.g. arsenic, antimony.

METALLURGY. Science and technology of metals; in particular, the extraction of metals from their ores.

METAMERISM. Type of *isomerism* (q.v.) exhibited by organic compounds of the same chemical class or type; caused by the attachment of different *radicals* (q.v.) to the same central atom or group. E.g. diethyl ether, $(C_2H_5)_2O$, and methyl propyl ether, $CH_3OC_3H_7$.

METASTABLE STATE. State of supercooled water (see *supercooling*) or of supersaturated solutions (see *supersaturation*) in which the phase which is normally stable under the given conditions does not form unless a small amount of the normally stable phase is already present. Thus supercooled water will remain as liquid water below 0° C. until a small crystal of ice is introduced.

METATHESIS (chem.). *Double decomposition* (q.v.).

METEORITE, meteor. Solid body from the outer space. A meteorite becomes incandescent ('shooting star') on entering the Earth's atmosphere owing to frictional forces set up at its surface. Consists of various materials, often of metallic iron.

METEOROLOGY. The science of the weather; the study of such conditions as atmospheric pressure, temperature, wind strength, humidity, etc., from which conclusions as to the forthcoming weather are drawn.

-METER. Suffix denoting measurer; e.g. *voltmeter* (q.v.).

METHACRYLIC ACID. $CH_2:C(CH_3)COOH$. Corrosive liquid, m.p. 15° C., b.p. 160·5° C. The polymer of its methyl ester, methyl methacrylate, is an important plastic ('Perspex').

METHANE, marsh gas, fire-damp. CH_4. First hydrocarbon of the *paraffin series* (q.v.). Odourless, invisible gas. Inflammable, forms an explosive mixture with air. Formed from decaying organic matter and in coal-mines ; occurs in coal-gas.

METHANOL. *Methyl alcohol* (q.v.).

METHYL ALCOHOL, wood spirit. CH_3OH. Colourless, poisonous liquid with a faint smell. B.p. 64·6° C. Obtained as wood naphtha by the *destructive distillation* (q.v.) of wood. Used for 'denaturing' methylated spirit, as a solvent, and in chemical industry.

METHYL CARBINOL. *Ethyl alcohol* (q.v.).

METHYL GROUP. The *univalent* (q.v.) organic radical CH_3.

METHYLATED SPIRIT. Liquid fuel consisting, by volume, of 90% ethyl alcohol, 9·5% methyl alcohol, 0·5% pyridine, together with small amounts of petroleum and methyl violet dye.

METHYLATED SPIRIT, INDUSTRIAL. A variety of methylated spirit free from pyridine; consists of ethyl alcohol with 5% methyl alcohol.

METHYLENE BLUE. $C_{66}H_{18}N_3SCl$. Soluble, intense blue dye. Used as a dyestuff, in medicine, and as a stain in biology.

METOL, *p*-methylaminophenol. $CH_3NH.C_6H_4OH$. White crystalline compound, m.p. 87° C. Used as a developer in photography. Term also often applied to the sulphate of the compound.

METRE. Unit of length in the metric system. Length of the International Prototype Metre (preserved in Paris). 39·37 inches.

METRE BRIDGE. See *Wheatstone bridge*.

METRE-CANDLE. See *lux*.

METRIC SYSTEM. System of weights and measures originally based upon the *metre* (q.v.). This was intended to be 1/10,000,000 of a quadrant of the Earth through Paris. See *weight, volume, length* (metric units of).

METRIC TON, tonne. 1000 kilograms; 2204·61 lb., 0·9842 ton.

MHO, reciprocal ohm. Unit of *conductance* (q.v.); ratio of the current flowing through a conductor, measured in amperes, to the potential difference between the ends of the conductor, measured in volts gives the conductance in mhos.

MICHELSON-MORLEY EXPERIMENT. An attempt to measure the velocity of the Earth through the 'ether', by measuring the effect which such a velocity would have upon the velocity of light. No such motion of the Earth relative to the ether was detected: a result of the greatest importance for the theory of relativity.

MICRO-. 1. Prefix denoting one-millionth, in metric units. 2. Prefix meaning 'very small'; on a small scale. See also *macro-*.

MICROBALANCE. Balance for weighing objects of very small weight, i.e. of the order of 10^{-3} to 10^{-6} gm.

MICROCOSMIC SALT. Sodium ammonium hydrogen phosphate, $NANH_4HPO_4.4H_2O$. White crystalline soluble salt.

MICROFARAD. One-millionth of a *farad* (q.v.).

MICROMETER. Instrument for the accurate measurement of small distances or angles.

MICRO-MICRON, $\mu\mu$. One-millionth of a *micron* (q.v.); 10^{-12} metre, ·01 Ångström units.

MICRO-MILLIMETRE. One-millionth of a millimetre; 10^{-9} metre, 10 Ångström units.

MICRON, μ. One-millionth of a metre. 10,000 Ångström units.

MICROPHONE. Device for converting sound-waves into electrical energy which may then be reconverted into sound after transmission by wire or radio. One common type consists of a diaphragm in contact with, or close to, loosely packed carbon granules. The vibration of the diaphragm which is set up by sound disturbs the packing of the carbon granules and alters the electrical resistance of the carbon. Thus an electric current flowing through the carbon will vary in a manner which depends upon the frequency and intensity of the vibrations produced by the sound on the diaphragm. See also *condenser microphone*.

MICROPHOTOMETER. Special form of *densitometer* (q.v.) enabling density variations over a very small area of the image to be measured.

MICROSCOPE, COMPOUND. Instrument consisting essentially of two converging lenses or systems of lenses called the *objective* and the *eye-piece* respectively. The objective, which is nearest the viewed object, forms a real inverted magnified image of the object just inside the focal distance (see *focal length*) of the eyepiece. This image is viewed through the eyepiece, which then acts as a simple microscope.

MICROSCOPE, SIMPLE; magnifying glass. A convex lens which is used to produce a virtual *image* (q.v.) larger than the viewed object.

MICROTOME. Apparatus for cutting thin sections of material, for microscopical examination.

MILK OF LIME. Suspension of *lime* (q.v.) in water.

MILK SUGAR. See *lactose*.

MILLI-. Prefix denoting one-thousandth, in metric units.

MILLIAMMETER. Sensitive *ammeter* (q.v.) graduated to measure *milliamperes* (q.v.).

MILLIAMPERE. One-thousandth of an *ampere* (q.v.).

MILLIBAR. Unit of atmospheric pressure, used in meteorology. 1000 dynes per square centimetre; approximately equal to 1/32 inch of mercury. See *pressure, units of*.

MILLICURIE. One-thousandth of a *curie* (q.v.); that quantity of a radio-active isotope which decays at the rate of 3.7×10^7 disintegrations per second.

MILLIGRAM. 1/1000 gram; ·0154 grain.

MILLILITRE, ml. Unit of volume, used for liquids; 1/1000 *litre* (q.v.). Very nearly equal to 1 cubic centimetre (c.c.).

MILLIMETRE, mm. 1/1000 metre; ·0394 inch. See *length, metric units*.

MILLIMICRON. 1/1000 *micron* (q.v.); 10^{-7} cm.

MINERAL. Occurring naturally in the earth. The term, although apply-ing mainly to inorganic compounds, also includes mineral oil, which consists chiefly of organic *hydrocarbons* (q.v.).

MINERAL OIL. See *paraffin oil*.

MINIM. British fluid measure; 1/60 of a fluid drachm; ·0591 c.c. See *apothecaries' fluid measure*.

MINIMUM (math.). See *maximum*.

MINOR PLANETS. See *asteroids*.

MINIUM. See *red lead*.

MIRROR. Surface which reflects regularly most of the light falling upon it, thus forming images. See *reflection*.

MIRROR IMAGE. Image of an object as viewed in a mirror; reversed in such a way that the image bears to the object the same relation as a right hand to a left.

MIRRORS, SPHERICAL. Mirrors the reflecting surfaces of which form a portion of a sphere. The surface of such a mirror may be regarded as being made up of an infinitely large number of very small plane mirrors, each at a tangent to the curve of the mirror. Thus a ray of incident light would be reflected at any point as if from such a small plane mirror. Spherical mirrors may be *convex*, with the reflecting surface on the outside of the sphere, or *concave*. The centre and radius of the sphere of which the mirror is considered to form a part, are termed the *centre* and *radius of curvature*; the centre of the mirror is the *pole*, and the line joining the centre of curvature to the pole is the *axis*. The *principal focus* (see *focus*) is at a point half-way between the pole and the centre of curvature. Regarding all distances as measured from the mirror and taking all distances in the direction opposite to that of the incident light as positive, the following relationship holds for spherical mirrors: $1/v + 1/u = 1/f = 2/r$, where u and v are the distances of object and image from the mirror, r the radius of curva-ture, and f the focal length.

MISCH METAL. Alloy of cerium with small amounts of other *rare earth* (q.v.) metals. Used for 'flints' in automatic lighters.

MISCIBLE. Capable of being mixed to form a *homogeneous* (q.v.) sub-stance; usually applied to liquids; e.g. water and alcohol are com-pletely miscible.

MISPICKEL, arsenical pyrites. Natural sulphide of iron and arsenic, FeAsS.

MIST. Droplets of water, formed by the condensation of water-vapour on dust particles.

MIXED CRYSTALS, *solid solutions* (q.v.).

MIXTURES, mechanical mixtures. These differ from chemical compounds in the following respects: 1. The constituents may be separated by suitable physical or mechanical means. 2. Most mixtures may be made in all proportions; in the case of *solutions* (q.v.) which may be regarded as molecular mixtures, there are often limits of solubility. 3. No heat effect (except in the case of solutions) is produced on formation; the formation of chemical compounds is invariably accompanied by the evolution or absorption of energy in the form of heat. 4. The properties of a mixture are an aggregate of the properties of the constituents, whereas a compound has individual properties, often quite unlike those of the component elements.

MODERATOR. Substance used in an *atomic pile* (q.v.) for the rapid slowing-down of the neutrons emitted as the result of *nuclear fission* (q.v.). Graphite, heavy water and beryllium can be used as moderators.

MODULATION. Alterations in the *amplitude* (q.v.) or *frequency* (q.v.) of an electrical oscillation by a frequency of a different (usually a lower) order.

MODULUS. Constant factor or multiplier for the conversion of units from one system to another. See also *elastic modulus*.

MOHS SCALE OF HARDNESS. A scale in which each mineral listed is softer than (i.e. is scratched by) all those below it. 1. Talc. 2. Gypsum. 3. Calcite. 4. Fluorite. 5. Apatite. 6. Orthoclase. 7. Quartz. 8. Topaz. 9. Corundum. 10. Diamond.

MOL, mole. Gram-molecular weight of a substance; the weight of it in grams numerically equal to its molecular weight.

MOLAR SOLUTION. Solution containing one *mol* or gram-molecule per litre.

MOLECULAR COMPOUNDS. Chemical compounds formed by the chemical combination of two or more complete molecules. E.g. the *hydrates* (q.v.) of salts.

MOLECULAR CONCENTRATION. Concentration of a solution expressed in terms of gram-molecules or *mols* (q.v.) in a given volume.

MOLECULAR FORMULA. *Formula* (q.v.) of a chemical compound, showing the kind and the number of atoms present in the molecule, but not their arrangement.

MOLECULAR SPECTRUM. *Spectrum* (q.v.) emitted by molecules. Caused by transitions between different states of molecular rotation, vibration, etc.

MOLECULAR WEIGHT. Weight of a molecule of an element expressed on a scale which is defined so that the weight of an oxygen atom is exactly 16; the sum of the atomic weights of the atoms in a molecule.

MOLECULAR WEIGHT DETERMINATION. The following are amongst the available methods: Determination of the *vapour density* (q.v.); applicable to gases and volatile liquids. Measurement of the *depression of freezing point, elevation of boiling point,* and *osmotic pressure* (q.v.) produced by a definite concentration of the substance in solution; used for soluble substances which do not dissociate or associate in solution. (See *dissociation, association.*) Determination of the *chemical equivalent* (q.v.) of the substance, with a knowledge of the equation for the reaction.

MOLECULE. Smallest portion of a substance capable of existing independently and retaining the properties of the original substance.

MOLYBDENUM. Mo. Element. A.W. 95·95, At. No. 42. Hard white metal resembling iron. S.G. 10·2, m.p. 2620° C. Occurs as molybdenite, MoS_2. Extracted by roasting the ore and reducing the oxide so formed in an electric furnace with carbon. Used for special steels and alloys.

MOMENT, MAGNETIC. See *magnetic moment.*

MOMENT OF A FORCE. Measure of the tendency of a force to rotate the body to which it is applied. Measured by multiplying the magnitude of the force by the perpendicular distance from the line of action of the force to the axis of rotation.

MOMENT OF INERTIA. The moment of inertia I of a body about any axis is the sum of the products of the mass dm of each element of the body and the square of r, its distance from that axis. $I = \Sigma r^2 dm$.

MOMENTUM. The product of the mass and the velocity of a body. For speeds approaching that of light, the variation of mass with velocity must be taken into account, and the value of m appropriate to the velocity of the body must be used in the expression for the momentum. See *relativity, theory of.*

MOMENTUM, CONSERVATION OF. See *conservation of momentum.*

MONAD. Element having a *valency* (q.v.) of one.

MONATOMIC MOLECULE. *Molecule* (q.v.) of an element, consisting of a single atom of the element. E.g. the molecules of the *inert gases* (q.v.).

MONAZITE. Mineral containing compounds of cerium, thorium and other *rare earths* (q.v.), with some occluded helium.

MOND PROCESS. Extraction of nickel by the action of carbon monoxide, CO, on the impure metal. This gives nickel carbonyl, $Ni(CO)_4$, a gas which decomposes when heated to 200° C. into pure nickel and carbon monoxide, the latter being used again.

MONEL METAL. Alloy of copper (25%–35%), nickel (60%–70%) and small amounts of iron, manganese, silicon and carbon. Used as an acid-resisting material in chemical industry.

MONO-. Prefix denoting one, single.

MONOBASIC ACID. An acid having one atom of acidic hydrogen in a molecule; acid giving rise to only one series of salts. E.g. nitric acid, HNO_3.

MONOCHROMATIC LIGHT. Light consisting of vibrations of the same or nearly the same frequency; light of one *colour* (q.v.).

MONOHYDRIC. Containing one *hydroxyl group* (q.v.) in a molecule.

MONOMER. Chemical compound consisting of single molecules; as opposed to a *polymer*, the molecules of which are built up by the repeated union of monomer molecules. See *polymerization*.

MONOSACCHARIDES, simple sugars. Group consisting chiefly of *sugars* (q.v.) having a molecular formula, $C_6H_{12}O_6$ (*hexoses*) or $C_6H_{10}O_5$ (*pentoses*); unlike the *polysaccharides* (q.v.), cannot be hydrolyzed to give simpler sugars.

MONOTROPIC. Existing in only one stable physical form, any other form obtainable being unstable under all conditions.

MONOVALENT, univalent. Having a *valency* (q.v.) of one.

MOON, THE. Satellite of the Earth. Mean distance from the Earth, 239,000 miles; synodic month 29·5 days, sidereal month 27·3 days. Mass approximately 1/81 that of the Earth; diameter quarter that of the Earth. Devoid of water or an atmosphere.

MORDANTS. Substances used in dyeing, especially fabrics of plant origin. The fabric is first impregnated with the mordant, which is generally a basic metal hydroxide for acidic dyes, or an acidic substance for basic dyes. The dye then reacts chemically with the mordant forming an insoluble *lake* which is firmly attached to the fabric.

MORPHIA. See *morphine*.

MORPHINE. $C_{17}H_{19}O_3N$. Member of the *alkaloids* (q.v.); occurs in opium. White solid, m.p. 253° C. Powerful narcotic, used medically for relieving pain. Dangerous habit-forming drug.

MORTAR. Building material consisting mainly of lime and sand; hardens on exposure through chemical action between the ingredients and atmospheric carbon dioxide.

MOSAIC GOLD. Crystalline stannic sulphide, SnS_2. Shining, golden-yellow scales.

MOTHER-LIQUOR. Solution from which substances are crystallized.

MOTION, EQUATIONS OF. Equations applying to bodies moving with uniform acceleration. If u = initial velocity, v = final velocity at the end of t seconds, f = acceleration, and s = distance moved in t seconds, (1) $v = u + ft$; (2) $s = ut + \frac{1}{2}ft^2$; (3) $v^2 = u^2 + 2fs$.

MOTION, LAWS OF. See *Newton's laws of motion*.

MOTOR. A device for converting other forms of energy into mechanical energy. Generally applied to the *internal-combustion engine* (q.v.) and the *electric motor* (q.v.).

MOTOR, ELECTRIC. See *electric motor*.

MULTIPLE PROPORTIONS, LAW OF. See *chemical combination, laws of*.

MUNTZ METAL. Alloy containing 3 parts of copper and 2 parts of zinc.

MURIATE. Chloride, salt of hydrochloric acid.

MURIATIC ACID. *Hydrochloric acid* (q.v.).

MUSTARD GAS. Dichlorodiethyl sulphide, $(CH_2CH_2Cl)_2S$. Oily liquid which has been used as a 'war gas'. Destroyed by oxidizing agents, e.g. bleaching powder.

MUTAROTATION. A change in the *optical rotation* (q.v.) of a substance.

MUTUAL INDUCTION. The induction of an E.M.F. in a circuit due to a changing current in a separate circuit with which it is magnetically linked. The induced E.M.F. is proportional to the rate of change of the current in the second circuit, the constant of proportionality being called the coefficient of mutual induction, or the *mutual inductance*. The unit of mutual inductance is the *henry* (q.v.).

MYDRIATIC. Substance used to dilate the pupil of the eye.

MYOPIA, short sight. Defect of vision. Subject is unable to see distant objects distinctly. Corrected by the use of concave spectacle lenses.

N

NADIR (astr.). Lowest point; point opposite the *zenith* (q.v.) on the *celestial sphere* (q.v.).

NAPHTHA. General name for mixtures of *hydrocarbons* (q.v.) in various proportions, obtained from paraffin oil, coal-tar, etc. Wood naphtha is impure *methyl alcohol* (q.v.), CH_3OH, produced by the *destructive distillation* (q.v.) of wood.

NAPHTHALENE. $C_{10}H_8$. *Cyclic hydrocarbon* (q.v.) occurring in coal-tar. White, shiny, crystalline solid with a penetrating smell. M.p. 79° C. B.p. 218° C. Used in the manufacture of organic dyes.

NARCOTIC. Producing sleep, stupor or insensibility.

NASCENT STATE. Certain elements, notably hydrogen, are more active when being set free in a chemical reaction than in their ordinary state; such 'nascent' elements are supposed to owe their activity to being composed of single atoms instead of molecules, or alternatively to some of the chemical energy liberated on the reaction being associated with the hydrogen instead of being released in the form of heat.

NATRIUM. *Sodium* (q.v.).

NATRON. Natural sodium sesquicarbonate,
$$Na_2CO_3.NaHCO_3.2H_2O.$$

NATURAL (chem.). Occurring in nature; not artificially prepared.

NATURAL GAS. Mixture of gaseous *hydrocarbons* (q.v.), often containing other gases, issuing from the earth in some localities, more particularly near deposits of mineral oil.

NAUTICAL MILE. 6082·66 feet; often used synonymously with the Admiralty mile, 6080 feet. Practically, may be taken as 1 minute of latitude.

NEAR INFRA-RED or ULTRA-VIOLET. The shortest *infra-red* (q.v.) or the longest *ultra-violet* (q.v.) wave-lengths; i.e. those wave-lengths of these two types of radiation which are 'nearest' in magnitude to those of visible light.

NEBULA (astr.). Cloudy, luminous patch in the heavens. Consists of 'universes' of stars, or of materials from which such universes or *galaxies* (q.v.) are being formed.

NEGATIVE (math. and phys.). In any convention of signs, regarded as being counted in the minus, or negative direction, as opposed to positive.

NEGATIVE, PHOTOGRAPHIC. See *photography*.

NEGATIVE POLE. The south-seeking pole of a magnet. See *magnetic pole*.

NEODYMIUM. Nd. Element. A.W. 144·27. At. No. 60. See *rare earths*.

NEON. Ne. Element. A.W. 20·183. At. No. 10. Colourless, odourless, invisible gas belonging to the *inert gases* (q.v.). Occurs in the atmosphere (1 part in 55,000). Obtained by the *fractional distillation* (q.v.) of liquid air. A discharge of electricity through neon at low pressures produces an intense orange-red glow; used for neon signs.

NEOPRENE, *trans*-polychloroprene, $(CH_2.CH:CCl.CH_2)_n$. A synthetic polymer material; variety of 'synthetic rubber'.

NEPHASCOPE. Grid-like instrument for determining speed of celestial objects (including clouds) by observation of time of transit.

NEPTUNE (astr.). Planet with one satellite. Orbit lies between those of Uranus and Pluto. Mean distance from the Sun, 2793 million miles. Sidereal period ('year'), 164·8 years. Mass approximately 17 times that of the Earth. Surface temperature probably below — 200° C.

NEPTUNIUM. Np. *Transuranic element* (q.v.), At. No. 93.

NESSLER'S SOLUTION. Solution of potassium mercuri-iodide, $KHgI_3$, in potassium hydroxide solution. Used as a test for ammonia, with which it forms a brown coloration or precipitate.

NEUTRAL (chem.). Neither acid nor alkaline.

NEUTRAL TEMPERATURE. The temperature of the hot junction of a *thermocouple* (q.v.) at which the electromotive force round the circuit is a maximum and the rate of change of E.M.F. with temperature is a minimum.

NEUTRALIZATION (chem.). Addition of acid to alkali, or *vice versa*, till neither is in excess and the solution is neutral.

NEUTRINO. Fundamental uncharged particle, the existence of which has been postulated in order to preserve the laws of *conservation of mass and energy* (q.v.) and *conservation of momentum* (q.v.) in certain *nuclear reactions* (q.v.). The neutrino has zero or very small *rest mass* (q.v.).

NEUTRON. Electrically uncharged particle possessing a slightly greater mass than the *proton* (q.v.). A constituent of all atomic nuclei (see *atom, structure of*) except the normal hydrogen nucleus, which is a single proton. Owing to the absence of electric charge, the neutron can pass readily through matter.

NEW CANDLE. See *candela*.

NEWTON'S LAW OF COOLING. The rate at which a body loses heat to its surroundings is proportional to the temperature difference between the body and its surroundings (an empirical law, true only for small differences of temperature).

NEWTON'S LAWS OF MOTION. The fundamental laws on which classical dynamics is based. 1. Every body continues in its state of rest or uniform motion in a straight line except in so far as it is compelled by external forces to change that state. 2. Rate of change of *momentum* (q.v.) is proportional to the applied force, and takes place in the direction in which the force acts. 3. To every action there is an equal and opposite reaction.

NEWTON'S RINGS. Coloured rings which may be observed round the point of contact of a convex lens and a plane reflecting surface. Caused by the *interference* (q.v.) effects which occur between light-waves reflected at the upper and lower surfaces of the air film separating the lens and the flat surface.

NEWTONIAN MECHANICS. System of mechanics developed from Newton's Laws of Motion. Provides an accurate means of determining the motions of bodies possessing ordinary velocities. The motions of particles having very high velocities must be treated by *relativistic mechanics*, i.e. a system of mechanics based on the theory of *relativity* (q.v.), as the change of mass of a particle with its velocity becomes important under such conditions.

NICKEL. Ni. Element. A.W. 58·69. At. No. 28. Silvery-white magnetic metal resembling iron. S.G. 8·90, m.p. 1452° C. Resists corrosion. Occurs combined with sulphur or arsenic in pentlandite, kupfernickel, smaltite and other ores. The ore is roasted to form the oxide, which is reduced to the metal by hydrogen, and the metal is then purified by the *Mond process* (q.v.). Used for nickel-plating, in coinage, for alloys such as *nickel steel*, *platinoid*, *constantan* (q.v.), and as a *catalyst* (q.v.).

NICKEL CARBONYL. See *Mond process*.

NICKEL PLATING. Depositing a thin layer of metallic nickel by an electrolytic process. See *electrolysis*.

NICKEL SILVER. Group of alloys of copper, nickel and zinc in varying proportions, containing up to 30% nickel. A typical composition is 60% copper, 20% nickel, 20% zinc.

NICKEL STEEL. Steel containing up to 6% nickel.

NICOL PRISM. Optical device, constructed from a crystal of calcite, used for obtaining plane polarized light. See *polarization of light*.

NICOTINE. $C_{10}H_{14}N_2$. *Alkaloid* (q.v.) occurring in tobacco leaves. Colourless, intensely poisonous oily liquid.

NICOTINIC ACID. Pyridine-3-carboxylic acid, $C_5H_4N.COOH$. *Vitamin* (q.v.) of the B complex.

NIOBIUM, columbium. Element. A.W. 92·91. At. No. 41. Grey metal, S.G. 8·4, m.p. 1950° C. Very rare.

NITON. Obsolete name for *radon* (q.v.).

NITRATE. Salt of *nitric acid* (q.v.).

NITRATION. Introduction of the nitro group, NO_2, into organic compounds by the use of nitric acid. Of importance in the production of *explosives* (q.v.), many nitro-derivatives of organic compounds being chemically unstable.

NITRE, saltpetre. See *potassium nitrate*.

NITRIC ACID, aqua fortis. HNO_3. Colourless, corrosive, acid liquid, b.p. 86° C. Powerful oxidizing agent. Attacks most metals and many other substances with evolution of brown fumes of nitrogen dioxide, NO_2. Manufactured by the action of concentrated sulphuric acid, H_2SO_4, on sodium or potassium nitrate, and by the oxidation of ammonia, NH_3, by passing a mixture of ammonia and air over heated platinum which acts as a *catalyst* (q.v.). Widely used in chemical industry.

NITRIC OXIDE. NO. Colourless gas, reacts with oxygen on contact to form nitrogen dioxide, NO_2.

NITRIFICATION. The process of conversion, by the action of bacteria, of nitrogen compounds from animal and plant waste and decay, into nitrates in the soil.

NITROBENZENE. $C_6H_5NO_2$. Pale yellow, oily, poisonous liquid, b.p. 208° C., with an odour of bitter almonds. Produced by the action of nitric acid on benzene; reduction of nitrobenzene yields *aniline* (q.v.).

NITROCELLULOSE. *Cellulose nitrate* (q.v.), the nitric acid *ester* (q.v.) of cellulose. Although the term nitrocellulose is chemically incorrect for this compound, it is extensively used.

NITROCHALK. Mixture of calcium carbonate, $CaCO_3$, and ammonium nitrate, NH_4NO_3, used as a fertilizer.

NITROGEN. N. Element. A.W. 14·008. At. No. 7. Odourless, invisible, chemically inactive gas, forming approximately 4/5 of the atmosphere. Chief natural compound is *Chile saltpetre* (q.v.). Compounds are used as *fertilizers* (q.v.) and in the manufacture of *nitric acid* (q.v.). The element is vital to living organisms, forming an essential part of the *proteins* (q.v.). See *fixation of atmospheric nitrogen; nitrogen cycle*.

NITROGEN CYCLE. The circulation of nitrogen compounds in nature through the various organisms to which nitrogen is essential. Inorganic nitrogen compounds in the soil are taken in by plants, and are combined by the plants with other elements to form *proteins* (q.v.), the form in which nitrogen can be utilized by the higher animals. The result of animal waste and decay is to bring the nitrogen which the animals had absorbed in the form of proteins, back into the soil in the form of simpler nitrogen compounds. Bacterial action of various kinds converts these into compounds suitable for use by plants again. In addition to this main circulation, a certain amount of atmospheric nitrogen is 'fixed' (i.e. combined) by the action of bacteria associated with the roots of leguminous plants, and by the action of atmospheric electricity; while some combined nitrogen is set free by the action of *denitrifying* bacteria. See Fig. 9.

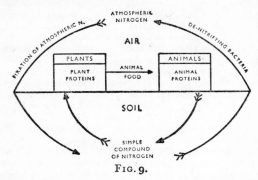

FIG. 9.

NITROGEN DIOXIDE, nitrogen peroxide, NO_2. Dark brown gas with a pungent smell, formed by the *reduction* (q.v.) of nitric acid and in the decomposition, by heat, of some nitrates. On cooling to a low temperature becomes paler in colour, owing to the *association* (q.v.) of the molecules to form N_2O_4.

NITROGLYCERIN, glyceryl trinitrate. $C_3H_5(NO_3)_3$. Pale yellow, heavy, oily liquid. Explodes with great violence when subjected to sudden shock or detonation. Used as an explosive, either alone or in the form of *dynamite* (q.v.).

NITROLIME. See *calcium cyanamide*.

NITROUS ETHER. *Ethyl nitrite* (q.v.).

NITROUS OXIDE, N_2O. *Laughing-gas* (q.v.).

NOBLE METALS. Metals such as silver, gold and platinum, which do not corrode or tarnish in air or water, and are not easily attacked by acids. From the chemical point of view, unreactive metals low in the *electromotive series* (q.v.).

NODAL POINTS. Two points on the axis of a lens system, such that if the incident ray passes through one, travelling in a given direction, the emergent ray passes through the other in a parallel direction.

NODES. Points of zero displacement in a system of stationary waves. See also *antinodes*.

NOISE (elec.). Effect observed in amplifying circuits due to the amplification, together with the input signal, of spurious voltages arising from such causes as the vibration of certain components, the random motion of the electrons constituting the current in the conductors, etc.

NON-ELECTROLYTES. Substances which do not yield *ions* (q.v.) in solution and which therefore form solutions of low electrical conductivity. See *electrolysis*.

NON-METALLIC ELEMENTS. Chemical elements not possessing the properties of the *metals* (q.v.).

NORDHAUSEN ACID, fuming sulphuric acid, pyrosulphuric acid. $H_2S_2O_7$. Oily, fuming liquid made by the action of sulphur trioxide, SO_3, on ordinary sulphuric acid, H_2SO_4.

NORMAL (math.). A line perpendicular to a surface.

NORMAL SOLUTION (chem.). A solution containing 1 gram-equivalent per litre. Term used in *volumetric analysis* (q.v.).

NORMAL STATE of atom. See *ground state*.

NORMALITY (chem.). Method of expressing concentrations of solutions; number of gram-equivalents of reagent per litre of solution. Thus, a solution containing 2 gram-equivalents per litre is a twice-normal or 2N solution.

NOTATION. Representation of numbers, quantities or other entities by symbols; a system of symbols for such a purpose.

NOVA. A star which suddenly flares up to a greatly increased brightness which subsides after a short period of time. Probably caused by a sudden contraction, accompanied by the liberation of vast amounts of energy, leaving a white dwarf star.

N.T.P.; S.T.P. Normal (standard) temperature and pressure. A pressure of 760 mm. of mercury and a temperature of 0° C.; standard conditions under which volumes of gases are compared.

NUCLEAR CHARGE. The positive electric charge on the nucleus of an atom. When expressed in units equal to the charge on the electron, this is numerically equal to the *atomic number* (q.v.) of the element, to the number of *protons* (q.v.) in the nucleus, and to the number of electrons surrounding the nucleus in the neutral atom. See *atom, structure of*.

NUCLEAR FISSION. The breaking up of a heavy atom, e.g. of uranium, into two or more new atoms of approximately equal mass, with an enormous release of energy. See *atomic bomb; atomic pile*.

NUCLEAR ISOMERS. Atoms of an element of the same mass but possessing different rates of radioactive decay.

NUCLEAR PHYSICS. The study of the physics of the atomic nucleus and of sub-atomic particles.

NUCLEAR REACTIONS. Reactions in which the nuclei of atoms are changed, yielding either atoms of a different element, or *isotopes* (q.v.) of the original element. Such reactions occur in Nature in radioactive elements, and are produced artificially by bombarding elements with particles (protons, neutrons, deuterons, etc.) of suitable energy.

NUCLEAR REACTOR. See *atomic pile*.

NUCLEAR TRANSMUTATIONS. The changing of atoms of one element into those of another by suitable *nuclear reactions* (q.v.).

NUCLEUS. Vital central point; particle of matter acting as centre; e.g. a particle of dust will act as a nucleus for the condensation of water in *mist* (q.v.).

NUCLEUS, ATOMIC. Positively charged body, consisting of positively charged *protons* (q.v.) and neutral *neutrons* (q.v.), constituting the main mass of the atom. See *atom, structure of.*

NUMERATOR. Number above the line in a vulgar fraction. E.g. 3 in $\frac{3}{16}$.

NYLON. Officially defined as 'a generic term applied to any long-chain synthetic polymeric amide which has recurring amide groups as an integral part of the main polymer chain, and which is capable of being formed into a filament in which the structural elements are oriented in the direction of the axis'. The familiar commercial form of nylon, as used for stockings, is a substance formed by the condensation *polymerization* (q.v.) of adipic acid with hexamethylene diamine. The solid polymer is melted and forced through fine jets to make filaments which are then collected in the form of yarn.

O

OBJECTIVE (phys.). Lens or system of lenses nearest the object in a *telescope* or compound *microscope* (q.v.).

OBLATE SPHEROID. See *spheroid.*

OBTUSE ANGLE. Angle greater than 90°.

OCCLUSION. Certain solids have the property of absorbing or occluding some gases, either by the formation of a chemical compound, or by forming a solid solution, or by the condensation of the gas on the surface of the solid.

OCHRE. Natural hydrated form of ferric oxide, Fe_2O_3, containing various impurities. Used as a red or yellow pigment.

OCTA-, OCTO-. Prefix denoting eight, eightfold.

OCTANE. C_8H_{18}. Hydrocarbon of the *paraffin series* (q.v.). Exists in several isomeric forms (see *isomerism*). Liquid, b.p. 126° C.

OCTANE NUMBER OF A FUEL. Defined as the percentage by volume of *iso*-octane, C_8H_{18} (2:2:4-trimethylpentane) in a mixture of *iso*-octane and normal heptane, C_7H_{16}, which is equal to the fuel in knock characteristics under specified test conditions.

OCTANT. Portion of a circle cut off by an arc and two radii at 45°; one-eighth of the area of a circle.

OCTAVES, LAW OF. An incomplete statement of the *Periodic Law* (q.v.) made by Newlands independently of Mendeleev.

OERSTED, THE. The unit of *magnetic field strength* or *magnetic intensity* (q.v.) in C.G.S. units.

OHM, THE. Unit of electrical resistance (q.v.). The *absolute ohm* is 10^9 *electromagnetic units* (q.v.) of resistance, and is that resistance in which energy is dissipated at the rate of 1 *watt* (q.v.) by the flow of one absolute *ampere* (q.v.) of current. The former *international ohm* (= 1·00048 absolute ohms) was defined as the resistance, at 0° C., of a column of mercury 106·3 cm. in length, of mass 14·4521 gm., and of uniform cross-sectional area.

OHM'S LAW. The ratio of the potential difference between the ends of a conductor and the current flowing in the conductor is constant. This ratio is termed the resistance of the conductor. For a potential difference of E volts and a current of I amperes, the resistance, R, in ohms is equal to E/I.

OIL, MINERAL. General name given to various mixtures of natural *hydrocarbons* (q.v.). See *paraffin oil*.

OIL OF VITRIOL. Concentrated *sulphuric acid* (q.v.).

OIL, SYNTHETIC. Natural mineral oils are composed of various *hydrocarbons* (q.v.). It is possible to make similar products artificially from coal, etc., by combining carbon or carbon monoxide with hydrogen. See *Bergius process; Fischer-Tropsch process*.

OILS. See *fats and oils*.

OLEFIANT GAS. *Ethylene* (q.v.).

OLEFINES, olefins. Ethylene series of hydrocarbons, having the general formula C_nH_{2n}.

OLEIC ACID. $C_{17}H_{33}COOH$. *Unsaturated* (q.v.) organic acid. Occurs in the form of *glycerides* (q.v.) in many fats and oils. Liquid, m.p. $14°$ C. A high proportion of *triolein* (q.v.), the glyceride of oleic acid, in a fat or oil makes it more liquid.

OLEIN. See *triolein*.

OLEUM. Fuming sulphuric acid; concentrated sulphuric acid, H_2SO_4, containing extra sulphur trioxide, SO_3.

OPAQUE. Not permitting a wave-motion (e.g. light, sound, X-rays) to pass. Usually applied to light; not transparent or translucent.

OPEN-CHAIN COMPOUNDS. Organic compounds not derived from ring compounds; *aliphatic compounds* (q.v.).

OPEN-HEARTH PROCESS, Siemens-Martin process. Process for steel manufacture. Pig-iron and steel scrap or iron ore in calculated amounts are heated together by *producer gas* (q.v.) on a hearth in a furnace. See *steel*.

OPIUM. The dried, milky juice from unripe fruits of the opium poppy, *Papaver somniferum*. Contains several *alkaloids* (q.v.), including morphine and codeine.

OPPOSITION (astr.). A planet having its orbit outside that of the Earth is in opposition when the Earth is in a line between the Sun and the planet.

OPTIC AXIS. The direction in a doubly refracting crystal in which light is propagated without *double refraction* (q.v.).

OPTICAL ACTIVITY, optical rotation. The property possessed by some substances and their solutions of rotating the plane of vibration of polarized light (see *polarization of light*). The amount of this rotation is proportional to the distance the light travels in the medium, and to the concentration of the solution. The amount of rotation also depends upon the wave-length (i.e. the colour) of the light used. This last phenomenon is termed *rotatory dispersion*.

OPTICAL AXIS. Line passing through the optical centre and the centre of curvature of a spherical mirror or lens. See *mirrors, spherical; lens*.

OPTICAL CENTRE OF THIN LENS. A point, situated for all practical purposes at the geometrical centre of the lens, through which an incident ray passes without being deviated. See *lens*.

OPTICAL ISOMERISM. Form of *isomerism* (q.v.) in which the isomers differ in their *optical activity* (q.v.). See *stereoisomerism*.

OPTICAL ROTATION. See *optical activity*.

OPTICS. The study of light.

OPTICS, GEOMETRICAL. Branch of optics built up on the laws of reflection and refraction, and assuming the rectilinear propagation of light; it involves no consideration of the physical nature of light. Mainly concerned with the formation of images by mirrors and lenses.

ORBIT. A path; in the atom, the path taken by electrons round the nucleus (see *atom, structure of*).

ORDINATE. In analytical geometry, the ordinate of a point is the perpendicular distance of the point from the axis.

ORDINARY RAY. When a ray of light is incident upon a crystal which exhibits *double refraction* (q.v.) so that the direction of the ray makes an angle with the *optic axis* (q.v.) of the crystal, the ray splits into two rays. One of these obeys the ordinary laws of refraction and is called the *ordinary ray*. The other is the *extra-ordinary ray*.

ORGANIC CHEMISTRY. Chemistry of the *organic compounds* (q.v.); chemistry of carbon compounds excluding the metal carbonates and the oxides of carbon. Originally, the chemistry of substances produced by living organisms, as distinct from the inorganic chemistry of substances of mineral origin.

ORGANIC COMPOUNDS. Chemical compounds containing carbon combined with hydrogen, and often also with oxygen, nitrogen and other elements. The molecules of organic compounds are often very complex, and contain a large number of atoms. They are not usually ionized in solution (see *dissociation*), and frequently show the phenomenon of *isomerism* (q.v.).

ORMOLU. Alloy of copper, zinc and tin in various proportions; generally containing at least 50% copper.

ORPIMENT. Natural arsenic trisulphide, As_2S_3. Yellow mineral.

ORTHO-. Prefix denoting right, straight, correct.

ORTHOCHROMATIC FILM. Photographic film sensitive to green in addition to blue and violet light, thus giving a more accurate representation of colours in monochrome than ordinary film. See *photography*.

ORTHOCLASE FELSPAR. Natural potassium aluminium silicate, $K_2O.Al_2O_3.6SiO_2$. Constituent of granite.

OSCILLOSCOPE. See *cathode ray oscilloscope*.

OSMIC ACID. Osmium tetroxide, OsO_4. Colourless, crystalline solid, m.p. 40° C.; solution used as a stain for fat globules in microscopy.

OSMIRIDIUM. Natural alloy of osmium, iridium, with smaller amounts of platinum, rhodium and ruthenium. Hard and resistant to corrosion; used for tipping pen-nibs.

OSMIUM. Os. Element. A.W. 190·2. At. No. 76. Hard, white crystalline metal. S.G. 22·48, m.p. 2700° C. Heaviest substance known. Occurs together with platinum (see *osmiridium*); used in alloys with platinum and iridium.

OSMOSIS. The flow of water (or other solvent) through a *semi-permeable membrane* (q.v.); i.e. a membrane which will permit the passage of the solvent but not of dissolved substances. There is a tendency for solutions separated by such a membrane to become equal in molecular concentration; thus water will flow from a weaker to a stronger solution, the solutions tending to become more nearly equal in concentration.

OSMOTIC PRESSURE of a solution. The pressure which must be applied to a solution in order to prevent the flow of solvent through a *semi-permeable membrane* (q.v.) separating the solution and the pure solvent. When a solvent is allowed to flow through such a membrane into a vessel or cell containing a solution, the solvent will flow into the cell (see *osmosis*) until such a pressure is set up as to balance the pressure of the solvent flowing in. The osmotic pressure of a dilute solution is analogous to gaseous pressure; a substance in solution, if not dissociated (see *dissociation*), exerts the same osmotic pressure as the gaseous pressure it would exert if it were a gas at the same temperature, and occupying the same volume. The osmotic pressure, temperature and volume of a dilute solution of a non-electrolyte are connected by laws exactly similar to the *gas laws* (q.v.).

OUNCE, AVOIRDUPOIS. 437½ grains. 28·3 grams.

OUNCE, FLUID. 8 fluid drachms; 28·41 c.c.

OUNCE, TROY. 480 grains; 31·1 grams.

OVERTONES. Notes of lesser intensity and higher pitch (i.e. of higher frequency) than the fundamental note, and superimposed upon the latter to give a note of characteristic *quality* (q.v.).

OXALATE. Salt of *oxalic acid* (q.v.).

OXALIC ACID. $(COOH)_2.2H_2O$. White crystalline poisonous soluble solid, m.p. 101° C. Salts occur in wood sorrel and other plants. Used in dyeing, bleaching, ink manufacture, metal polishes and for removing ink stains.

OXIDASE. An *enzyme* (q.v.) which acts by oxidation.

OXIDATION. Combination with oxygen; addition of oxygen or other *electronegative* (q.v.) atom or group; removal of hydrogen or other *electropositive* (q.v.) atom or group.

OXIDE. *Binary compound* (q.v.) with oxygen.

OXY-ACETYLENE BLOWPIPE. Device for obtaining a very high-temperature flame (3300° C.) for welding, by burning a mixture of oxygen and acetylene in a special jet.

OXYGEN. O. Element. A.W. 16·0000 (taken as the standard of *atomic weight*, q.v.). Odourless, invisible gas; the most abundant of all the elements; forms approximately one-fifth of the atmosphere. Chemically very active; burning and respiration both involve combination with oxygen. Essential to most forms of life. Compounds (oxides) are very widely distributed. The pure element is made by the fractional distillation of liquid air. Used for welding and metal-cutting.

OXY-HAEMOGLOBIN. Unstable compound formed by the action of oxygen on haemoglobin in respiration (q.v.).

OXY-HYDROGEN BLOWPIPE. Device similar to the *oxy-acetylene blow-pipe* (q.v.), giving a temperature of about 2400° C.

OZOKERITE, earth-wax. Natural mixture of solid *hydrocarbons* (q.v.). Brownish or greyish mass, resembling paraffin wax.

OZONE. O_3. *Allotropic form* (q.v.) of oxygen, containing three atoms in the molecule. Bluish gas, very active chemically, powerful oxidizing agent. Formed when oxygen or air is subjected to a silent electric discharge. Occurs in ordinary air in very small amounts only; the health-giving effects sometimes attributed to it in sea-air are probably due to other causes. Used for purifying air.

P

PACKING FRACTION of an atom. The ratio of the *mass defect* (q.v.) to the mass number (see *isotopic weight*) of an atom. The packing fraction gives an indication of the stability of the atomic nucleus.

PAINT. Liquid containing a coloured material (pigment) in suspension. The application of the paint to a surface and the evaporation or hardening of the liquid cover the surface with the pigment in the form of a skin. The liquid generally consists of linseed oil, a 'thinner' of turpentine or other volatile liquid, and a 'drier' to accelerate drying or hardening of the linseed oil.

PAIR PRODUCTION. See *cosmic ray showers*.

PALLADIUM. Pd. Element. A.W. 106·7. At. No. 46. Silvery-white metal which occurs with and resembles platinum. S.G. 11·40, m.p. 1555° C. Used in alloys and as a catalyst.

PALMITIC ACID. $C_{15}H_{31}COOH$. Organic *fatty acid* (q.v.); occurs in the form of *tripalmitin* (q.v.) in palm oil and many natural fats. Wax-like solid, m.p. 64° C.

PALMITIN. See *tripalmitin*.

PANCHROMATIC FILM. Photographic film sensitive to light of all colours including red, thus giving a more accurate representation of colours in monochrome than *orthochromatic film* (q.v.). See *photography*.

PAPER. Paper normally consists of sheets of *cellulose* (q.v.), mainly obtained from wood pulp from which *lignin* (q.v.) and other non-cellulosic materials have been removed.

PARA-. Prefix denoting beside, beyond; or wrong, irregular.

PARABOLA. Curve traced out by a point which moves so that its distance from a fixed point, the *focus*, is equal to its distance from a fixed straight line, the *directrix*.

PARABOLIC MIRROR. Device for producing a parallel beam of light from a source. Consists of a curved reflector the section of which is a parabola. Such a reflector will bring a parallel beam of light to a focus, and conversely, if a source of light is placed at the focus, the light will be reflected in a parallel beam.

PARABOLOID OF REVOLUTION. The surface obtained by rotating a *parabola* (q.v.) about its axis of symmetry.

PARACHOR. A relation showing the influence of temperature upon the surface tension of a liquid; interpreted as the molecular volume measured at a standard internal pressure. The value is composed, approximately, of a sum of terms for separate atoms, and of constants for various types of linkage between the atoms, thus giving a method for the determination of the constitution and structure of molecules.

PARAFFIN (chem.). Hydrocarbon of the *paraffin series* (q.v.).

PARAFFIN OIL, kerosine. Mixture of *hydrocarbons* (q.v.) obtained in the distillation of petroleum. The boiling range of the kerosines is 150° C.–300° C. Used for paraffin lamps, oil-burning engines, domestic heaters.

PARAFFIN SERIES. *Homologous series* (q.v.) of *hydrocarbons* (q.v.) having the general formula C_nH_{2n+2}. Chemically inert, stable, inflammable. The first four members of the series (methane, ethane, propane, butane) are gases at ordinary temperatures; the next eleven are liquids, and form the principal constituents of various mineral oils; the higher members are solids, forming the chief constituents of paraffin wax.

PARAFFIN WAX. White, translucent solid melting to a colourless liquid in the range 50° C.–60° C. Consists of a mixture of the higher hydrocarbons of the *paraffin series* (q.v.). Used for candles, waxed paper, polishes.

PARAFORM, paraformaldehyde. Solid *polymer* (q.v.) of *formaldehyde* (q.v.), readily converted into formaldehyde on heating. Used in fumigation.

PARALDEHYDE. $(CH_3CHO)_3$. *Polymer* (q.v.) of *acetaldehyde* (q.v.). Liquid, b.p. 124° C. Used in medicine as a *hypnotic* (q.v.).

PARALLAX. Difference in direction, or a shift in the apparent position, of a body, due to a change in position of the observer.

PARALLAX, ANNUAL, OF A STAR. The angle between the direction in which a star appears as observed from the Earth, and the direction in which it would appear from the centre of the Sun.

PARALLEL BEAM OF LIGHT. A beam of light which neither converges nor diverges; theoretical concept of a beam of light from an infinitely great distance, so that the rays composing the beam may be considered to be parallel; e.g. light from the Sun.

PARALLEL, CONDUCTORS IN. Electrical conductors joined in parallel between two points A and B, so that each conductor joins A to B. If R_1, R_2, R_3, etc., are the resistances of the separate conductors, the total resistance R between A and B is given by the formula

$$\frac{1}{R} = \frac{1}{R_1} + \frac{1}{R_2} + \frac{1}{R_3} \ldots \text{etc. See Fig. 10.}$$

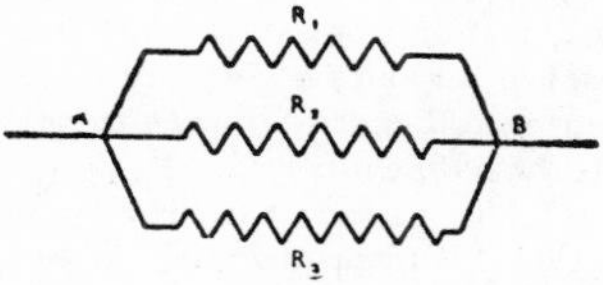

FIG. 10.

PARALLELEPIPED. Solid figure having six faces, all parallelograms; all opposite pairs of faces being similar and parallel.

PARALLELOGRAM. Plane, four-sided, rectilinear figure having its opposite sides parallel. It may be proved that in all parallelograms the opposite sides and angles are equal; the diagonals bisect each other; and the diagonals bisect the parallelogram. The *area* of a parallelogram is given by (a) the product of the base and the vertical height, and (b) the product of two adjacent sides and the *sine* of the angle between them. (See *trigonometrical ratios*.)

PARALLELOGRAM OF FORCES. If a particle is under the action of two forces which are represented in direction and magnitude by the two sides of a parallelogram drawn from a point, the resultant of the two forces is represented by the diagonal of the parallelogram drawn from that point.

PARALLELOGRAM OF VELOCITIES. If a body has two component velocities, represented in magnitude and direction by two adjacent sides of a parallelogram drawn from a point, the resultant velocity of the body is represented by the diagonal of the parallelogram drawn from that point.

PARAMAGNETIC. Substance possessing a *magnetic permeability* (q.v.) slightly greater than unity; i.e. possessing a small positive *magnetic susceptibility* (q.v.). The atoms of a paramagnetic substance possess a permanent *magnetic moment* (q.v.) due to unbalanced electron *spins* (q.v.) or unbalanced orbital motions of the electrons around the nucleus (see *atom, structure of*). Application of a magnetic field to such a substance tends to align the magnetic axes of the atoms in the direction of the field, giving the substance a resultant magnetic moment.

PARAMETER. A variable; the term is used in at least two different senses. 1. In two-dimensional co-ordinate geometry it is often convenient to express the variables (x, y) each in terms of a third variable t, such that x and y are functions of t; $x = f(t)$, $y = g(t)$. The equations are termed parametric equations, and t is a *parameter*. 2. A variable which may be kept constant while the effect of other variables is investigated.

PARIS GREEN, Schweinfurt green. Double salt of copper arsenite and acetate, $Cu(CH_3COO)_2 . 3Cu(AsO_2)_2$.

PARSEC. Astronomical unit of distance, corresponding to a parallax of one second of arc. 19×10^{12} miles, 3·3 light-years.

PARTIAL PRESSURES, Dalton's law of. The total pressure of a mixture of two or more gases or vapours is equal to the sum of the pressures that each component would exert if it was present alone and occupied the same volume as the whole mixture.

PASCAL'S LAW OF FLUID PRESSURES. Pressure applied anywhere to an enclosed body of fluid is transmitted equally in all directions. This pressure acts at right angles to every portion of the surface of the container, the force per unit area being uniform throughout.

PASCHEN'S LAW. The breakdown or 'sparking potential' for a pair of parallel electrodes situated in a gas, i.e. the potential which must be applied between them for sparking to occur, is a function only of the product of the pressure of the gas and the separation of the electrodes.

PASSIVE IRON. Iron made chemically unreactive by the surface action of concentrated nitric acid or other powerful oxidizing agent, which produces a protective film of iron oxide on the surface of the metal.

PASTEURIZATION. Partial sterilization, especially of milk; heating to a temperature sufficiently high to kill bacteria, but not spores of bacteria.

PATHOGENIC. Causing disease.

PAULI EXCLUSION PRINCIPLE. Each electron moving round the nucleus of a neutral atom can be characterized by values of four so-called *quantum numbers*. These quantum numbers are measures of such properties as the contribution to the atomic angular momentum of the electron, etc. The principle states that no two electrons in a neutral atom can have the same set of four quantum numbers. The principle is of great importance in the theoretical building-up of the *periodic table* (q.v.).

PEARL. Secretion consisting mainly of calcium carbonate, $CaCO_3$, produced by various molluscs.

PEARL ASH. *Potassium carbonate* (q.v.), K_2CO_3, made from wood ashes.

PEARL SPAR. See *dolomite*.

PEAT. Early stage in the formation of *coal* (q.v.) from vegetable matter. Accumulation of partly decomposed plant material, used as fuel.

PECTINS. Class of complex *polysaccharides* (q.v.) occurring in plants, particularly fruits. Solutions have the power of setting to a jelly; this is probably responsible for the 'setting' of jams.

PELTIER EFFECT. When an electric current flows across the junction between two different metals, a quantity of heat, proportional to the total charge crossing the junction, is evolved or absorbed, depending on the direction of the current. This effect is due to the existence of an electromotive force at the junction of the two metals.

PENCIL LEAD. A mixture of *graphite* (q.v.) with clay in various proportions, to give different degrees of hardness.

PENCIL OF LIGHT (phys.). A collection of *rays* (q.v.) proceeding from or towards a point.

PENDULUM, SIMPLE. Device consisting of a weight or 'bob' swinging on the end of a string or wire. In the case of an ideal pendulum, when the angle described by the pendulum is small, the string has negligible weight, and the mass of the pendulum is concentrated at one point, the time of one complete swing, T, is given by the formula $2\pi\sqrt{l/g}$, where l is the length of the string, and g the *acceleration due to gravity* (q.v.).

PENICILLIN. Class of chemically related *antibiotics* (q.v.) produced by the *Penicillium* mould. A very powerful agent for preventing the growth of several types of disease bacteria.

PENNYWEIGHT. 24 grains, 1/20 troy ounce. See *troy weight*.

PENTA-. Prefix denoting five, fivefold.

PENTANE. C_5H_{12}. Fifth member of the *paraffin series* (q.v.). Exists in three isomeric forms (see *isomerism*). Contained in light petroleum; n-pentane has b.p. 36° C.

PENTODE. *Thermionic valve* (q.v.) containing five electrodes: a cathode, an anode or plate, a control grid, and (between the two latter) two other grids called the screen grid and the suppressor grid.

PENUMBRA. Half-shadow, formed when an object in the path of rays from a large source of light cuts off a portion of the light. See *shadow*.

PEPSIN. Digestive *enzyme* (q.v.) produced in the stomach. Converts *proteins* (q.v.) into *peptones* (q.v.); acts only in an acid medium.

PEPTONES. Organic substances produced by the *hydrolysis* (q.v.) of *proteins* (q.v.) by the action of *pepsin* (q.v.) in the stomach. Soluble in water, absorbed by the body.

PER-. Prefix denoting, in chemical nomenclature, an excess of the normal amount of an element in a compound; e.g. peroxide.

PERCUSSION CAP. Device used in fire-arms. A small copper cylinder containing *fulminate of mercury* (q.v.) or other violent explosive which will explode on being struck, thus initiating the explosion of the main charge.

PERFECT GAS, ideal gas. Theoretical concept of a gas which would obey the *gas laws* (q.v.) exactly. Such a gas would consist of perfectly elastic molecules, the volume occupied by the actual molecules, and the forces of attraction between them, being zero or negligible.

PERI-. Prefix denoting around, about.

PERICLASE. Natural magnesium oxide, MgO.

PERIGEE. The Moon or the Sun are said to be in perigee when they are at their least distance from the Earth.

PERIHELION. The time of, or the point of, the nearest approach of a planet to the Sun.

PERIMETER. The distance all round a plane figure; e.g. the perimeter of a circle is its circumference.

PERIOD (phys.). If any quantity is a function of the time, and this function repeats itself exactly after constant time intervals T, the quantity is said to be periodic, and T is called the *period* of the function.

PERIOD OF DECAY. See *half-value period*.

PERIODIC LAW. The statement that 'the properties of the elements are in periodic dependence upon their atomic weights', published by Mendeleev in 1869. The law is brought out clearly when the elements are arranged in a *periodic table* (q.v.).

PERIODIC SYSTEM. Arrangement of the chemical elements in the *periodic table* (q.v.).

PERIODIC TABLE. An arrangement of the chemical elements in order of their *atomic numbers* (q.v.) in such a way as to demonstrate the *periodic law* (q.v.). In such an arrangement elements having similar properties occur at regular intervals and fall into groups of related elements. From the position of an element in the periodic table its properties may be predicted with a fair measure of success; Mendeleev was able to forecast the existence and properties of then undiscovered elements by means of his original table.

PERIPHERY. The external surface or boundary of a body; the circumference or *perimeter* (q.v.) of any closed figure.

PERISCOPE. Device for viewing objects which are above the eye-level of the observer, and so situated that direct vision is obstructed. Essentially consists of a long tube, at each end of which is a right-angled prism, so situated that by, or *total internal reflection* (q.v.) at the longest faces, light is turned through an angle of 90° by each prism. Thus light from a viewed object enters the observer's eye in a direction parallel to, but below, the original direction of the object.

PERMALLOY. Class of iron-nickel alloys with high *magnetic permeability* (q.v.). Used in parts of electrical machinery which are subject to alternating magnetic fields; causes only low losses of energy due to hysteresis.

PERMANENT GAS. Gas which cannot be liquefied by pressure alone; gas above its *critical temperature* (q.v.).

PERMANENT HARDNESS OF WATER. *Hardness* (q.v.) which is not destroyed by boiling the water. See *hard water*.

PERMANENT MAGNETISM. Magnetic properties of substances (especially steel) possessed without the influence of an external magnetic field.

PERMANGANATE. Salt of permanganic acid, $HMnO_4$. Term commonly applied to *potassium permanganate* (q.v.).

PERMEABILITY. A body is said to be permeable to a substance if it allows the passage of the substance through itself.

PERMEABILITY, MAGNETIC. See *magnetic permeability*.

PERMITTIVITY. See *specific inductive capacity*.

PERMUTATION (math.). An arrangement of a specified number of different objects. E.g. the six possible permutations of the digits 123 are 123, 132, 213, 231, 312, 321. The number of possible permutations of n objects if all are taken each time, denoted by ^nP_n, is *factorial* (q.v.) n. The number of permutations of n different objects taken r at a time,

$$^nP_r, \text{ is } \frac{\lfloor n}{\lfloor n-r}.$$

PEROXIDE. Oxide which yields hydrogen peroxide with an acid; term also applied to an oxide which contains more oxygen than the normal oxide of an element.

PEROXIDE OF HYDROGEN. See *hydrogen peroxide*.

PERPENDICULAR. At right angles; a straight line making an angle of 90° with another line or plane.

PERPETUAL MOTION. Concept of a machine which, once set in motion, will go on for ever without receiving energy. It is impossible to make a machine which will go on for ever and be able to do work, i.e. create energy without receiving energy from outside.

PERSISTENCE OF VISION. The sensation of light, as interpreted by the brain, persists for a brief interval after the actual light stimulus is removed; successive images, if they follow one another sufficiently rapidly, produce a continuous impression. Use is made of this in the cine-projector.

PERSONAL EQUATION. Time interval or lag peculiar to a person between the perception and recording of any event. In many physical observations an error is introduced by the time-lag between the actual occurrence of the observed event, its perception by the observer, and its recording.

PETRIFACTION. Turning of organic structures, such as trees, into a stony or mineral structure. Generally caused by dissolved hydrated silica, SiO_2, penetrating into the pores and gradually losing its water.

PETROL, gasoline. Complex mixture consisting mainly of *hydrocarbons* (q.v.), such as hexane, heptane and octane; other fuels and special ingredients are often added.

PETROLATUM, petroleum jelly, 'Vaseline'. Purified mixture of hydrocarbons; semi-solid whitish or yellowish mass.

PETROLEUM, mineral oil. Natural mixture of *hydrocarbons* (q.v.) and other organic compounds. Composition of various petroleums varies according to source; e.g. American petroleum contains a high proportion of *paraffins* (q.v.) while Russian petroleum is rich in *cyclic hydrocarbons* (q.v.). *Fractional distillation* (q.v.) yields petrol, paraffin oil, lubricating oil, Vaseline and paraffin wax.

PETROLEUM ETHER. Mixture of the lower hydrocarbons of the *paraffin series* (q.v.) consisting mainly of pentane and hexane. B.p. 30° C.–70° C.

PETROLOGY. The study of the origin, structure and composition of rocks.

PEWTER. Alloy of approximately 4 parts of tin to 1 of lead, with small amounts of antimony.

p_H **VALUE.** Measure of the *hydrogen-ion concentration* (q.v.), and hence of the acidity or alkalinity of a solution, expressed on a scale of numbers ranging from 0 for a solution containing 1 gram-ion of hydrogen ions per litre, corresponding to extreme acidity, to 14 for a solution containing 1 gram-ion of hydroxyl ions per litre.

PHARMACOGNOSY. Knowledge or study of drugs.

PHARMACOLOGY. Study of the action of chemical substances upon animals and man.

PHARMACOPHORE. The portion of a molecule of a substance which is regarded as determining the special physiological action of the substance.

PHARMACY. The preparation and dispensing of drugs and medicines.

PHASE (chem.). Separate part of a heterogeneous body or system. E.g. a mixture of ice and water is a two-phase system, while a solution of salt in water is a system of one phase.

PHASE (phys.). Points in the path of a *wave motion* (q.v.) are said to be points of equal phase if the displacements at those points at any instant are exactly similar; i.e. of the same magnitude and varying in the same manner.

PHASE RULE. $F + P = C + 2$. For a heterogeneous system in equilibrium, the sum of the number of *phases* (q.v.) plus the number of *degrees of freedom* (q.v.) is equal to the number of *components* (q.v.), plus two. E.g. with ice, water and water vapour in equilibrium, the number of phases is 3, the number of components 1, and hence the number of degrees of freedom is 0; the system is said to be *invariant*, since no single variable can be changed without causing the disappearance of one phase from the system.

PHENOL, carbolic acid. C_6H_5OH. White crystalline solid, m.p. 41° C., with a characteristic 'carbolic' smell. Soluble in water, corrosive and poisonous. Used as a disinfectant and in the manufacture of plastics and dyes.

PHENOLPHTHALEIN. $C_{20}H_{14}O_4$. Colourless crystalline solid, m.p. 261° C. Solution in alcohol turns a deep purple-red in the presence of alkalies, and is used as an *indicator* (q.v.). Also used in dye manufacture and as a laxative.

PHENOLS, THE. Class of organic compounds of the aromatic or benzene series; *hydroxy-derivatives* (q.v.) of the hydrocarbons of the benzene series; correspond to the alcohols in the aliphatic series.

PHENYL. The univalent radical C_6H_5.

PHLOGISTON THEORY. A theory of *combustion* (q.v.) which was generally accepted during the eighteenth century until refuted by Lavoisier. All combustible substances were supposed to be composed of phlogiston, which escaped on burning, and a calx or ash, which remained. Replacement of phlogiston into the calx would restore the original substance.

PHON. A unit of loudness, used in measuring the intensity of sounds. The loudness, in phons, of any sound is equal to the intensity in *decibels* (q.v.) of a sound of frequency 1000 which seems as loud to the ear as the given sound.

PHOSGENE, carbonyl chloride. $COCl_2$. Colourless, poisonous gas with a penetrating smell resembling musty hay. Used extensively as a poison gas during 1915–1918.

PHOSPHATE. Salt of phosphoric acid, H_3PO_4. Phosphates are used as *fertilizers* (q.v.) to rectify a deficiency of phosphorus in the soil.

PHOSPHINE. PH_3. Colourless, inflammable poisonous gas with an unpleasant smell.

PHOSPHOR BRONZE. Alloy of copper (80%–95%), tin (5%–15%), and phosphorus (0.25%–2.5%). Hard, tough and elastic.

PHOSPHORESCENCE. Property of shining after exposure to light.

PHOSPHORIC ACID. H_3PO_4. Crystalline, very soluble solid; m.p. 41° C.; commonly met with as a thick, syrupy liquid. Strong tribasic acid.

PHOSPHORUS. P. Element. A.W. 30.975. At. No. 15. Occurs in several *allotropic forms* (q.v.), white phosphorus and red phosphorus being the commonest. The former is a waxy white, very inflammable and poisonous solid, m.p. 44° C. Red phosphorus is a non-poisonous, dark red powder, not very inflammable. The element occurs only in the combined state, mainly as calcium phosphate, $Ca_3(PO_4)_2$. Extracted by heating with coke and silica (sand) in an electric furnace, and distilling off the phosphorus. Essential to life; calcium phosphate is the main constituent of animal bones. Compounds are used as *fertilizers* (q.v.).

PHOT. Unit of illumination; an illumination of one *lumen* (q.v.) per square centimetre.

PHOTOCHEMICAL REACTIONS. Chemical reactions which are initiated, assisted or accelerated by exposure to light. E.g. hydrogen and chlorine combine explosively on exposure to sunlight but only slowly in the dark.

PHOTO-CONDUCTIVE EFFECT. A *photo-electric effect* (q.v.) in which the electrical conductivity of certain substances, notably selenium, increases with the intensity of the light to which the substance is exposed.

PHOTO-ELECTRIC CELL. Device used for the detection and measurement of light. The cell may depend for its action upon (1) the normal *photo-electric effect* (q.v.); the cell is then called a photo-emissive cell;

(2) the *photo-voltaic effect* (q.v.) (rectifier or barrier layer cell); or (3) the *photo-conductive effect* (q.v.) (conductivity cell). Photo-emissive cells consist of two electrodes, a plane cathode coated with a suitable photo-sensitive material, and an anode which is maintained at a positive potential with respect to the cathode and which attracts the photo-electrons liberated by the latter. These electrodes are arranged in an envelope which is either evacuated, or, for greater sensitivity, contains a gas at low pressure. The current passing through the cell is a measure of the light intensity incident on the cathode. For rectifier or barrier cells, the potential difference developed across the boundary gives rise to a current when the faces of the cell are connected externally. This current can be measured directly by suitable means such as a galvanometer. Rectifier cells require no external source of E.M.F. and are very convenient for photographic exposure meters, etc. The conductivity cell is simply an arrangement for measuring the resistance of a layer of material, usually selenium, which shows the photo-conductive effect.

PHOTO-ELECTRIC EFFECT. In general, any effect arising as a result of a transfer of energy from light incident on a substance to electrons in the substance. The term is normally restricted to one type of the effect, namely the emission of electrons by substances when irradiated with light of a frequency greater than a certain minimum *threshold frequency* (q.v.). Electrons liberated in this way are called *photo-electrons*, and constitute a *photo-electric current* when the system is included in a suitable circuit.

PHOTO-ELECTRONS. See *photo-electric effect*.

PHOTO-VOLTAIC EFFECT. A *photo-electric effect* (q.v.) in which light falling on a specially prepared boundary between certain pairs of substances (e.g. copper and cuprous oxide) produces a potential difference across the boundary.

PHOTOGRAPHY. By means of a system of lenses in the *camera* (q.v.) an image of the object to be photographed is thrown for a definite length of time on to a plate or film made of glass, celluloid, or other transparent material and covered with an emulsion containing silver bromide, AgBr, or silver chloride, AgCl. The effect of this exposure of the film is to make the silver compound easily *reduced* (see *reduction*) to metallic silver by the chemical action of *developers* (q.v.); these produce a black deposit of fine particles of metallic silver on those portions of the film which had been exposed to light, thus giving a negative image. *Fixing* (q.v.) consists of the chemical action of sodium thiosulphate, $Na_2S_2O_3$, ('hypo'), and other reagents on the unchanged silver salts to give a soluble compound, which is then washed out with water, leaving a negative which is free of light-sensitive silver salts. By placing the finished negative over a piece of sensitive paper similar to film, and exposing to light, the silver salts in the paper are affected in a similar way to those in the original film; those portions of the negative which were darkest let through least light, and thus give the whitest portions on the developed paper. The negative image is thus again reversed, and a correct image or photograph is obtained on the paper, which is then fixed and washed as before.

PHOTOMETER. Instrument for comparing the *luminous intensity* (q.v.) of sources of light.

PHOTON. *Quantum* (q.v.) of radiant energy.

PHOTOSPHERE. The visible, intensely luminous portion of the Sun.

PHOTOSYNTHESIS. The formation of *carbohydrates* (q.v.) from carbon dioxide, CO_2, and water in the presence of sunlight by green plants containing *chlorophyll* (q.v.) according to the equation

$$6CO_2 + 6H_2O = C_6H_{12}O_6 + 6O_2.$$

It is held that the catalytic action of the chlorophyll (see *catalysis*) enables the plant to reduce carbon dioxide to formaldehyde, HCHO, which then rapidly polymerizes (see *polymerization*) to sugar.

PHYSICAL CHANGE. Any change in a body or substance which does not involve an alteration in its chemical composition.

PHYSICS. The study of the properties of matter and energy.

PHYSIOLOGY. The study of the functioning of the various organs of living beings.

PHYTAMINS. See *auxins*.

PI, π. Symbol for the ratio of the circumference of any *circle* (q.v.) to its diameter. $3 \cdot 14159 \ldots$ (Approximately $22/7$).

PICRIC ACID, trinitrophenol. $C_6H_2(NO_2)_3OH$. Bright yellow crystalline solid, m.p. $122°$ C. Explosive, poisonous. Formerly used as an explosive (see *lyddite*), as a dye, and (in solution) for treating burns.

PIEZO-ELECTRIC EFFECT. A property of certain *asymmetric* (q.v.) crystals. When such crystals are subjected to a pressure, charges of positive and negative electricity are produced on opposing faces; the signs of these charges are reversed if the pressure is replaced by a tension. The *inverse piezo-electric effect* occurs if such crystals are subjected to an electric potential, an alteration in size of the crystal taking place.

PIG-IRON, cast iron. Impure form of iron obtained from iron ores by the *blast furnace* (q.v.) process.

PIGMENT. Coloured substance which, when applied to a surface, colours the surface. Distinct from a dye, which penetrates the fibres or tissues of the surface; in general, pigments are insoluble materials which may be removed by mechanical means.

PIGMENT COLOUR, body colour. The colour of most natural objects is due to the differential absorption by the substance of the different wave-lengths (i.e. colours) present in the incident white light. The incident light penetrates a small distance into the substance, undergoes this absorption and is then diffusely reflected out again. The colour the body appears is determined by the wave-lengths absorbed the least. Thus, a substance which absorbs chiefly the red and yellow will appear blue. See also *surface colour*.

PILE, VOLTAIC. See *voltaic pile*.

PINK SALT. Ammonium chlorostannate, $(NH_4)_2SnCl_6$. Used as a *mordant* (q.v.) in dyeing.

PINKING. See *knocking*.

PIPETTE. Glass tube with the aid of which a definite volume of liquid may be transferred.

PITCH. Name given to numerous hard, dark substances which melt to viscous, tarry liquids; applied to the residue from the *destructive distillation* (q.v.) of wood and coal-tar, to *asphalt* (q.v.), various bitumens, etc.

PITCH OF A NOTE. Measure of the *frequency* (q.v.) of vibration of the source producing the note; a high frequency produces a note of high pitch. See *sound*.

PITCH OF A SCREW. The distance between adjoining crests of the thread, measured parallel to the axis of the screw.

PITCHBLENDE. Natural ore consisting mainly of uranium oxide, U_3O_8. Occurs in Saxony, Bohemia, East Africa and Colorado. Contains small amounts of *radium* (q.v.), of which it is the principal source.

PLANCK'S CONSTANT, h. The universal constant connecting the frequency of a radiation with its *quantum* (q.v.) of energy. The value of the quantum in ergs is equal to the product $h\nu$, where ν is the frequency of the radiation in cycles per sec. $h = 6.624 \times 10^{-27}$ erg. sec.

PLANE (math.). A flat surface; mathematically defined as a surface containing all the straight lines passing through a fixed point and also intersecting a straight line in space.

PLANE-POLARIZED LIGHT. See *polarization of light*.

PLANETOIDS. *Asteroids* (q.v.).

PLANETS. Heavenly bodies revolving in definite orbits about the Sun. Mercury, Venus, the Earth, Mars, Jupiter, Saturn, Uranus, Neptune and Pluto.

PLASMOLYSIS. The effect of *osmosis* (q.v.) on cells of living organisms. A cell placed in a solution which is of a greater molecular concentration than (i.e. is *hypertonic* to) the contents of the cell becomes *plasmolyzed;* the water in the cell sap flows out through the cell wall and the cell contents contract.

PLASTER OF PARIS. Powdered calcium sulphate, $2CaSO_4.H_2O$, obtained by heating *gypsum* (q.v.) to 120° C.–130° C. With water, sets and hardens.

PLASTICIZERS. Substances added to *plastics* (q.v.) to improve their plastic properties; i.e. to make them softer, more flexible, etc.

PLASTICS. Many different definitions have been given. In general, the term may be taken to cover materials which are stable in normal use, but which at some stage of their manufacture are plastic, and can be shaped or moulded by heat, pressure, or both. Most plastics are polymers (see *polymerization*), and are classified into *thermoplastic* and *thermosetting* (q.v.) materials.

PLATINIZED ASBESTOS. *Asbestos* (q.v.) in the fibres of which a black deposit of finely-divided platinum has been formed. Used as a *catalyst* (q.v.).

PLATINOID. Alloy of 60% copper, 24% zinc, 14% nickel and 2% wolfram.

PLATINUM. Pt. Element. A.W. 195·23. At. No. 78. Hard, silvery-white, ductile and malleable metal. S.G. 21·45. M.p. 1773·5° C. Very resistant to heat and acids. Coefficient of expansion very nearly equal to that of glass. Occurs as the metal, alloyed with osmium, iridium and similar metals. Used for electrical contacts, scientific apparatus, as a catalyst (see *platinized asbestos*) and in jewellery.

PLUMBAGO, black-lead, *graphite* (q.v.). Natural *allotropic form* (q.v.) of carbon.

PLUTO. Planet with its orbit outside that of Neptune. Discovered in 1930. Mean distance from the Sun,3, 671 million miles. Siderea! period ('year') 248·4 years. Mass approximately that of the Earth. Surface temperature probably below — 200° C.

PLUTONIUM. Pu. At. No. 94. *Transuranic element* (q.v.). Different *isotopes* (q.v.) of plutonium can be produced by suitable *nuclear reactions* (q.v.). The isotope $_{94}Pu^{239}$ is produced in the *atomic pile* (q.v.) and is of considerable importance since it undergoes *nuclear fission* (q.v.) when bombarded by slow neutrons.

POINT SOURCE OF LIGHT. Theoretical concept of a source of light in which all the light is emitted from a single point.

POISE. Unit of *viscosity* (q.v.) in C.G.S. units.

POISEUILLE'S EQUATION. The volume V of a liquid flowing through a cylindrical tube per second is given by the equation $V = \dfrac{\pi p a^4}{8 l \eta}$, where p is the pressure difference between two points on the axis of the tube at a distance l apart, η is the coefficient of *viscosity* (q.v.) and a is the radius of the tube. The result assumes uniform *streamline flow*, and also that the liquid in contact with the walls of the tube is at rest.

POISSON'S RATIO. The ratio of the lateral strain to the longitudinal strain in a stretched wire. Given by the ratio of d/D to l/L, where D = original diameter, L = original length, d = decrease in diameter, and l = increase in length.

POLAR CO-ORDINATES. The position of any point P lying in a plane can be completely determined by (1) its distance, r, from any selected point O in the plane, termed the *origin*, and (2) the angle θ which the line joining P to O (called the *radius vector*) makes with any co-planar reference line passing through O. The angle is taken as positive when measured anti-clockwise from the reference line. The polar co-ordinates of the point P are r and θ, denoted by (r, θ).

POLAR MOLECULE. A molecule, the configuration of charge in which constitutes a permanent electric *dipole* (q.v.).

POLARIMETER. Apparatus for measuring the rotation of the plane of vibration of polarized light by optically active substances. See *polarization of light* and *optical activity*.

POLARISCOPE. See *polarimeter*.

POLARIZATION, ANGLE OF. The angle of reflection from a *dielectric* (q.v.) medium, e.g. glass, at which the reflected ray is completely polarized, the plane of vibration being at right angles to the plane of incidence.

POLARIZATION, ELECTRIC. See *electric polarization*.

POLARIZATION, ELECTROLYTIC. Increase in the electrical resistance of an electrolyte due to various causes; chiefly associated with the accumulation of gaseous molecules on the electrodes, where they are liberated.

POLARIZATION OF LIGHT. Ordinary light consists of electric (E) and magnetic (H) vibrations taking place in all possible planes containing the ray, the vibrations themselves being at right angles to the direction of the light path; i.e. light is a *transverse wave motion*. For each E vibration the associated H vibration takes place in a plane at right angles to it. In *plane-polarized light*, the E vibrations are confined to one plane, called the *plane of vibration*, and hence the associated H vibrations are also confined to one plane, the plane at right angles to this, called the *plane of polarization*. See also *circularly* and *elliptically polarized light*.

POLAROID. Trade name of thin transparent films which produce plane-polarized light on transmission. Consist of thin sheets of cellulose nitrate packed with ultra-microscopic doubly-refracting crystals with their *optic axes* (q.v.) parallel. The crystals produce plane-polarized light by differential absorption of the ordinary and extraordinary rays.

POLE, MAGNETIC. See *magnetic pole*.

POLE OF MIRROR. See *mirrors, spherical*.

POLE STRENGTH. See *magnetic pole strength*.

POLONIUM. Po. Radium-F. Radioactive element decaying by alpha-particle emission. A.W. 210. At. No. 84. Forms a stage in the radio-active disintegration of radium.

POLY-. Prefix denoting many, several, numerous.

POLYBASIC. Acid containing more than one atom of *acidic hydrogen* (q.v.) in a molecule.

POLYGON. Plane figure bounded by straight lines.

POLYGON OF FORCES. If any number of forces, acting on a particle, can be represented in magnitude and direction by the sides of a polygon taken in order, the forces will be in equilibrium.

POLYHEDRON. A solid figure having polygons for its faces. A regular polyhedron has all its faces equal in all respects; the five possible types of regular polyhedra are: (1) *tetrahedron*, 4 triangular faces;

(2) *cube*, 6 square faces; (3) *octahedron*, 8 triangular faces; (4) *dodeca-hedron*, 12 five-sided faces; (5) *icosahedron*, 20 triangular faces.

POLYMER. Product of *polymerization* (q.v.).

POLYMERIZATION. Originally understood to be the chemical union of two or more molecules of the same compound to form larger molecules, resulting in the formation of a new compound of the same *empirical formula* (q.v.) but of greater molecular weight. E.g. paraldehyde, $(CH_3CHO)_3$, is formed by the polymerization of acetaldehyde, CH_3CHO, and each molecule of the *polymer* is made up of three molecules of the acetaldehyde *monomer*. The meaning of the term has been extended to cover (1) *addition polymerization*, in which the molecule of the polymer is a multiple of the monomer molecule, as in the case of paraldehyde; (2) *condensation polymerization*, in which the monomer molecules are joined by *condensation* (q.v.) into a polymer molecule, which differs in empirical formula from the monomer; and *co-polymerization*, in which the polymer molecule is built up from two or more different kinds of monomer molecules. Many important products, such as plastics and textile fibres, consist of polymeric substances, either natural (e.g. *cellulose*, q.v.) or synthetic (e.g. *nylon*, q.v.).

POLYMORPHISM. The existence of the same substance in more than two different crystalline forms.

POLYSACCHARIDES. Large class of natural *carbohydrates* (q.v.). Molecules are derived from the *condensation* (q.v.) of several, frequently very many, molecules of simple sugars (*monosaccharides*, q.v.). Class includes cellulose and starch.

POLYTHENE, polyethylene, 'Alkathene'. Tough, waxy *thermoplastic* (q.v.) material, made by the addition *polymerization* (q.v.) of ethylene, C_2H_4. Used as an insulating material and for many other purposes where a flexible, chemically resistant plastic material is required.

PORCELAIN. Hard, white material made by the firing of a mixture of pure kaolin (china clay) with felspar and quartz, or with other materials containing silica.

POSITION CIRCLE. Circle with centre at an observed point and radius such that the circumference passes through the place of observation. The portion of the circumference near the place of observation approximates to a *position line* (q.v.) if the radius is large.

POSITION LINE. A line of position on which the observer is situated at a given time. The intersection of two position lines, determined at the same time, fixes the position of the observer.

POSITIVE (math., phys.). In any convention of signs, regarded as being counted in the plus, or positive direction, as opposed to negative.

POSITIVE MAGNETIC POLE. The north-seeking pole of a magnet. See *magnetic pole*.

POSITIVE RAY ANALYSIS. *Positive rays* (q.v.) may be separated out into a mass spectrum by means of suitably disposed magnetic and electric fields. The deflection of any one ion in these fields is a function of the ratio of its mass to its charge, m/e. Such a spectrum can be made to affect a photographic plate, and will appear as a number of lines each corresponding to a definite value of m/e. *Isotopes* (q.v.) were first discovered in this way.

POSITIVE RAYS. Streams of *ions* (q.v.) bearing positive electric charges. May be produced by means of an electric discharge in a rarefied gas (see *discharge in gases*).

POSITRON. Elementary positive charged particle having the same mass as, and charge numerically equal to, that of the *electron* (q.v.). Positrons are emitted by many artificial radioactive elements and are produced in the process of 'pair production' (see *cosmic ray showers*).

POTASH. Potassium carbonate, K_2CO_3. Term also applied to potassium hydroxide, KOH (caustic potash) and, loosely, to potassium salts in general.

POTASSIUM, kalium. K. Element. A.W. 39·100. At. No. 19. Silvery-white, soft, highly reactive metal, strongly resembling sodium. S.G. 0·86, m.p. 62·3° C. Widely distributed in the form of various salts (e.g. *carnallite*, q.v.); essential to life; found in all living matter. Salts used as *fertilizers* (q.v.).

POTASSIUM BICARBONATE, bicarbonate of potash. $KHCO_3$. White, soluble salt.

POTASSIUM BROMIDE. KBr. White, crystalline salt, used in medicine and photography.

POTASSIUM CARBONATE, potash, carbonate of potash. K_2CO_3. White, very soluble, deliquescent salt.

POTASSIUM DICHROMATE, dichromate or bichromate of potash. $K_2Cr_2O_7$. Red, crystalline, soluble salt, m.p. 398° C., prepared from *chrome iron ore* (q.v.). Used as an oxidizing agent, and in the paint and dye industries.

POTASSIUM HYDROXIDE, caustic potash. KOH. White, deliquescent solid, m.p. 360·4° C., dissolves in water to give an alkaline solution.

POTASSIUM NITRATE, nitre, saltpetre. White, soluble crystalline salt, m.p. 336° C. When hot, acts as an oxidizing agent. Used in medicine, for pickling meat, and in gunpowder.

POTASSIUM PERMANGANATE, permanganate of potash. $KMnO_4$. Deep purple, crystalline, soluble salt, dissolves in water to give a purple solution which acts as a powerful oxidizing agent. Used as a disinfectant and in *volumetric analysis* (q.v.).

POTENTIAL. See *electric potential*.

POTENTIAL DIFFERENCE. If two points have a different *electric potential* (q.v.) there is said to be a potential difference (P.D.) between them; if the points are joined by an electric conductor, a current of electricity will flow between them. Defined as the work performed when a unit positive electric charge is moved from one of the points to the other. Also referred to as electromotive force, E.M.F. The practical unit of P.D. and E.M.F. is the *volt* (q.v.).

POTENTIAL ENERGY. *Energy* (q.v.) which a body possesses by virtue of its position. E.g. a coiled spring, or a vehicle at the top of a hill, possesses potential energy. Measured by the amount of *work* (q.v.) the body performs in passing from that position to a standard position in which the potential energy is considered to be zero.

POTENTIAL SERIES. See *electromotive series*.

POTENTIOMETER. An instrument for measuring direct current E.M.F. or potential differences, which does not draw current from the circuit containing the E.M.F. to be measured. In its simplest form consists of a uniform resistance *AB* (see Fig. 11) in the form of a single wire, connected to a source of E.M.F., *E*. A slide wire contact *C* is connected in series with a sensitive galvanometer *G*, to one terminal of the E.M.F. to be measured. The other terminal is connected to *A*, so that the E.M.F.'s across *XY* and *AC* are in opposition through *G*. Contact *C* is then adjusted until no current flows through the galvanometer. The required E.M.F. is then given by El_1/L, where *L* is the total length of the resistance *AB*, and l_1 is the length *AC* for zero current through *G*.

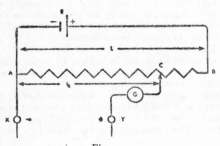

Fig. 11.

POUND. British unit of weight. The weight, in vacuo, of a platinum cylinder called the *Imperial standard pound*. 453·592 gm. Used as a unit of *force* (q.v.), the force of attraction of the Earth upon a mass of one pound; and as a unit of *mass* (q.v.).

POUNDAL. Unit of *force* (q.v.) in the foot-pound-second system of units. That force which, acting on a mass of 1 pound, will impart to it an acceleration of 1 foot per second per second. Approximately 1/32 of a force of 1 pound weight.

POWER (math.). A quantity successively multiplied by itself is said to be raised to a power, the magnitude of the power being the number of times that the quantity occurs in the multiplication. Thus $2 \times 2 \times 2 \times 2$ is 2 raised to the fourth power, 2 to the fourth, denoted as 2^4, 4 being the index or exponent.

POWER (phys.). Rate of doing work. Measured in units of *work* (q.v.) per unit time. See *watt, horse-power*.

POWER ALCOHOL. Industrial *ethyl alcohol* (q.v.) used as a fuel.

POWER FACTOR. The power factor of an electrical circuit is the ratio of the power dissipated in the circuit to the product of the electromotive force and current in the circuit.

PRASEODYMIUM. Pr. Element. A.W. 140·92. At. No. 59. See *rare earths*.

PRECESSIONAL MOTION. A rotating body is said to precess when, as a result of an applied *couple* (q.v.), the axis of which is at right angles to the rotation axis, the body turns about the third mutually perpendicular axis.

PRECIPITATE (chem.). An insoluble substance formed in a solution as the result of a chemical reaction.

PRECIPITATION (chem.). The formation of a *precipitate* (q.v.). A common type of precipitation, much used in chemical analysis and preparations, occurs by *double decomposition* (q.v.) when two solutions are mixed if each of the solutions contains one *radical* (q.v.) of an insoluble compound.

PRESBYOPIA. Long sight. Defect of vision normally occurring in elderly people. Subject is able to see distant objects clearly, but is unable to accommodate the eye to see near objects distinctly. Corrected by the use of convex spectacle lenses.

PRESSURE. The force per unit area acting on a surface.

PRESSURE, ATMOSPHERIC. See *atmosphere, the normal or standard*.

PRESSURE, UNITS OF. In C.G.S. units, 1 bar $= 10^6$ dynes/sq. cm. See also *atmosphere, the normal or standard*.

PRIMARY CELL, voltaic cell. Device, usually irreversible, for producing an *electromotive force* (q.v.) and delivering a current of electricity by chemical action. See *Daniell cell, Leclanché cell*.

PRIMARY COIL. The input coil of a *transformer* (q.v.) or *induction coil* (q.v.).

PRIMARY COLOURS (phys.). Red, green, and a bluish-violet. Any colour may be obtained by suitably combining light producing these (see *colour vision*). Term also used for the *pigment colours* (q.v.) red, yellow, and blue, which cannot be imitated by mixing any other pigment colours.

PRIME NUMBER (math.). Number possessing no factors (i.e. divisible by no whole number, other than itself and one).

PRINCIPAL FOCUS. See *mirrors, spherical; lens*.

PRINCIPAL PLANE (phys.). In a crystal exhibiting *double refraction* (q.v.), a principal plane is a plane containing the *optic axis* (q.v.) and either the ordinary ray (*principal plane of ordinary ray*) or the extra-ordinary ray (*principal plane of extra-ordinary ray*).

PRINCIPAL POINTS (phys.). Two points on the axis of a thick lens or combination lens system, such that if the object distance is measured from one and the image distance from the other, the equations obtained relating object-image distance, etc., are similar to those obtained for a thin *lens* (q.v.).

PRINCIPAL SECTION (phys.). A principal section of a crystal exhibiting *double refraction* (q.v.) is a plane passing through the *optic axis* (q.v.) and at right angles to one of the crystal surfaces.

PRINCIPLE OF SUPERPOSITION. See *Huygens' principle of superposition*.

PRISM (math.). Solid figure having two identically equal faces (bases) consisting of polygons in parallel planes; the other faces being parallelograms equal in number to the number of sides of one of the bases.

PRISM, optical. Triangular prism made of material transparent to the light being used; e.g. glass for visible light, quartz for ultra-violet rays and near infra-red rays.

PRISMATIC. In the shape of a prism.

PRISMATIC OPTICAL INSTRUMENTS. Instruments (field-glasses, etc.) in which a right-angled prism is used to invert the inverted image produced by the objective.

PROBABILITY, MATHEMATICAL. If an event can happen in a ways and fail in b ways, and, except for the numerical difference between a and b, is as likely to happen as to fail, the mathematical probability of its happening is $\dfrac{a}{a+b}$ and of its failing, $\dfrac{b}{a+b}$.

PRODUCER GAS. Mixture of carbon monoxide, CO, and nitrogen; formed by passing air over excess of red-hot coke, thus partially burning the coke.

PRODUCT (math.). The product of two or more quantities is the result of multiplying them together.

PROJECTILE. Body thrown or projected. If the projectile is discharged with a velocity v at an angle a to the horizontal, the following formulae hold true if the resistance of the air is neglected (g being the acceleration due to gravity):

Time to reach highest point of flight $= \dfrac{v \sin a}{g}$

Total time of flight $= \dfrac{2v \sin a}{g}$

Maximum height $= \dfrac{v^2 \sin^2 a}{2g}$

Horizontal range $= \dfrac{v^2 \sin 2a}{g}$

PROLATE SPHEROID. See *spheroid*.

PROMETHIUM. The element of At. No. 61.

PRONTOSIL. Organic compound derived from chrysoidine (an *azo dye*, q.v.) which has been used for destroying certain types of disease bacteria in the living body. The earliest used of the *sulphonamide* (q.v.) group of drugs.

PROOF SPIRIT. *Ethyl alcohol* (q.v.) containing 49·28% alcohol by weight, or 57·10% by volume, and having a specific gravity of 0·91976 at 60° F. Formerly defined as the weakest solution of alcohol which would fire gunpowder when brought into contact with it and ignited.

PROOF SPIRIT, DEGREES. The number of degrees under proof is the volume percentage of water in a solution regarded as containing *proof spirit* (q.v.) and water; degrees over proof is the volume increase obtained when 100 volumes of the spirit are diluted with sufficient water to obtain proof spirit.

PROPANE. C_3H_8. Third hydrocarbon of the *paraffin series* (q.v.). Inflammable gas.

PROPER MOTION OF A STAR. Its real change of place arising from the actual motion of the star itself.

PROPORTION (math.). An equality between two *ratios* (q.v.). If $a/b = c/d$, the four quantities a, b, c, d are in proportion.

PROPYL. The univalent *alkyl radical* (q.v.). C_3H_7.

PROTARGOL. Powder containing finely-divided silver and protein; with water, forms a colloidal solution of silver.

PROTEASES, proteinases. Group of *enzymes* (q.v.) capable of breaking up *proteins* (q.v.) into *amino-acids* (q.v.), of building up amino-acids into proteins, and of substituting one amino-acid for another in protein molecules. Occur in all living tissues; conduct the processes of protein *metabolism* (q.v.) in the living organism.

PROTECTIVE FOODS. Foods which protect against *deficiency diseases* (q.v.).

PROTEINS. Class of organic compounds of very high molecular weights (18,000–10,000,000) which compose a large part of all living matter. Protein molecules invariably contain the elements carbon, hydrogen, oxygen and nitrogen; often also sulphur and sometimes phosphorus. *Hydrolysis* (q.v.) of proteins yields a mixture of various *amino-acids* (q.v.). Proteins are essential in food; their function is to be built into the body-tissues. The usefulness of a protein in food depends upon the nature of the amino-acids from which the particular protein is built up, since some amino-acids necessary to the human body cannot be made within the body. Typical proteins are *albumin* (q.v.) in egg-white; *casein* (q.v.) in cheese; foods containing a high percentage of proteins include cheese, lean meat, fish and eggs.

PROTEIN-SPARERS. *Proteins* (q.v.) may be used by the body to supply energy by being oxidized, in the same way as *carbohydrates* (q.v.) and fats; this, however, causes the proteins so used to be lost for their more important function of body-building. Carbohydrates and fats when eaten with proteins in a food thus act as *protein-sparers*, providing energy while the proteins are utilized for building tissue.

PROTEOLYTIC, proteoclastic. Having the power of decomposing or hydrolyzing *proteins* (q.v.).

PROTOACTINIUM. Pa. Radioactive element. A.W. 231. At. No. 91. See *radioactivity*.

PROTON. Positively-charged particle having mass approximately 1840 times greater than that of the electron (i.e. $1\cdot00757$ *atomic mass units*, q.v.) and charge numerically equal to that of the electron. Constituent of all atomic nuclei. See *atom, structure of*.

PROTOPLASM. Highly complex colloidal substance containing protein-like materials; essential constituent of all living cells.

PROTYLE. Primary 'element' from which atoms of all other elements were supposed to be formed; considered by Prout (1816) to be hydrogen.

PRUSSIAN BLUE. Potassium ferric ferrocyanide, $KFe[Fe(CN)_6]$. Deep blue substance obtained by the action of a ferric salt on potassium ferrocyanide.

PRUSSIC ACID. Solution of *hydrocyanic acid* (q.v.), HCN. Intensely poisonous.

PSYCHROMETRY. Measurement of the humidity of the atmosphere.

PTOMAINES. Name given to a class of extremely poisonous organic compounds formed during the putrefaction of *proteins* (q.v.) of animal origin. Food poisoning, frequently misnamed ptomaine poisoning, is almost invariably due to causes other than the ptomaines.

PTYALIN. *Enzyme* (q.v.) in the saliva; serves to convert starch into sugar.

PUDDLING PROCESS. Preparation of nearly pure *wrought iron* (q.v.) from cast iron which contains a high percentage of carbon. The cast iron is heated with haematite, Fe_2O_3, the oxygen in which oxidizes the carbon.

PURINES. Class of organic chemical compounds derived from *uric acid* (q.v.).

PURITY, CHEMICAL. A substance is theoretically pure if it contains no trace of any other substance; in practice the determination of purity is limited by the accuracy of the analytical methods employed; a chemically pure substance is generally understood to contain no detectable impurities. A constant melting point, boiling point and crystalline form are amongst the criteria of purity of a substance.

PURPLE OF CASSIUS. A purple pigment, consisting of a mixture of colloidal gold and stannic acid. Used for making ruby glass.

PUTREFACTION. Chemical decomposition, by the action of bacteria, of the bodies of dead animals and plants; especially the decomposition of *proteins* (q.v.) with the production of offensive substances.

PUTTY. Material composed of powdered chalk mixed with linseed oil.

PUTTY POWDER. Impure tin oxide, SnO_2.

PYKNOMETER. Apparatus for determining the density and coefficient of expansion of a liquid. A glass vessel which is graduated to hold a definite volume of liquid at a given temperature. By weighing it full of liquid at different temperatures, the variations in density, and therefore the apparent expansion, may be found.

PYRAMID (math.). Solid figure having a polygon for one of its faces (termed the *base*), the other faces being triangles with a common vertex. The volume of a pyramid is one-third of the product of the area of the base and the vertical height.

PYRENE. 1. The hydrocarbon $C_{16}H_{10}$, yellow crystals, m.p. 149° C., found in coal-tar. 2. Fire extinguisher consisting of carbon tetrachloride, CCl_4.

PYRIDINE. C_5H_5N. *Heterocyclic* (q.v.) organic compound. Colourless liquid with an unpleasant smell. B.p. 115° C. Occurs in *bone-oil* (q.v.) and coal-tar. Used for making methylated spirit unpalatable; compounds derived from it are used in medicine.

PYRITES. Natural sulphides of certain metals. Iron pyrites is FeS_2; copper pyrites ('fools' gold') is $CuFeS_2$.

PYRO-. Prefix denoting fire, strong heat. In chemical nomenclature denotes a substance obtained by heating; e.g. pyroboric acid, obtained by heating boric acid.

PYROELECTRICITY. The property of certain crystals, e.g. tourmaline, of acquiring electric charges on opposite faces when the crystals are heated.

PYROGALLOL, pyrogallic acid. 1, 2, 3-trihydroxybenzene. $C_6H_3(OH)_3$. White, crystalline soluble solid, m.p. 132° C. Powerful reducing agent; alkaline solution rapidly absorbs oxygen. Used in photographic developers and in gas analysis for the estimation of oxygen.

PYROLIGNEOUS ACID. Watery liquid obtained by the *destructive distillation* (q.v.) of wood. Contains acetic acid, CH_3COOH, methyl alcohol, CH_3OH, acetone, $(CH_3)_2CO$, and small amounts of other organic compounds.

PYROLUSITE. Natural manganese dioxide, MnO_2. Black crystalline solid, S.G. 4·8; principal ore of *manganese* (q.v.).

PYROLYSIS. Chemical decomposition by the action of heat.

PYROMETERS. Instruments for measuring high temperatures. The four main types are: (1) platinum resistance thermometers, which make use of the increased electrical resistance of platinum wire with rise in temperature; (2) thermo-electric thermometers, using the principle of the *thermocouple* (q.v.); (3) optical pyrometers, in which the temperature is estimated by the intensity of the light emitted by the body in a narrow wave-length range; and (4) radiation pyrometers, which detect the radiant heat energy from the hot body (see *radio-micrometer*).

PYROPHORIC ALLOYS. Alloys which emit sparks when scraped or struck, and are therefore used as 'flints' in lighters. See *misch metal; Auer metal*.

PYROTECHNICS. Fireworks.

PYTHAGORAS, THEOREM OF. In a right-angled triangle the square on the hypotenuse is equal to the sum of the squares on the other two sides.

Q

Q-VALUE, nuclear energy change, nuclear heat of reaction. The net amount of energy released in a *nuclear reaction* (q.v.); usually expressed in million *electron-volts* (q.v.), *Mev*, per individual reaction.

QUADRANT, quarter-circle. *Sector* (q.v.) of a circle bounded by an arc and two radii at right angles.

QUADRATIC EQUATION. An *equation* (q.v.) involving the square or second power of the unknown quantity; satisfied by two values (known as roots) of the unknown quantity. Any quadratic equation may be written in the form $ax^2 + bx + c = 0$; the roots of this equation are given by the expression $x = \dfrac{-b \pm \sqrt{b^2 - 4ac}}{2a}$.

Thus any quadratic equation may be solved by substitution of the appropriate values in the above expression.

QUADRILATERAL. Plane figure bounded by four straight lines.

QUALITATIVE. Dealing only with the nature, and not the amounts, of the substances under consideration.

QUALITATIVE CHEMICAL ANALYSIS. Determination of the chemical nature of substances; identification of substances present in a mixture.

QUALITY OF SOUND. Most sounds are not 'pure'; i.e. they are composed of vibrations of more than one frequency. A note consists of a *fundamental*, of greatest intensity and lowest pitch; and several *overtones*, of much lesser intensity and of frequencies which are simple multiples of that of the fundamental. The various overtones produce a characteristic quality or *timbre* in the note.

QUANTITATIVE. Dealing with quantities as well as the nature of the substances under consideration.

QUANTITATIVE CHEMICAL ANALYSIS. Determination of the amounts of substances present, by chemical means.

QUANTUM. A definite amount of energy associated with *electromagnetic waves* (q.v.), e.g. light, X-rays, gamma-rays; dependent only on the frequency of the radiation; thus, if v is the frequency of the radiation, its quantum of energy is hv, where h is *Planck's constant* (q.v.).

QUANTUM THEORY. The body of theories, rules and processes of calculation which followed Planck's introduction of discontinuity into atomic physics and the theory of radiation. The quantum theory has now been superseded by *wave mechanics* (q.v.), which has been much more versatile in the explanation of physical phenomena and, being free of the *ad hoc* hypotheses which were necessary in the quantum theory, is more satisfactory.

QUARTZ. Natural crystalline silica, SiO_2. Sometimes occurs in clear, colourless crystals ('rock crystal'); more frequently as a white, opaque mass.

QUARTZ CLOCK. A clock regulated by a quartz crystal which vibrates with a definite constant frequency under the effect of an alternating electric field tuned to this *resonance* (q.v.) frequency of the crystal. (See *piezo-electric effect*.) Much more accurate than a pendulum-regulated clock; used for astronomical and other very precise work.

QUARTER-WAVE PLATE. Plate of doubly refracting material cut parallel to the *optic axis* (q.v.) of the crystal, and of such a thickness that a phase difference of $\pi/2$ or $90°$ is introduced between the ordinary and extraordinary rays for light of a particular wave-length (usually sodium light). Plane-polarized light incident normally upon such a plate, with its plane of vibration making an angle of $45°$ with the optic axis, emerges from the plate *circularly polarized* (q.v.). A quarter-wave plate is often used in the analysis of polarized light.

QUARTERNARY AMMONIUM COMPOUNDS. Compounds of the general formula NR_4OH; theoretically derived from ammonium hydroxide, NH_4OH, by replacement of the hydrogen atoms by organic radicals.

QUENCHING OF STEEL. Rapid cooling by immersion into water or oil, to harden the steel.

QUICKLIME. Calcium oxide, CaO. Combines with water, with evolution of heat, to give slaked lime, calcium hydroxide, $Ca(OH)_2$. Used in mortar, etc.

QUICKSILVER. See *mercury*.

QUININE. $C_{20}H_{24}O_2N_2$. *Alkaloid* (q.v.) occurring in Cinchona bark. Colourless, crystalline solid with a bitter taste. Basic in chemical character, gives rise to salts. Used in medicine.

QUINQUEVALENT. Having a *valency* (q.v.) of five.

R

RACEMIC ACID, racemic tartaric acid, *dl*-tartaric acid. *Racemic form* (q.v.) of *tartaric acid* (q.v.).

RACEMIC FORM. Isomeric form of a substance which exhibits *stereo-isomerism* (q.v.). Consists of an *equimolecular mixture* (q.v.) of the two optically active forms. Such a racemic form is denoted by the letters *dl.*, e.g. *dl*-tartaric acid; it is optically inactive and is said to be *externally compensated*.

RADAR. A generic term covering a variety of electronic systems of direction-finding and navigation. The basic characteristic of all such systems is a very high frequency radio transmitter which sends out a *beam* (q.v.) of *electromagnetic waves* (q.v.) of very small wave-length, in the range of from a few centimetres to 1 metre, in the form of short pulses. Distant objects, e.g. aeroplanes, in the path of the beam reflect these pulses back to the transmitter where they are received. The direction in which the beam is being transmitted when this reflection is observed gives the direction of the object. The time taken for any one pulse to travel to the object and back is measured electronically.

A knowledge of the velocity with which electromagnetic waves travel in air gives the distance of the object from the transmitter.

RADIAN. Measure of angle; the angle subtended at the centre of a circle by an arc equal in length to the radius of the circle.

RADIATION. In general, the emission of any rays, wave motion or particles (e.g. alpha particles, beta particles, neutrons) from a source; usually applied to the emission of *electromagnetic waves* (q.v.).

RADIATION POTENTIAL, resonance potential. The energy (expressed in *electron-volts*, q.v.) necessary to transfer an electron from its normal position in an atom to some other possible position; i.e. to an *energy level* (q.v.) of greater energy.

RADICAL, radicle (chem.). A group of atoms, present in a series of compounds, which maintains its identity through chemical changes which affect the rest of the molecule. E.g. the ammonium radical, NH_4; ethyl, C_2H_5.

RADIOACTIVE EQUILIBRIUM. A state ultimately reached when a radio-active substance of slow decay (see *radioactivity*) yields a radioactive product on disintegration. This product may also decay to give a further radioactive substance, and so on. The amount of any of the daughter radioactive products present after equilibrium has been reached remains constant, the loss due to decay being counterbalanced by gain from the decay of the immediate parent.

RADIOACTIVE SERIES. See *radioactivity*.

RADIOACTIVE TRACING. Any two *isotopes* (q.v.) of an element are chemically identical. Thus, by introducing a small amount of a radio-active isotope, called a *tracer*, the course taken by the stable isotope of the same element can be followed or traced by detecting the course of the accompanying radioactive isotope by suitable means. This can be done in various ways ; e.g. *Geiger counter* (q.v.).

RADIOACTIVITY. The spontaneous disintegration of unstable atomic nuclei (see *atom, structure of*) to give more stable product nuclei, usually accompanied by the emission of charged particles (e.g. *alpha* or *beta particles*, q.v.) and *gamma rays* (q.v.). The most common types of radioactive change result in beta-particle emission and are (1) a neutron present in the unstable nucleus is converted into a proton with the emission of an electron and a *neutrino* (q.v.). The product nucleus is an *isotope* (q.v.) of an element of *atomic number* (q.v.) exceeding that of the original element by unity. (2) A proton present in the unstable nucleus is converted into a neutron with the emission of a *positron* (q.v.) and a neutrino. The resulting isotope has an atomic number one less than the original nucleus. Alpha-particles are emitted only by certain radioactive isotopes of the heavier elements. Alpha-particle emission results in a daughter nucleus of an atomic number smaller by two than that of the parent. Gamma-rays accompany the alpha or beta particles when the product nucleus is formed in an excited state.

Radioactive isotopes of the heavier elements occur naturally. Radioactive isotopes of practically every element can be made artificially by suitable *nuclear reactions* (q.v.), especially by submitting the elements to neutron bombardment in an *atomic pile* (q.v.). The number of atoms of a radioactive isotope decaying in unit time is proportional to the number of radioactive atoms present, the constant of proportionality being called the *transformation constant* (q.v.), a constant characteristic of the particular isotope considered (see also *half-value period*). The naturally occurring radioactive isotopes may be arranged in three radioactive series. Each isotope in such a series is the product of decay of the preceding isotope of the series.

The radiations emitted by radioactive isotopes are extensively used in the treatment of disease, as a means of following the course taken by elements in *radioactive tracing* (q.v.) and in many other applications.

RADIO-AUTOGRAPH. Image obtained by placing a thin biological or other specimen, containing a radioactive isotope (see *radioactivity*), in contact with a photographic plate, exposing for a suitable period and developing. The resulting image shows the distribution of the radioactive element in the specimen.

RADIOGRAPHY. The formation of images on fluorescent screens or photographic material by short wave-length radiation, such as *X-rays* and *gamma rays* (q.v.).

RADIOLOGY. The science of X-radiation and radioactivity.

RADIO-MICROMETER. Extremely sensitive instrument for measuring heat radiations. Consists of a *thermocouple* (q.v.) connected directly into a single copper loop forming the coil of a sensitive galvanometer (q.v.).

RADIO TELEGRAPHY, wireless telegraphy. Transmission of messages in morse code by means of *electromagnetic waves* (q.v.). The general principle is similar to that used in radio telephony (q.v.).

RADIO TELEPHONY, wireless telephony, 'radio'. Transmission of sound through the agency of *electromagnetic waves* (q.v.). The radio transmitter emits a continuous *carrier wave* (q.v.) of a definite frequency. The sound impulses are converted into electrical impulses by means of a *microphone* (q.v.); the carrier wave is modulated (see *modulation*) by having these impulses superimposed upon it. The receiver is tuned (see *tuning*) to the carrier wave. This received signal can then be amplified (high frequency amplification) and gives, after *rectification* (q.v.), a direct current which varies in amplitude in accordance with the sound impulses applied to the carrier wave. This current, usually after further (low frequency) amplification, is passed through a telephone receiver or loud-speaker, causing mechanical vibrations which produce sounds corresponding to those injected at the transmitter.

RADIO-THERAPY. The treatment of disease by means of radiation, particularly *X-rays* (q.v.) and techniques involving *radioactivity* (q.v.).

RADIUM. Ra. Naturally occurring radioactive element. A.W. 226.05.

At. No. 88. Very rare metal, chemically resembling barium. See *radioactivity*.

RADIUM EMANATION. See *radon*.

RADIUS. See *circle*.

RADIUS OF CURVATURE. Consider any point P on a curve S lying in a plane. A circle can be drawn with centre at a unique point O on the normal to S at P, such that the curve and the circle are tangential at P. The radius of this circle, OP, is the *radius of curvature* of the curve at P. The concept may be extended to a point on a three-dimensional curved surface. In this case, an infinite number of radii of curvature exist, corresponding to the infinite number of plane curves which can form the line of intersection of the curved surface and the plane containing the normal at P. Of these curves, two are unique, one having a maximum radius of curvature at P and the other a minimum. These two are called the principal radii of curvature at P.

RADIUS OF GYRATION. The *moment of inertia* (q.v.) I, of a body of mass M about a given axis can be expressed in the form $I = Mk^2$. k is called the radius of gyration about that axis.

RADIUS VECTOR (astr.). A line drawn from a central body (the focus) to a planet in any position in its orbit.

RADIUS VECTOR (math.). The position of any point P in space with respect to a given origin O may be completely defined by the direction and length of the line OP. This line is called the *radius vector* of the point P.

RADON. Rn. Radium emanation, niton. Element. A.W. 222. At. No. 86. Naturally occurring radioactive gas, the immediate disintegration product of radium; chemically belongs to the *inert gases* (q.v.).

RAINBOW. A colour effect produced by the *refraction* (q.v.) and internal reflection of sunlight in minute droplets of water in the air; the effect is visible only when the observer has his back to the Sun.

RAMAN EFFECT. When *monochromatic light* (q.v.) passes through a transparent medium, some of the light is scattered. If the *spectrum* (q.v.) of this scattered light is examined, it is found to contain, apart from light of the original wave-length, weaker lines differing from this by constant amounts. Such lines are called *Raman lines*, and are important in the study of molecular energy states.

RAMSDEN EYE-PIECE. *Eye-piece* (q.v.) consisting of two plano-convex lenses (curved surfaces inwards) of equal focal length f, and separated by a distance of $2/3 f$. The eye-piece has low spherical aberration, is fairly achromatic (see *aberration*) and is very useful when cross-wires or a scale are desired in the eye-piece.

RAOULT'S LAW. When a solute which does not dissociate (see *ionic hypothesis*) in solution is dissolved in a solvent to form a dilute solution, then (1) the ratio of the decrease in vapour pressure to the original vapour pressure is equal to N_1/N_2, N_1 and N_2 being the total numbers of molecules present of solute and solvent respectively; or, alternatively (2) the elevation of the boiling point of the solution above that of the pure solvent is proportional to N_1/N_2; or (3) the depression of the freezing point of the solution below that of the pure solvent is proportional to N_1/N_2. See *depression of freezing point; elevation of boiling point*.

RARE EARTH ELEMENTS, 'rare earths'. Group of metals, most of them very rare, closely resembling one another, and very similar to aluminium in many properties. They comprise the elements of atomic numbers 57 to 71. Occur in *monazite* (q.v.) and other rare minerals.

RARE GASES. See *inert gases*.

RATIO. The numerical relation one quantity bears to another of the same kind. E.g. 6 tons and 4 tons, and 30 and 20, are both in the ratio of 3 to 2.

RAY. Term to denote the rectilinear path along which any radiation, e.g. light, travels in any direction from a point in the source of the radiation. Loosely used to denote radiation of any kind.

RAYON. Formerly 'artificial silk', the term has been used to describe all types of man-made textile fibres, as distinct from those produced directly by plants (e.g. cotton) or animals (wool, silk). The use of the term *rayon* to include fibres not made from cellulose and its derivatives has not, however, been universally accepted. The two most important types of rayon from cellulose are (1) *viscose rayon*, made by forcing a solution of *viscose* (q.v.) through fine holes into a solution which decomposes the viscose to give threads of cellulose, and (2) *cellulose acetate rayon*, made by forcing a solution of *cellulose acetate* (q.v.) through fine holes into warm air and allowing the solvent to evaporate, thus leaving threads of cellulose acetate.

R.D.X. *Cyclonite* (q.v.).

REACTANCE of an alternating current circuit X. Quantity which, together with the resistance, makes up the impedance of a given circuit; given by the expression $X = wL - 1/wC$, where L is the *self-inductance* (q.v.) of the circuit, C the *capacity* (q.v.) and w is the angular frequency ($w = 2\pi n$, n being the frequency of the alternating current).

REACTION, CHEMICAL. See *chemical reaction*.

REACTIVE (chem.). Readily entering into chemical reactions; chemically active.

REAGENT. Chemical substance used to produce a chemical reaction.

REALGAR. Natural red arsenic disulphide, As_2S_2.

RÉAUMUR SCALE. Temperature scale in which the melting point of ice is taken as 0° R. and the boiling point of water as 80° R.

RECIPROCAL OF A QUANTITY. 1 divided by the quantity; e.g. the reciprocal of 5 is $\frac{1}{5}$.

RECIPROCAL PROPORTIONS, law of. See *chemical combination, laws of*.

RECTIFICATION (chem.). Purification of a liquid by *distillation* (q.v.).

RECTIFICATION (math.). The process of determining the length of a curve.

RECTIFICATION (phys.). Conversion of an alternating into a direct current. See *rectifier, rectifying valve*.

RECTIFIER (phys.). Device for transforming an alternating current into a direct one; consists of an arrangement which presents a much higher resistance to an electric current flowing in one direction than in the other. See *rectifying valve; crystal detector*.

RECTIFYING VALVE. The thermionic vacuum valve commonly used for rectification is the *diode* (q.v.). The valve will pass current only when the anode is at a positive potential with respect to the cathode. Hence if an alternating potential is applied to a circuit containing such a valve, a direct current will flow through the circuit.

RECTILINEAR. In a straight line; consisting of straight lines.

RECTILINEAR PROPAGATION OF LIGHT. To a first approximation light travels in straight lines, as is evident from the formation of *shadows* (q.v.) and other everyday experience; see, however, *diffraction*.

RED LEAD, minium. Pb_3O_4. Bright scarlet powder, used as a pigment, in glass manufacture, and as an oxidizing agent.

REDUCTION (chem.). Removal of oxygen or other *electronegative* (q.v.) atom or group from a compound; or the addition of hydrogen or other *electropositive* atom or group. The opposite process to oxidation. E.g. copper oxide is reduced by hydrogen to metallic copper, the hydrogen being oxidized to water.

REDUCED TEMPERATURE, PRESSURE and **VOLUME.** Ratios of the temperature, the pressure and the volume to the *critical temperature* (q.v.), *critical pressure* (q.v.) and *critical volume* (q.v.) respectively.

REFLECTION, ANGLE OF. The angle between a ray of light reflected from a surface, and the *normal* (q.v.) to the surface at that point.

REFLECTION OF LIGHT. Certain surfaces have the property of reflecting or returning rays of light which fall upon them, according to definite laws (see *reflection of light, laws of*).

REFLECTION OF LIGHT, LAWS OF. 1. The incident ray, the reflected ray, and the normal to the reflecting surface at the point of incidence lie in the same plane. 2. The angle between the incident ray and the normal (i.e. the angle of incidence) is equal to the angle between the reflected ray and the normal.

REFLECTION, TOTAL INTERNAL. See *total internal reflection*.

REFLEX ANGLE. Angle greater than 180° and less than 360°.

REFLUX. Flow back; e.g. a reflux condenser is a *condenser* (q.v.) used so that the vapour over a boiling liquid is condensed to a liquid which flows back into the vessel, so preventing its contents from boiling dry.

REFRACTION, ANGLE OF. The angle between the refracted ray and the normal to the surface at the point of *refraction* (q.v.).

REFRACTION, LAWS OF. 1. The incident ray, the refracted ray, and the normal to the surface of separation of the two media at the point of incidence lie in the same plane. 2. Snell's law. The ratio of the sine of the angle of incidence to the sine of the angle of refraction is a constant for any pair of media. (See *refractive index*.)

REFRACTION OF LIGHT. When a ray of light travels obliquely from one medium to another, it is bent or refracted at the surface separating the two media. The ray before refraction is termed the *incident ray;* on being refracted it becomes the *refracted ray.* A line perpendicular to the refracting medium at the point where the incident ray enters it is the *normal.* Glass, water, etc., cause the incident ray to be turned towards the normal when the ray enters from a medium less optically dense, such as air. Similar considerations apply to wave-motions other than light. See Fig. 12.

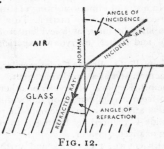

FIG. 12.

REFRACTIVE INDEX of a medium, μ. The ratio of the sine (see *trigonometrical ratios*) of the angle of incidence to the sine of the angle of refraction when light is refracted from a vacuum (or, to a very close approximation, from air) into the medium. This is equivalent to the fundamental definition: the ratio of the velocity of light in free space to that in the medium.

REFRACTOMETER. Apparatus for the measurement of the *refractive index* (q.v.) of a substance.

REFRACTORY (chem.). A material not damaged by heating to high temperatures.

REGELATION OF ICE. The melting point of ice is lowered by increased pressure; therefore ice near its melting point is melted by sufficient pressure, and solidification or *regelation* takes place again when the pressure is removed.

RELATIVE DENSITY. See *specific gravity.*

RELATIVE HUMIDITY, hygrometric state of the atmosphere. Can be defined either as (1) the ratio of the pressure of the water vapour actually present in the atmosphere to the pressure of the vapour which would be present if the vapour were saturated at the same temperature, or (2) the ratio of the mass of water vapour per unit volume of the air to the mass of water vapour per unit volume of saturated air at the same temperature. The numerical difference between the two is very small and can normally be neglected. The relative humidity is usually expressed as a percentage. Its value may be determined from a knowledge of the *dew-point* (q.v.), since the saturated vapour pressure at the dew-point is equal to the aqueous vapour pressure at the temperature of the experiment. The result is then obtained by reference to tables which give the saturated vapour pressure at different temperatures.

RELATIVITY, THEORY OF. A theory, formulated by Einstein, which recognizes the impossibility of determining absolute motion and leads to the concept of a four-dimensional space-time continuum. The *special theory*, which is limited to the description of events as they appear to observers in a state of uniform motion relative to one another, is developed from two axioms: (1) the laws of natural phenomena are the same for all observers, and (2) the velocity of light is the same constant to all observers. The more important consequences of this theory are (a) the mass m of a body is a function of its velocity, given by the formula $m = \dfrac{m_0}{\sqrt{1 - v^2/c^2}}$, where m_0 is the rest mass of the body, v its velocity, and c the velocity of light; (b) the *mass-energy equation* (q.v.) for the inter-conversion of mass and energy; (c) the *Fitzgerald-Lorentz contraction* (q.v.) appears as a natural consequence of the theory. The *general theory*, applicable to observers not in uniform relative motion, leads to a novel concept of the theory of gravitation. The validity of the theory of relativity has been amply confirmed in modern physics.

RELAY, ELECTRICAL. A device by which the current flowing in one circuit can open or close a second circuit and thus control the switching on and off of a current in the second circuit.

REMANENCE. The residual magnetization of a ferromagnetic substance subjected to a *hysteresis cycle* (q.v.) when the magnetizing field is reduced to zero.

RENNET. An extract of the fourth stomach of the calf, containing *rennin* (q.v.).

RENNIN. *Enzyme* (q.v.) having the power of coagulating the *protein* (q.v.) in milk.

REPRODUCTION FACTOR, k, of an atomic pile or nuclear reactor is the average number of neutrons released in a single fission process which go on to produce further fissions. If k is greater than 1, the chain reaction (see *atomic pile*) will build up. By subsequently reducing k to unity, the reaction can be maintained at any desired level. If k is further reduced, the chain reaction can no longer maintain itself, and begins to decay.

RESISTANCE, ELECTRICAL, of a conductor is the ratio of the potential difference between the ends of a conductor to the current flowing in the conductor. See *Ohm's law*. The practical unit of resistance is the *ohm* (q.v.).

RESISTANCE THERMOMETER. The electrical *resistance* (q.v.) of a conductor varies with temperature, normally increasing with rise in temperature. This forms the basis of a convenient and accurate thermometer, in which the temperature is deduced from the measurement of the resistance of a spiral of a metal (usually platinum) in the form of a wire.

RESISTIVITY, specific resistance. A constant for a given material; the resistance of unit length of the material per unit cross-sectional area. Usually stated in microhms per centimetre cube.

RESOLVING POWER. The ability of an optical system (e.g. microscope, telescope, the eye, etc.) to produce separate images of objects very close together.

RESONANCE. If, to a system capable of oscillation, a small periodic force is applied, the system is in general set into forced oscillations of small *amplitude* (q.v.). As the frequency f of the exciting force approaches the natural frequency of the system, f_o, the amplitude of the oscillations builds up, becoming a maximum when $f = f_o$. The system is then said to be *in resonance with the exciting force*, or simply *in resonance*.

REST MASS. The mass of a body when at rest relative to the observer. The mass of a body varies with its velocity (see *relativity, theory of*), a result of great importance when velocities approaching those of light are considered, e.g. in nuclear physics.

RESTITUTION, COEFFICIENT OF. *e.* A measure of the elasticity of bodies upon impact. For two smooth spheres of a given material colliding, e is equal to the ratio of the relative velocity of the spheres along their line of centres immediately after impact to their relative velocity before impact.

RESULTANT (phys.) of two or more forces or velocities is a single force or velocity which produces the same effect as the two or more forces or velocities acting together.

RETARDATION (phys.). Negative *acceleration* (q.v.); rate of decrease of velocity.

RETORT (chem.). A glass vessel consisting of a large bulb with a long neck narrowing somewhat towards the end. In industrial processes, any vessel from which distillation takes place; in the canning industry, a large autoclave for heating sealed cans by superheated steam under pressure.

RETORT CARBON. See *gas carbon*.

REVERBERATORY FURNACE. Furnace designed for operations in which it is not desirable to mix the material with the fuel; the roof is heated by flames, and the heat is radiated down on to the material off the roof.

REVERSIBLE PROCESS (in *thermodynamics*, q.v.). A process which can be performed in the reverse direction, the whole series of changes constituting the process being exactly reversed. A reversible process can take place only in infinitesimal steps about equilibrium states of the system.

REVERSIBLE REACTION. A chemical reaction which may be made, under suitable conditions, to proceed in either direction. See *chemical equilibrium*.

REYNOLDS NUMBER, *R*. A dimensionless quantity applied to a liquid flowing through a cylindrical tube, given by $R = \dfrac{V\rho a}{\eta}$, where $V =$ velocity of flow, $\rho =$ density of the liquid, and η the coefficient of viscosity of the liquid. At low velocities, the flow of the liquid is *stream-line* (q.v.). At a certain value of R, corresponding to a critical velocity V_c, the flow becomes turbulent.

RHENIUM. Re. Element. A.W. 186·31. At. No. 75. Hard, heavy grey metal, S.G. 20·53, m.p. 3167° C. Used in thermocouples.

RHEOLOGY. Study of the deformation and flow of matter.

RHEOSTAN. Alloy of 52% copper, 25% nickel, 18% zinc and 5% iron; used for electrical resistance wire.

RHEOSTAT. Variable electrical resistance.

RHODIUM. Rh. Element. A.W. 102·91. At. No. 45. Silvery-white hard metal, S.G. 12·5, m.p. approximately 2000° C. Occurs with and resembles platinum. Used in alloys, catalysts and thermocouples.

RHODOPSIN, visual purple. Complex organic compound formed in the retina of the eye. Makes the eye more sensitive in very dim light; lack of it causes night blindness. Formed with the aid of vitamin A.

RHOMBUS. Quadrilateral having all its sides equal.

RIGIDITY MODULUS. *Elasticity modulus* (q.v.) applied to a body under a shearing strain.

RING COMPOUND (chem.). Chemical compound in the molecule of which some or all of the atoms are linked in a closed ring. See *carbo-cyclic, heterocyclic compounds*.

ROCHELLE SALT. COOK.(CH.OH)$_2$.COONa.4H$_2$O. Sodium potassium tartrate. White, crystalline, soluble salt, used in the preparation of baking-powder, Seidlitz powders, etc.

ROCHON PRISM. Prism used for obtaining plane-polarized light (see *polarization of light*) and in other related problems. Such a prism, made of quartz, may be used for work with *ultra-violet* (q.v.) light.

ROCK CRYSTAL. Pure natural crystalline form of silica, SiO$_2$.

ROCK SALT. Natural crystalline sodium chloride, NaCl.

ROCKET. Projectile which is driven through space by the recoil or reaction on the rocket of explosions produced within its structure. The driving force is not due to any pushing effect of the jet against the air.

RODINAL. Photographic *developer* (q.v.) consisting of an alkaline solution of *para*-aminophenol, NH$_2$C$_6$H$_4$OH, with sodium bisulphite, NaHSO$_3$.

RONGALITE. Compound of sodium sulphoxylate and formaldehyde, NaHSO$_2$.HCHO. Used as a reducing agent in dyeing.

ROENTGEN, THE. r. The amount of X- or gamma-radiation which will produce ions carrying 1 electrostatic unit of electricity of either sign in 1 c.c. of dry air.

ROENTGEN RAYS. See *X-rays*.

ROOT (math.). One of the equal factors of a number or quantity. The square root, $\sqrt[2]{}$ or $\sqrt{}$, is one of two equal factors; e.g. $9 = 3 \times 3$ or -3×-3; hence $\sqrt[2]{9} = \pm 3$. Similarly the cube or third root is denoted by $\sqrt[3]{}$, etc. May also be denoted by a fractional index; thus $\sqrt[2]{x} = x^{\frac{1}{2}}$; $\sqrt[3]{x} = x^{\frac{1}{3}}$. The *root of an equation* is a value of the unknown quantity which satisfies the equation.

ROOT MEAN SQUARE VALUE OF ALTERNATING QUANTITY. If y is a periodic function of t, of period T, the root mean square (R.M.S.) value of y is the square root of the mean of the square of y taken over a period. The R.M.S. value I of an alternating current is important since it determines the heat generated (RI^2) in a resistance R (see *electric current, heating effect of*). All ordinary A.C. measuring instruments give R.M.S. values of current, etc. If the alternating quantity can be represented by a pure sine wave, the R.M.S. value of the quantity A is related to the maximum value a of the quantity (i.e. *amplitude*, q.v.) by the expression $A = a/\sqrt{2}$.

ROOT MEAN SQUARE VALUE OF VARIABLE. R.M.S. Given by the expression

$$\text{R.M.S.} = \sqrt{\frac{\text{(Sum of squares of the individual values of the variable)}}{\text{(total number of values)}}}$$

ROSE'S METAL. Alloy of 50% bismuth, 25% lead and 25% tin; m.p. 94° C.

ROTARY DISPERSION. See *optical activity*.

ROTATION, OPTICAL. See *optical rotation*.

RUBBER. Elastic solid obtained from the latex (a milky juice) of the *Hevea brasiliensis* tree. Raw natural rubber consists mainly of the *cis*-form of polyisoprene, $(CH_2.CH:C(CH_3):CH_2)_n$, a hydrocarbon polymer, with molecular weight of about 300,000. Nearly all rubber articles are made by 'compounding' raw rubber, i.e. mixing it with other ingredients and then vulcanizing it in moulds by heating with sulphur and 'accelerators' (*catalysts*, q.v.).

RUBBER, SYNTHETIC. Class of substances having the 'rubbery' properties of the natural product; made from simple molecules by *polymerization* (q.v.). See *Neoprene, Buna, butyl rubber*.

RUBIDIUM. Rb. Element. A.W. 85.48. At. No. 37. Soft, extremely reactive white metal resembling sodium. S.G. 1.53, m.p. 38.4° C. Occurs in a few rare minerals.

RUBY. Red form of *corundum* (q.v.), Al_2O_3, which owes its colour to traces of chromium.

RUST. Hydrated oxide of iron, mainly $Fe_2O_3.H_2O$, formed by iron by exposure to moisture and air.

RUTHENIUM. Ru. Element. A.W. 101·7. At. No. 44. Hard, brittle metal, S.G. 12·2, m.p. 2450° C. Occurs together with platinum.

RUTILE. Crystalline form of natural titanium dioxide, TiO_2.

RYDBERG CONSTANT. Constant relating to those atomic spectra which are similar to the hydrogen atom spectrum. The Rydberg constant for hydrogen is 109,678 cm.$^{-1}$.

S

SACCHARIMETER. Apparatus for determining the concentration of a sugar solution by measuring the angle of rotation of the plane of vibration of polarized light passing through a tube containing the solution. See *optical activity; polarization of light*.

SACCHARIN. $C_6H_4SO_2CONH$. White, crystalline, sparingly soluble solid; m.p. 227° C. When pure, has about 550 times the sweetening power of sugar, but has no food value, and may have harmful effects if used to excess. Manufactured from toluene, $C_6H_5CH_3$.

SACCHAROMETER. Type of *hydrometer* (q.v.) used for finding the concentration of sugar solutions by determining their density; usually graduated to read the percentage of sugar direct.

SACCHAROSE. See *sucrose*.

SAFETY LAMP, Davy lamp. An oil-lamp which will not ignite inflammable gases, e.g. methane (fire-damp). Has a cylinder of wire gauze acting as a chimney; the heat of the flame is conducted away by the gauze, and while fire-damp will burn inside the gauze, the temperature of the gauze does not rise sufficiently high to ignite the gas outside.

SAL VOLATILE. Commercial 'ammonium carbonate', actually consisting of a mixture of ammonium bicarbonate, NH_4HCO_3, ammonium carbamate, $NH_4O.CO.NH_2$, and ammonium carbonate, $(NH_4)_2CO_3$.

SAL-AMMONIAC. *Ammonium chloride*, NH_4Cl (q.v.).

SALINOMETER. Type of *hydrometer* (q.v.) used for the determination of concentration of salt solutions by measuring their density.

SALT (chem.). Chemical compound formed when the hydrogen of an acid has been replaced by a metal. Salts are named according to the acid and the metal from which the salt is derived; thus copper sulphate is a salt derived from copper and sulphuric acid.

SALT, COMMON. Sodium chloride, NaCl.

SALTCAKE. Sodium sulphate, $Na_2SO_4.10H_2O$.

SALTPETRE, nitre. *Potassium nitrate* (q.v.).

SALTS OF LEMON. Potassium quadroxalate, $KH_3C_4O_8.2H_2O$. White, soluble, poisonous, crystalline salt. Used for removing ink-stains.

SAMARIUM. Sm. Element. A.W. 150·43. At. No. 62. See *rare earths*.

SAND. Hard, granular powder, generally composed of granules of impure silica, SiO_2.

SAPONIFICATION. *Hydrolysis* (q.v.) of an *ester* (q.v.); term often confined to the hydrolysis of an ester using an alkali, thus forming a salt (a 'soap' in the case of some of the higher fatty acids) and the free alcohol. See *soap*.

SAPONIFICATION NUMBER. One of the characteristics of a fat or oil; the number of milligrams of potassium hydroxide required for the complete *saponification* of the fat or oil.

SAPPHIRE. Natural crystalline form of blue, transparent corundum (alumina, Al_2O_3); the colour being due to traces of cobalt or other metals.

SATELLITES. Bodies rotating in orbits round the planets; e.g. the Moon is a satellite of the Earth.

SATURATED COMPOUND (chem.). A compound which does not form *addition compounds*; a compound the molecule of which contains no double or multiple valency bonds between the atoms.

SATURATED SOLUTION. A solution which can exist in equilibrium with excess of solute. The saturation concentration is a function of the temperature.

SATURATED VAPOUR. A vapour which can exist in equilibrium with its liquid.

SATURATED VAPOUR PRESSURE. The pressure exerted by a saturated vapour. This pressure is a function of the temperature.

SATURN (astr.). Planet, with nine small satellites, and surrounded by characteristic rings (see *Saturn's rings*). Orbit lies between those of Jupiter and Uranus. Mean distance from the Sun, 886 million miles. Sidereal period ('year'), 29·46 years. Mass, approximately 95 times that of the Earth. Surface temperature, about − 150° C.

SATURN'S RINGS. Three concentric rings, probably composed of the remains of a broken-up satellite, which are seen round the planet Saturn.

SCALAR QUANTITY. Any quantity which is sufficiently defined when the magnitude is given in appropriate units. Compare *vector*.

SCANDIUM. Sc. Element. A.W. 44·96. At. No. 21. See *rare earths*.

SCATTERING OF LIGHT. When a beam of light traverses a material medium, scattering of the beam takes place. Two types of scattering occur: (1) by random reflection; i.e. small particles suspended in the medium act as tiny mirrors and, being randomly orientated with respect to the beam, produce random reflections. This type occurs when the size of the particles is large in comparison with the *wave-length* (q.v.) of the light; (2) by *diffraction* (q.v.); this occurs when particles which are small compared with the wave-length of the light are present in the medium. Owing to diffraction phenomena, the particles act as centres of radiation and each particle scatters the light in all directions. In this type, the degree of scattering is proportional to the inverse fourth power of the wave-length of the light. Thus, blue light is scattered to a greater extent than red. The blue colour of the sky is due to scattering by the actual molecules of the atmosphere.

SCHEELE'S GREEN. Bright green precipitate, probably consisting of cupric arsenite, $Cu_3(AsO_3)_2.2H_2O$. Used as a pigment and insecticide.

SCHWEITZER'S REAGENT. Deep blue solution formed by the action of ammonia solution on cupric hydroxide, $Cu(OH)_2$. Dissolves cellulose, which is re-precipitated by the action of dilute acids; this is the basis of the cuprammonium process of *rayon* (q.v.) manufacture.

SCLEROPROTEINS. Class of complex *proteins* (q.v.) forming the framework of many animal tissues.

-SCOPE. Suffix applied to names of instruments for observing or watching, usually as distinct from measuring. E.g. telescope.

SCRUPLE. 1/24 ounce Troy. See *troy weight*.

SEA-WATER. The approximate composition (not including inland seas such as the Dead Sea) is water, 96·4%; common salt, NaCl, 2·8%; magnesium chloride, $MgCl_2$, 0·4%; magnesium sulphate, $MgSO_4$, 0·2%; calcium sulphate, $CaSO_4$, and potassium chloride, KCl, 0·1% each.

SECANT. A straight line cutting a circle or other curve.

SECANT (trig.). See *trigonometrical ratios*.

SECOND. 1. Fundamental unit of time; 1/86,164·100 of a *sidereal day* (q.v.); 1/86,400 of a mean *solar day* (q.v.). 2. Measure of angle: 1/60 of a minute, 1/3600 of a degree.

SECONDARY CELL. See *accumulator*.

SECONDARY EMISSION of electrons. When a primary beam of rapidly-moving electrons strikes a metal surface, secondary electrons are emitted from the surface. The effect is of importance in the *thermionic valve* (q.v.), the *electron multiplier* (q.v.), etc. In the thermionic valve, the emission occurs when the electrons strike the anode, and may be suppressed or controlled in multi-electrode tubes (*tetrode, pentode*, q.v.) by various grids called the *suppressor* and *screen* grids.

SECTOR. See *circle*.

SECULAR VARIATION OF MAGNETIC DECLINATION. If the Earth's magnetic North pole is considered to rotate round the geographical North pole, completing a cycle in about 960 years, a representation of a steady variation of *magnetic declination* (q.v.), known as the secular variation, will be seen. Thus, the magnetic declination in London is at present westerly, and decreasing until it is due to become zero at the beginning of the twenty-second century.

SEEBECK EFFECT. If two wires of different metals are joined at their ends to form a circuit and the two junctions are maintained at different temperatures, a current flows round the circuit.

SEGER CONES. Device for estimating the approximate temperature of a furnace. Cones made of material softening at a definite temperature.

SEGMENT. See *circle*.

SEISMOGRAPH. Instrument for recording earthquake shocks.

SELENIUM. Se. Element. A.W. 78·96. At. No. 34. Non-metal resembling sulphur in its chemical properties. S.G. 4·81, m.p. 217° C. Exists in several *allotropic forms* (q.v.). The so-called 'metallic' selenium, a silvery-grey crystalline solid, varies in electrical resistance on exposure to light and is used in *photo-electric cells* (q.v.). Occurs as selenides of metals, together with their sulphides; used in the manufacture of rubber and of ruby glass.

SELENIUM CELL. *Photo-electric cell* (q.v.) depending for its action on the *photo-conductive effect* (q.v.), or the photo-voltaic effect.

SELF-INDUCTANCE. Coefficient of *self-induction* (q.v.).

SELF-INDUCTION. The magnetic field associated with an electric current cuts the conductor carrying the current. When the current changes, so does the magnetic field, resulting in an induced E.M.F. (See *induction, electromagnetic.*) This phenomenon is called self-induction. The induced E.M.F. is proportional to the rate of change of the current, the constant of proportionality being called the coefficient of self-induction, or the *self-inductance.* The magnitude of the self-inductance is a function only of the geometry of the electrical circuit and can be calculated in a few simple cases. The unit of self-inductance is the *henry* (q.v.).

SEMI-CONDUCTOR. Electrical conductor characterized by the fact that its resistance decreases with rise in temperature and the presence of impurities, in contrast to the normal metallic conductor for which the reverse is true. Examples include graphite, silicon, and the *thermistor* (q.v.).

SEMI-PERMEABLE MEMBRANE. A membrane allowing the passage of some substances and not of others; a partition which permits the passage of pure solvent molecules more readily than those of the dissolved substance. E.g. copper ferrocyanide, $Cu_2Fe(CN)_6$, is permeable to water, but only very slightly permeable to dissolved substances. Used as a partition between solution and solvent in osmotic measurements (see *osmotic pressure*) and in *dialysis* (q.v.).

SERIES (math.). A sequence of numbers or mathematical expressions such that the nth term may be written down in general form, and any particular term (say, the rth) may be obtained by substituting r for n; e.g. x^n is the general term of the series $1, x, x^2, x^3 \ldots x^n$.

SERIES, RESISTANCES IN. If a number of conductors of electricity are connected *in series*, i.e. one after the other, so that the current flows through each in turn, the total resistance is the sum of the separate resistances of the conductors. See Fig. 13.

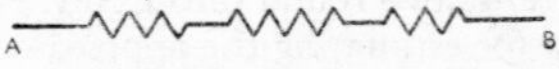

FIG. 13.

SERPEK PROCESS. Process for the fixation of *atmospheric nitrogen* (q.v.). Aluminium is made to react with nitrogen to form aluminium nitride, which is then decomposed by steam to give ammonia.

SERUM. The liquid which remains after the clotting and removal of blood corpuscles and fibrin from the blood; any similar body liquid.

SEXTANT. Instrument for determining the angle between two objects (e.g. horizon and star). Commonly employed for determining the radius of a *position circle* (q.v.).

SHADOW. A dark patch formed by a body which obstructs rays of light. A shadow cast by an object in front of a *point source* (q.v.) of light is as sharply defined area; a source of light of appreciable size produce two distinct regions, the *umbra* or full shadow, and the *penumbra* or half-shadow. See Fig. 14.

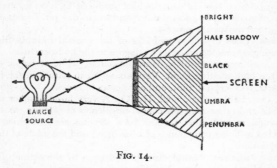

FIG. 14.

SHEAR. A stress applied to a body in the plane of one of its faces.

SHELLAC, lac. Coloured, resinous substance produced as an incrustation on tree bark by the *coccus lacca* insect. Used for varnishes.

SHOOTING-STAR. *Meteorite* (q.v.) which has become incandescent by friction on entering the Earth's atmosphere.

SHORT CIRCUIT. If a *potential difference* (q.v.) exists between two points A and B (e.g. the terminals of an electrical supply), a system of conductors connecting A and B constitutes a circuit. If now A and B are placed in contact, or joined by a conductor of much lower resistance than the rest of the circuit, most of the current will flow direct between A and B, which are then said to be short-circuited or 'shorted'.

SHORT SIGHT. See *myopia*.

SHUNT, ELECTRICAL. A device for altering the amount of electric current flowing through a piece of apparatus, such as a galvanometer. Consists of a conductor connected in parallel with the apparatus.

SIDE-CHAIN (chem.). An *aliphatic radical* (q.v.) or group attached to a benzene or other cyclic group in the molecule of an organic compound. E.g. in toluene, $C_6H_5.CH_3$, the methyl group, CH_3, is a side-chain attached to a benzene nucleus.

SIDEREAL DAY. The period of a complete rotation of the Earth upon its axis, with respect to the fixed stars.

SIDEREAL PERIOD OF A PLANET. The 'year' of a planet. The actual period of its revolution round the Sun.

SIDEREAL YEAR. The time interval in which the Sun appears to perform a complete revolution with reference to the fixed stars. 365·2564 mean solar days.

SIDERITE. Natural ferrous carbonate, $FeCO_3$. Important ore of iron.

SIEMENS-MARTIN PROCESS. See *open-hearth process*.

SIGN, ALGEBRAICAL. The plus or minus sign, $+$ or $-$, indicating opposite senses or directions; thus $+5$ is numerically equal, but opposite in sign, to -5.

SILAGE. Stored form of cattle-fodder produced by a limited fermentation of green fodder pressed down and stored in a pit. *Lactic acid* (q.v.) is formed during the process.

SILANES. Class of silicon hydrides of the general formula Si_nH_{2n+2}, forming a homologous series analogous to the hydrocarbons.

SILICA. Silicon oxide. SiO_2. Hard, insoluble, white or colourless solid with a high melting point. Very abundant in nature in the forms of quartz, rock-crystal, flint, and as silicates in rocks.

SILICATE. Salt of silicic acid, H_2SiO_3. A very large number of rocks, earths and other minerals consist of silicates of calcium, aluminium, magnesium and other metals. Such silicates are conveniently considered as being compounds of *silica* (q.v.) and the oxide of the metal in question.

SILICOL PROCESS. Manufacture of hydrogen by the action of sodium hydroxide (caustic soda, $NaOH$) solution on silicon.

SILICON. Si. Element. A.W. 28·09. At. No. 14. Non-metal similar to carbon in its chemical properties. Occurs in two *allotropic forms* (q.v.); a brown amorphous powder and dark grey crystals; S.G. 2·42, m.p. 1420° C. Occurs in nature as *silica* (q.v.) and as various *silicates* (q.v.). Used in alloys.

SILICONES. Term originally applied to compounds of the general formula R_2SiO, where R stands for hydrocarbon radicals. Now defined as polymeric (see *polymerization*) organosiloxanes of the general type $(R_2SiO)_n$. Used as lubricants, for water-repellent finishes, high-temperature resisting resins and lacquers.

SILK. A thread-like substance produced by the silkworm. Consists mainly of the proteins *sericin* and *fibroin*.

SILVER. Ag. Element. A.W. 107·88. At. No. 47. White, rather soft metal; S.G. 10·5, m.p. 960·5° C. Extremely malleable and ductile; the best-known conductor of electricity. Occurs as the metal, and as argenite or silver glance, Ag_2S; horn silver, $AgCl$; and other compounds. Extracted by alloying with lead, and then separating the lead by *cupellation* (q.v.) and other methods. Used in coinage and jewellery; compounds used in *photography* (q.v.).

SILVER BROMIDE. AgBr. Pale yellow, insoluble salt, used in *photography* (q.v.).

SILVER GLANCE. *Argentite* (q.v.).

SILVER NITRATE, lunar caustic. $AgNO_3$. White, soluble crystalline salt, m.p. 209° C. Used in marking-inks, medicine and chemical analysis.

SILVER PLATING. Depositing a layer of metallic silver, generally by electrolysis. See *electroplating*.

SIMPLE HARMONIC MOTION. S.H.M. A point moves in simple harmonic motion when it oscillates along a line about a central point O so that its acceleration towards O is always proportional to its distance from O; e.g. the projection of a point moving in a circle with constant *angular velocity* (q.v.) on to any fixed diameter of the circle moves in simple harmonic motion.

SINE. See *trigonometrical ratios*.

SIPHON. Bent tube used for transferring liquid from one level to a lower level *via* a third level higher than either. If the shorter arm of an inverted U-tube filled with liquid is immersed below the liquid surface in A (see Fig. 15), liquid will flow from A to C through the tube. The siphon depends for its action on the fact that the pressure at A tending to force the liquid up the tube is $P - P_{ab}$ and the pressure acting upwards on the liquid at C is $P - P_{bc}$, where P = external atmospheric pressure, and P_{ab} and P_{ac} are the pressures due to the weights of the liquid columns AB and AC respectively. Hence flow from A to B will occur provided BC is greater than AB.

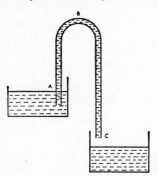

FIG. 15.

SKIP DISTANCE. There is a minimum angle of incidence at the ionosphere below which a *sky wave* (q.v.) of a given frequency cannot be reflected, but is transmitted through to outer space. Consequently there is a region surrounding a radio transmitter within which no sky wave can be received. The minimum distance at which reception of the sky wave is possible is called the *skip distance*.

SKY WAVE. A wireless wave may pass from transmitter to receiver by one of two paths; either directly along the ground following the curvature of the Earth (ground wave) or by reflection at the *Heaviside-Kennelly layer* (q.v.); in this case it is termed the *sky wave*.

SLAG. Non-metallic material obtained during the smelting of metallic ores; generally formed as a molten mass floating on top of the molten metal.

SLAKED LIME. Calcium hydroxide, $Ca(OH)_2$, formed by the action of water on quicklime, CaO.

SLAKING. The addition of water.

SLATE. Natural form of aluminium silicate formed from *clay* (q.v.) hardened by pressure.

SLIDE RULE. Mathematical instrument used for rapid calculations; in principle consists of a grooved ruler with a scale, with another similarly marked ruler sliding inside the groove. Multiplication and division are carried out by adding or subtracting lengths on the two rulers, the divisions on which are in a logarithmic scale, by a process analogous to addition and subtraction which could be carried out on two rulers by adding or subtracting lengths.

SMELTING. Extraction of a metal from its ores by a process involving heat. Generally the process is one of chemical *reduction* (q.v.) of the oxide of the metal with carbon in a suitable furnace.

SMOKE. A suspension of fine particles of a solid in a gas; smoke from coal consists mainly of fine particles of carbon.

SNELL'S LAW. See *refraction, laws of.*

SOAP. A mixture of the sodium salts of stearic acid, $C_{17}H_{35}COOH$, palmitic acid, $C_{15}H_{31}COOH$, and oleic acid, $C_{17}H_{33}COOH$; or of the potassium salts of these acids ('soft soap'). Made by the action of caustic soda or caustic potash on fats, the process of hydrolysis or *saponification* (q.v.) giving the soap, with glycerin as a by-product. The term soap is also applied to fatty acid salts of metals other than sodium or potassium, although such compounds are unlike the ordinary soaps.

SODA. Term applied to various sodium compounds; *washing soda*, sodium carbonate, $Na_2CO_3.10H_2O$; *baking soda*, bicarbonate of soda, $NaHCO_3$; *caustic soda*, NaOH.

SODA-LIME. A solid mixture of sodium hydroxide, NaOH, and calcium hydroxide, $Ca(OH)_2$, made by slaking quicklime (see *slaked lime*) with a solution of sodium hydroxide and drying by heat.

SODA NITRE. Impure natural sodium nitrate, *caliche* (q.v.).

SODA WATER. Water containing carbon dioxide, CO_2, under pressure; releasing the pressure lowers the solubility of the gas, and thus causes effervescence.

SODIUM. Na. (Natrium.) Element. A.W. 22·997. At. No. 11. Soft, silvery-white metal, S.G. 0·971, m.p. 97·5° C. Very reactive, tarnishes rapidly in air; reacts violently with water to form sodium hydroxide,

NaOH, and hydrogen gas. Compounds are very abundant and widely distributed; the commonest is sodium chloride, NaCl (common salt). Essential to life. The metal is used in the preparation of organic compounds.

SODIUM BICARBONATE, $NaHCO_3$. White, soluble salt, used in baking-powder.

SODIUM CARBONATE, washing soda. $Na_2CO_3 . 10H_2O$. White, crystalline, soluble salt, used in the household.

SODIUM CHLORIDE, common salt, salt. NaCl.

SODIUM HYDROXIDE, caustic soda, NaOH. White deliquescent solid, m.p. 318·4° C. Dissolves in water to give an alkaline solution.

SODIUM NITRATE, $NaNO_3$. White, soluble, crystalline salt, occurs naturally as Chile saltpetre; used as a *fertilizer* (q.v.) and in the manufacture of nitric acid.

SODIUM PEROXIDE, Na_2O_2. Yellow powder, formed when sodium metal burns in air. Reacts with water to give sodium hydroxide and oxygen gas.

SODIUM SILICATE, Na_2SiO_3. White, soluble, crystalline salt, used in the household as 'water-glass'.

SODIUM SULPHATE, Glauber's salt. $Na_2SO_4 . 10H_2O$. White, soluble, crystalline salt.

SODIUM THIOSULPHATE, sodium hyposulphite, 'hypo'. $Na_2S_2O_3 . 5H_2O$. White, crystalline, very soluble salt, used in photography.

SOFT IRON. Iron containing little carbon, as distinct from steel; iron which does not retain magnetism permanently, but loses most of it when the magnetizing field is removed.

SOFT SOAP. Potassium *soap* (q.v.).

SOFT WATER. Water which forms an immediate lather with soap. See *hard water*.

SOIL. Soils vary enormously in their chemical composition. The inorganic portion of a soil is composed of *silicates* (q.v.) of various metals, mainly of aluminium, but also of iron, calcium, magnesium, etc.; free silica (sand) and other inorganic matter, depending on the source. Organic matter in the soil is mainly derived from decomposed plants; much of it is in the form of a class of black, sticky substances known collectively as *humus*.

SOL. See *colloidal solution*.

SOLAR CONSTANT. The energy which would (in the absence of the atmosphere) be received per minute by an area of 1 sq. cm. placed at the mean distance of the Earth from the Sun and at right angles to the incident radiation; approximately 2 calories per minute per square centimetre.

SOLAR DAY. The variable interval between two successive returns of the Sun to the meridian. The *mean solar day* is the average value of this. See *time, measurement of*.

SOLAR SYSTEM, THE. A system of nine planets – Mercury, Venus, the

Earth, Mars, Jupiter, Saturn, Uranus, Neptune and Pluto – and of a belt of *asteroids* (q.v.) revolving in elliptical orbits round the Sun. The orbits are nearly circular, and lie very nearly in the same plane.

SOLDER. An alloy for joining metals. *Soft solders* are alloys of tin and lead in varying proportions; *brazing solders* are usually composed of copper and zinc.

SOLENOID. A coil of wire wound uniformly on a cylindrical former, having a length which is large compared with the radius, r. When a current of i electromagnetic units is passed through the solenoid, a uniform magnetic field H is produced inside the coil parallel to its axis. The magnitude of H in *oersteds* (q.v.) is given by $H = 4\pi ni$, where n is the number of turns per unit length of the solenoid.

SOLID (math.). A three-dimensional figure, having length, breadth and thickness; a figure occupying space or having a measurable volume.

SOLID ANGLE. The ratio of the area of the surface of the portion of a sphere enclosed by the conical surface forming the angle, to the square of the radius of the sphere.

SOLID SOLUTION. A solid homogeneous mixture of two or more substances. E.g. some alloys are solid solutions of the metals in each other, the process of solution having taken place in the molten state.

SOLID STATE (phys.). State of matter in which the molecules of the substance are considered to be vibrating, with small *amplitude* (q.v.) about equilibrium positions. A solid is said to possess *cohesion*, remaining the same shape unless changed by external forces. This is due to the large forces of attraction between neighbouring molecules.

SOLIDIFYING POINT. The constant temperature at which a liquid solidifies under a given pressure, usually the standard *atmosphere* (q.v.).

SOLSTICE. The time (or, more accurately, the point) at which the Sun reaches its greatest declination North or South. The points are situated upon the *ecliptic* (q.v.) half-way between the equinoxes; the times are approximately June 21 and December 21.

SOLUBILITY. The extent to which a solute will dissolve in a solvent. Usually expressed in grams per 100 gm. of solvent at a specified temperature.

SOLUBILITY PRODUCT. The product of the concentrations of the *ions* (q.v.) of a dissolved electrolyte when in equilibrium with undissolved substance. For sparingly soluble electrolytes, the solubility product is a constant for a given substance at a given temperature. When the solubility product for a given compound is exceeded in a solution, some of it is precipitated until the product of the ionic concentrations falls to the constant value.

SOLUBLE. Capable of being dissolved (usually in water).

SOLUTE. A substance which is dissolved in a solvent to form a solution.

SOLUTION. A homogeneous molecular mixture of two or more substances of dissimilar molecular structure; term commonly applied to solutions of solids in liquids. Other types of solutions include gases in liquids, the solubility of gases decreasing with rise in temperature; gases in solids, forming a solid solution; liquids in liquids; and solids in solids (e.g. some alloys).

SOLVAY PROCESS, ammonia-soda process. Industrial preparation of washing-soda, $Na_2CO_3 . 10H_2O$, from common salt, NaCl, and calcium carbonate, $CaCO_3$. By the action of ammonia, NH_3, and carbon dioxide (obtained by heating $CaCO_3$) on salt solution, the less soluble sodium bicarbonate, $NaHCO_3$, is precipitated. The action of heat on this gives the required sodium carbonate, while the ammonia is recovered from solution by the action of the lime which remains when the calcium carbonate is heated.

SOLVENT. Substance (usually liquid) having the power of dissolving other substances in it; that component of a solution which has the same physical state as the solution itself. E.g. in a solution of sugar in water, water is the solvent, while sugar is the *solute*.

SOUND. A physiological sensation received by the ear. It is caused by a vibrating source and transmitted as a longitudinal pressure wave motion (see *longitudinal waves*) through a material medium such as air.

SOUND, VELOCITY OF. The velocity of propagation of sound waves (see *wave motion*). This velocity is a function of the temperature and of the nature of the propagating medium. In gases it is independent of the pressure. In air at 0° C. it is 1120 feet or 332 metres per second, approximately 760 miles per hour.

SOXHLET EXTRACTION APPARATUS. Device for extracting the soluble portion of any substance by a continuous circulation of the boiling solvent through it.

SPACE-TIME. The development of the theory of *relativity* (q.v.) has led to the disappearance of a clear-cut distinction between a three-dimensional *space* and an independent *time*; in the modern view, space and time are considered as being welded together in a four-dimensional *space-time continuum*.

SPARK. See *electric spark*.

SPARK COIL. See *induction coil*.

SPARKING-PLUG. Device for providing an electric spark for exploding the mixture of air and petrol vapour in the cylinder of the internal-combustion engine.

SPARKING POTENTIAL, sparking voltage. The difference in potential (i.e. the voltage) required for an electric spark to pass across a given gap. See *Paschen's law*.

SPECIFIC GRAVITY, S.G. The ratio of the *density* (q.v.) of a substance at the temperature under consideration to the density of water at the temperature of its maximum density (4° C.). Numerically equal to the density in grams per cubic centimetre, but is stated as a pure number, while the density is stated as mass per unit volume.

SPECIFIC HEAT. See *heat, specific*.

SPECIFIC INDUCTIVE CAPACITY, dielectric constant of a substance.

The ratio of the capacity of a condenser with the given substance as dielectric to the capacity of the same condenser with air (or vacuum) as dielectric. See *condenser, electrical*.

SPECIFIC RESISTANCE. See *resistivity*.

SPECIFIC VOLUME. The volume, at a specified temperature and pressure, occupied by 1 gm. of the substance. The reciprocal of the *density* (q.v.).

SPECTRAL LINES. See *line spectrum*.

SPECTRAL SERIES. The emission *spectrum* (q.v.) of any substance may be analyzed into one or more groups of frequencies (or wave-lengths), the frequencies in each group forming a series. For example, the spectrum of the hydrogen atom possesses series given by the expression

$$\nu = \text{constant}\left(\frac{1}{n_0{}^2} - \frac{1}{n^2}\right),$$

where ν is the frequency of the spectral lines. For the different series, n_0 takes the values 1, 2, 3, 4, etc. For any one value of n_0, n may have all integral values from $n_0 + 1$ upwards, the expression then giving the frequencies of all the lines in that particular series.

SPECTROGRAPH. Instrument by which spectra may be photographed; a photograph taken by means of such an instrument. See *spectrum analysis*.

SPECTROSCOPE. Instrument for *spectrum* (q.v.) analysis or observation.

SPECTRUM. The result obtained when radiations of *electromagnetic waves* (q.v.) are resolved into their constituent *wave-lengths* (q.v.) or frequencies. In the visible region (i.e. light waves) a well-known example is provided by the coloured bands produced when white light is passed through a prism or *diffraction grating* (q.v.). The colours of this spectrum, in order of decreasing wave-lengths, are: red, orange, yellow, green, blue, indigo, violet. Spectra formed from bodies emitting radiations are termed *emission spectra*. When white light is passed through a semi-transparent medium, selective absorption of radiations of certain wave-lengths or bands of wave-lengths takes place; the spectrum of the transmitted light is called an *absorption spectrum*. A *continuous spectrum* is one in which all wave-lengths, between certain limits, are present. A *line spectrum* is one in which only certain wave-lengths or 'lines' appear. The emission and absorption spectra of a substance are fundamental characteristics of it and are often used as a means of identification. Such spectra arise as a result of transitions between different *stationary states* (q.v.) of the atoms or molecules of the substance, electromagnetic waves being emitted or absorbed simultaneously with the transition. The frequency ν of the emitted or absorbed radiation is given by $E_1 - E_2 = h\nu$, where E_1 and E_2 are the energies of the first and second states respectively between which the transition takes place, and h is Planck's constant. When E_1 is greater than E_2, electromagnetic waves are emitted; in the converse case, they are absorbed.

SPECTRUM ANALYSIS. Investigation of the chemical nature of a substance by the examination of its *spectrum* (q.v.), using the fact that the position of emission and absorption lines and bands in the spectrum of a substance is characteristic of it.

SPECTRUM COLOURS. The colours visible in the continuous spectrum of white light. Red, orange, yellow, green, blue, indigo and violet.

SPECULAR REFLECTION. Perfect or regular reflection of *electromagnetic waves* (q.v.), e.g. light. Occurs whenever the reflecting surface is flat to approximately 1/8 of a wave-length of the radiation incident upon it.

SPECULUM METAL. Alloy of 2/3 copper and 1/3 tin; used for mirrors and reflectors.

SPEED. Ratio of the distance covered to the time taken by a moving body. Speed in a specified direction is *velocity*.

SPELTER. Commercial zinc, about 97% pure, containing lead and other impurities.

SPERMACETI. White, waxy solid consisting mainly of cetyl palmitate, $C_{15}H_{31}COOC_{16}H_{33}$. M.p. 40° C.–50° C. Obtained from the head of the sperm whale. Used in the manufacture of soaps and cosmetics.

SPHERE (math.). Solid figure generated by the revolution of a semicircle about a diameter as axis. The flat surface of a section cut by a plane passing through the centre is a *great circle*; surface of a section cut off by any other plane is a *small circle*. The solid cut off by a plane of a great circle is a *hemisphere*; that cut off by a small circle is a *segment*. The volume of a sphere having radius $r = \frac{4}{3}\pi r^3$; surface area = $4\pi r^2$.

SPHERICAL ABERRATION. See *aberration, spherical*.

SPHERICAL TRIANGLE. A triangle drawn on a spherical surface, bounded by the arcs of three *great circles* (q.v.). The properties of such triangles differ from those of plane triangles; calculations relating to them form the purpose of spherical trigonometry.

SPHERICAL TRIGONOMETRY. *Trigonometry* (q.v.) which deals with *spherical triangles*.

SPHEROID. Solid figure generated by an ellipse rotating about its minor axis (*oblate spheroid*, a 'flattened sphere') or about its major axis (*prolate spheroid*, an 'elongated sphere').

SPHEROMETER. Instrument for the accurate measurement of small thicknesses, or curvature of spherical surfaces.

SPIEGEL, spiegeleisen. Alloy of iron, manganese and carbon, used in the manufacture of steel by the *Bessemer process* (q.v.).

SPIN. Term of special significance in nuclear physics. Sub-atomic particles (electrons, neutrons, nuclei, mesons, etc.) may possess, in addition to other forms of energy such as energy of translation, energy due to the spinning of the particle about an axis within itself. This gives rise to a spin energy term in the quantum analysis (see *quantum* *theory*) of permissible *energy levels* (q.v.). Further, this motion may produce an associated *magnetic moment* (q.v.), whether the particle be charged or not.

SPINELS. Group of minerals having the general composition $MO.R_2O_3$, M being a bivalent metal (magnesium, ferrous iron, manganese, zinc) and R a tervalent metal (aluminium, chromium, ferric iron).

SPIRITS OF SALT. Solution of *hydrochloric acid* (q.v.).

SPIRITS OF WINE. *Ethyl alcohol* (q.v.).

SPUTTERING. Process for depositing a thin uniform film of a metal on to a surface. A disc of the metal to be 'sputtered' is made the cathode of a low-pressure discharge system (see *discharge in gases*). The material to be coated is placed between cathode and anode, the whole arrangement being enclosed and evacuated to a pressure of between 1 and ·01 mm. A discharge is set up by applying a voltage (1000–20,000 volts) between anode and cathode. Metallic atoms are ejected from the cathode and are deposited on the surface to be coated.

SQUARE. 1. Quadrilateral having all its sides equal and all its angles right angles. 2. The square of a quantity is that quantity raised to the second power, i.e. multiplied by itself.

SQUARE ROOT. See *root*.

SQUARING THE CIRCLE. The problem of constructing a square exactly equal in area to a given circle. The exact area of a circle cannot be determined, except in terms of π, which cannot be expressed as an exact fraction or decimal, although any required degree of approximation can be obtained. The problem, therefore, appears to be impossible of solution.

STABILIZATION (chem.). Prevention of chemical decomposition of a substance by the addition of a 'stabilizer' or 'negative catalyst'.

STABLE (chem.). Not readily decomposed.

STABLE EQUILIBRIUM (phys.). A body at rest is in stable equilibrium if, when slightly displaced, it tends to return to its original position of equilibrium. If the displacement tends to increase, the body is said to be in *unstable equilibrium*. Positions of stable equilibrium are positions of minimum *potential energy* (q.v.); those of unstable equilibrium are of maximum potential energy.

STAINLESS STEEL. A class of chromium steels containing 70%–90% iron, 12%–20% chromium, 0·1%–0·7% carbon.

STALACTITE. Downward growth of calcium carbonate, $CaCO_3$, formed on the roof of a cave by the trickling of water containing calcium compounds.

STALAGMITE. Upward growth from the floor of a cave; of the same nature and origin as a *stalactite* (q.v.).

STALAGMOMETRY. The measurement of *surface tension* (q.v.) by determining the weight (or volume) of a drop of the liquid hanging from the end of a tube.

STALLOY. Steel containing 3·5% silicon, having low energy losses due to *hysteresis* (q.v.). Used in portions of electrical apparatus which are subjected to alternating magnetic fields.

STANDARD ATMOSPHERE. See *atmosphere, the normal or standard*.

STANDARD CELL. A specially prepared *primary cell* (q.v.), e.g. the Weston cell, characterized by a high constancy of E.M.F. over long periods of time. The E.M.F. is a function of the temperature, and in the Weston cell it decreases by about 1 part in 10^5 per 1° rise.

STANDARD TEMPERATURE AND PRESSURE. S.T.P. See *N.T.P.*

STANNIC. Compound of *quadrivalent* (q.v.) tin.

STANNOUS. Compound of *bivalent* (q.v.) tin.

STANNUM. *Tin* (q.v.).

STARCH, amylum. *Carbohydrate* (q.v.) stored by plants in the form of granules. White, tasteless, insoluble powder. *Hydrolysis* (q.v.) by boiling with dilute acids gives firstly *dextrin* (q.v.) and finally *glucose* (q.v.).

STARCH GUM. See *dextrin*.

STARS. Fixed stars. Heavenly bodies of a nature similar to that of the Sun; intensely hot, glowing masses, situated at enormous distances from the solar system, the nearest being over 4 *light-years* (q.v.) away.

STASSFURT DEPOSITS. Natural deposits of several inorganic salts. The deposit consists of several strata, of a total estimated thickness of 2500 feet. Source of potassium and sodium compounds in the form of *carnallite* (q.v.); also of magnesium bromide, $MgBr_2.6H_2O$, and rock-salt.

STATES OF MATTER. The solid, liquid and gaseous states, the three states in which a substance can exist.

STATIC ELECTRICITY. See *electricity, static*.

STATICS. Branch of *mechanics* (q.v.); the mathematical and physical study of the behaviour of matter under the action of forces, dealing with cases where no motion is produced.

STATIONARY STATES. Term used in the *quantum theory* (q.v.). If only certain energy values or *energy levels* (q.v.) for the total energy of a system are permissible, the energy is said to be *quantized*. These levels are characteristic of the state of the system. Such states are called *stationary states*. A transition from one stationary state to another can occur only with the emission or absorption of energy in the form of *photons* (q.v.); i.e. electromagnetic waves are emitted or absorbed.

STATISTICS. Collection and study of numerical facts or data.

STEAM. Water, H_2O, in the gaseous state; water above its boiling point. Invisible gas; the white clouds which are frequently termed 'steam' consist of droplets of liquid water formed by the condensation of steam.

STEAM ENGINE. Machine utilizing steam power; either a steam turbine (see *turbine*) or a reciprocating steam engine, consisting essentially of a cylinder in which a piston is moved backwards and forwards by steam under pressure.

STEAM POINT. The temperature at which the maximum vapour pressure of water is equal to standard atmospheric pressure (see *atmosphere*), i.e. the normal boiling point. In the Centigrade scale of temperature the steam point is given the value of 100° C.

STEARIC ACID. $C_{17}H_{35}COOH$. Organic compound belonging to the group of *fatty acids* (q.v.). White solid, m.p. 69° C. Occurs in the form of *tristearin* (q.v.), a glyceride, in many fats.

STEARIN. *Tristearin* (q.v.); term also sometimes applied to a mixture of palmitic and stearic acids (see *stearine*).

STEARINE. Hard, white waxy solid consisting mainly of stearic and palmitic acids. Made by the *saponification* (q.v.) of natural fats.

STEEL. Iron containing from 0·1% to 1·5% carbon in the form of cementite (iron carbide, Fe_3C). The properties of different steels vary according to the percentage of carbon and of metals other than iron, and also according to the method of preparation. Prepared by the *open-hearth* and *Bessemer* processes (q.v.).

STEELYARD. Weighing-machine for heavy loads. In principle consists of a long, rigid bar, with a pan or hook at one end for taking the load to be weighed. The rod is pivoted about a fixed point or *fulcrum* near the centre of gravity, which is fairly near the end with the pan or hook. The other portion of the bar is graduated, and a movable weight slides along this, the weight balanced by it being proportional to its distance from the centre of gravity. See Fig. 16.

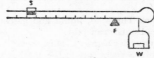

FIG. 16.

STEFAN'S LAW. The total energy emitted in the form of heat radiation per unit time from unit area of a black body is proportional to the fourth power of its absolute temperature (see *black body radiation*). The constant of proportionality, *Stefan's constant*, $= 5·75 \times 10^{-5}$ erg. cm.$^{-2}$ sec.$^{-1}$ deg.$^{-4}$.

STELLITE. Alloy of cobalt (35%–80%), chromium (15%–40%), tungsten (10%–25%), molybdenum (0%–40%) and iron (0%–5%). Hard and non-corroding; used for surgical instruments.

STERADIAN. Unit of *solid angle* (q.v.). That solid angle which encloses a surface on the sphere equal to the square of the radius.

STERE. Metric unit of volume; 1 cubic metre.

STEREOCHEMISTRY. Chemistry involving consideration of the arrangement in space of the atoms in a molecule. If a molecule is considered as a three-dimensional entity in space, possibilities of *stereoisomerism* or space *isomerism* (q.v.) arise; thus, a molecule consisting of four different radicals or atoms attached to a central carbon atom can exist in two distinct space arrangements, one being a mirror image of the other. Such isomerism is associated with *optical activity* (q.v.).

STEREOISOMERISM. *Isomerism* (q.v.) caused by possibilities of different arrangement in three-dimensional space of the atoms within a molecule, resulting in two isomers which are mirror images of each other.

STEREOSCOPE. Optical device by which two-dimensional pictures are given the appearance of depth and solidity.

STEROLS. Class of complex organic *alcohols* (q.v.), including *cholesterol* and *ergosterol* (q.v.); present in most living organisms and play many essential parts in the body processes.

STIBINE, antimony hydride. SbH_3. Poisonous gas.

STIBNITE. Natural antimony sulphide, Sb_2S_3. Principal ore of antimony.

STOICHIOMETRY. Part of chemistry dealing with the composition of substances; more particularly with the determination of combining proportions or *chemical equivalents* (q.v.).

STOKES' LAW. A small sphere falling under the action of gravity through a viscous medium ultimately reaches a constant velocity equal to

$$v = \frac{2gr^2(d_1 - d_2)}{9\eta}$$ where r = radius of the sphere, d_1 = density of the sphere, d_2 = density of the medium, and η = the coefficient of viscosity of the medium.

STORAGE BATTERY. See *accumulator*.

STRAIN (phys.). When a body is deformed by an applied *stress* (q.v.) the strain is the ratio of the dimensional change to the original or unstrained dimension. The strain may be a ratio of lengths, areas or volumes.

STRAIN GAUGE, ELECTRICAL. Consists essentially of a grid of fine resistance wire supported on a paper base. This is attached by a suitable adhesive to the surface under test, so that any strains set up in the latter are accurately transferred to the gauge wire. The electrical resistance of the gauge is proportional to the *strain* (q.v.), so that methods of measuring resistance may be used for measuring strain. The gauge is suitable for measuring strains of the order of 10^{-4} to 10^{-2}.

STRATOSPHERE. Layer of the atmosphere beginning approximately 7 miles above the surface of the Earth.

STRATUM. Layer.

STREAM-LINE. A *stream-line* is a line in a fluid such that the tangent to it at every point is in the direction of the velocity of the fluid particle at that point, at the instant under consideration. When the motion of the fluid is such that, at any instant, continuous stream-lines can be drawn through the whole length of its course, the fluid is said to be in *stream-line flow*.

STREPTOMYCIN. *Antibiotic* (q.v.) substance produced by the *Actinomyces* mould. Effective against several types of disease bacteria, including some against which *penicillin* (q.v.) is inactive.

STRESS (phys.). A force per unit area. When a stress is applied to a body (within its *elastic limit*, q.v.) a corresponding strain is produced, and the ratio of stress to strain is a characteristic constant of the body. See *elastic modulus.*

STROBOSCOPE. An instrument with the aid of which it is possible to view objects which are moving rapidly with a periodic motion (*see period*) and to see them as if they were at rest. For example, if a disc, rotating at n revolutions per second, is illuminated by a source which is flashing at the same frequency, then at any particular flash the eye will see the disc in exactly the same position as it was for the previous flash. The disc will therefore appear stationary. If the frequency of the motion is not quite equal to that of the flashing, the disc will appear to rotate slowly.

STRONTIUM. Sr. Element. A.W. 87·63. At. No. 38. Reactive metal resembling calcium. S.G. 2·6; m.p. 752° C. Occurs as celestine, $SrSO_4$, and strontianite, $SrCO_3$. Compounds colour a flame crimson; used in fireworks. Strontium oxide, SrO, combines with cane-sugar to form an insoluble 'saccharate'; this is used in sugar refining.

STRYCHNINE. $C_{21}H_{22}N_2O_2$. *Alkaloid* (q.v.) which occurs in the seeds of *nux vomica*. White, crystalline substance, slightly soluble in water; m.p. 284°C. Has an intensely bitter taste and a powerful and very dangerous action on the nervous system. Used in medicine in minute doses.

SUB-. Prefix denoting under, below.

SUB-ATOMIC. Term applied to particles smaller than, or forming a part of, the atom. See *atom, structure of.*

SUBLIMATE. Solid obtained by the direct condensation of a vaporized solid without passing through the liquid state.

SUBLIMATION (chem.). The conversion of a solid direct into vapour, and subsequent condensation, without melting.

SUBSTANTIVE DYES. See *direct dyes.*

SUBSTITUTION PRODUCT. A compound obtained by replacing an atom or group by another atom or group in a molecule.

SUBTEND (math.). Two points, A and B, are said to *subtend* the angle ACB at the point C.

SUCCINIC ACID. $(CH_2COOH)_2$. White crystalline organic dibasic acid, m.p. 185° C. Used in the manufacture of dyes, lacquers and other products.

SUCCINITE. *Amber* (q.v.).

SUCROCLASTIC. Sugar-splitting; applied to *enzymes* (q.v.) which have the power of hydrolyzing complex carbohydrates. E.g. *invertase* (q.v.).

SUCROSE. Cane-sugar, beet sugar, saccharose. Common 'sugar' of the household. $C_{12}H_{22}O_{11}$. White, sweet, crystalline solid, m.p. 160° C.–186° C. Found in numerous plants, particularly the sugar cane, sugar beet and maple tree sap.

SUCTION. This is not a positive force which 'draws' a liquid up; a liquid raised by so-called suction is actually pushed up by atmospheric pressure, which is greater than the pressure of the partial vacuum caused by the suction.

SUGAR. In general, any sweet, soluble *carbohydrate* (q.v.); term commonly applied to *sucrose* (q.v.).

SUGAR OF LEAD. *Lead acetate* (q.v.).

SULPHATE. Salt of *sulphuric acid* (q.v.).

SULPHATE OF AMMONIA. See *ammonium sulphate*.

SULPHIDE. A *binary compound* (q.v.) of an element or group with sulphur; a salt of hydrogen sulphide, H_2S.

SULPHITE. Salt of sulphurous acid, H_2SO_3.

SULPHONAMIDE DRUGS. A group of organic compounds, containing the sulphonamide group $SO_2.NH_2$ or its derivatives; includes prontosil, sulphanilamide, uleron, M. & B. 693 and numerous others. Of immense value in the treatment of several bacterial diseases.

SULPHUR. S. Element. A.W. 32·066. At. No. 16. Non-metallic element occurring in several *allotropic forms* (q.v.). The stable form under ordinary conditions is rhombic or *alpha*-sulphur, a pale-yellow brittle crystalline solid, S.G. 2·07, m.p. 112·8° C., b.p. 444·6° C. Burns with a blue flame to give sulphur dioxide; combines with many metals to form sulphides. Occurs as the element in many volcanic regions and as sulphides of many metals. Extracted in vast quantities in Texas by the *Frasch process* (q.v.). Used in the manufacture of sulphuric acid, carbon disulphide, for vulcanizing rubber, in the manufacture of dyes and various chemicals, for killing moulds and pests, and in medicine. Essential to life.

SULPHUR DIOXIDE. SO_2. Colourless gas with a choking, penetrating smell; liquid SO_2 is used in refrigerators.

SULPHUR POINT. The temperature of equilibrium between liquid sulphur and its vapour at a pressure of one standard atmosphere; 444·6° C.

SULPHUR TRIOXIDE. SO_3. White crystalline solid, m.p. 16·8° C. Combines with water to form sulphuric acid.

SULPHURETTED HYDROGEN. See *hydrogen sulphide*.

SULPHURIC ACID. Vitriol, oil of vitriol. Colourless, oily liquid. S.G. 1·84. Extremely corrosive, reacts violently with water with evolution of heat, chars organic matter. Dibasic acid. Prepared by the *lead chamber* and the *contact* processes. Used extensively in many processes in chemical industry, and in the lead *accumulator* (q.v.).

SULPHURIC ACID, FUMING. *Oleum* (q.v.).

SULPHURIC ETHER. See *ether*.

SUN, THE. Incandescent, approximately spherical, heavenly body, round which the planets rotate in elliptical orbits (see *solar system*). Mean distance from the Earth, approximately 93 million miles; diameter, about 866,000 miles; mass, 2×10^{27} tons; mean temperature, 5700° C.; average density 1·4. *Spectrum analysis* (q.v.) shows that it is composed of many of the elements found in the Earth, and no others.

SUN-SPOTS. Large patches, which appear black by contrast with their surroundings, visible upon the surface of the Sun. Owing to the rotation of the Sun, they appear to move across its surface. Their appearance is spasmodic, but their number reaches a maximum approximately every eleven years. Connected with such phenomena as magnetic storms and the Aurora Borealis.

SUPER-. Prefix denoting over, above.

SUPER-CONDUCTIVITY. The electrical resistance of a metal or alloy is a function of temperature, decreasing as the temperature falls and tending to zero at the *absolute zero* (q.v.). It is found that for certain metals and alloys (e.g. lead, vanadium, tin) the resistance changes abruptly, becoming vanishingly small at a temperature in the neighbourhood of a few degrees *above* absolute zero. This phenomenon is termed super-conductivity, and the temperature at which it sets in is the *transition temperature*.

SUPERCOOLING, undercooling. The *metastable* (q.v.) state of a liquid cooled below its freezing point. A supercooled liquid will usually freeze on the addition of a small particle of the solid substance, and often on the addition of any solid particle or even on shaking; the temperature then rises to the freezing point.

SUPERHEATED STEAM. Steam above a temperature of $100°$ C.; obtained by heating water under a pressure greater than atmospheric.

SUPERHEATING. Heating a liquid above its boiling point, when the liquid is in a *metastable* (q.v.) state. See *supercooling*.

'SUPERHET'. Superheterodyne receiver. Electronic circuit used in radio receivers which employs *intermediate frequency* (q.v.) amplification.

SUPERPHOSPHATE. Artificial *fertilizer* (q.v.) consisting mainly of calcium dihydrogen phosphate, $Ca(H_2PO_4)_2$.

SUPERSATURATION. The *metastable* (q.v.) state of a solution holding more dissolved solute than is required to saturate the solution.

SUPERSONICS, ultrasonics. High-frequency pressure waves of the same nature as sound waves, but of a frequency above the limit of *audibility* (q.v.). Such vibrations may be produced by the rapid vibration of a quartz crystal making use of the inverse *piezo-electric effect* (q.v.).

SUPPLEMENTARY ANGLES. Angles together totalling $180°$, or two right angles.

SURD. Irrational quantity; a *root* (q.v.) which cannot be expressed as an exact number or fraction; e.g. $\sqrt{2}$.

SURFACE ACTIVE AGENT. Substance introduced into a liquid in order to affect (usually to increase) its spreading, wetting, and similar properties. Many *detergents* (q.v.) fall into this class.

SURFACE COLOUR. Certain reflecting surfaces, e.g. metal surfaces exhibit selective reflection of light waves; i.e. they reflect some wavelengths (colours) more readily than others. When illuminated by white light, such surfaces reflect light deficient in certain wave-lengths, and the body appears coloured. The body is then said to show surface colour, as opposed to *pigment colour* (q.v.). Bodies showing surface colour when viewed by transmitted light appear to be of the *complementary colour* (q.v.) to that observed when viewed by reflected light. Substances which show pigment colour appear the same colour whether viewed by reflected or transmitted light.

SURFACE TENSION. An open surface of a liquid is under a state of tension, causing a tendency for the portions of the surface to separate from each other; the surface thus shows properties similar to those of a stretched elastic film over the liquid. The tension is an effect of the forces of attraction existing between the molecules of a liquid. Measured by the force per unit length acting in the surface at right angles to an element of any line drawn in the surface. A surface tension exists in any boundary surface of a liquid.

SUSCEPTIBILITY, MAGNETIC. See *magnetic susceptibility*.

SUSPENSION (chem.). A two-phase system (see *phase*) consisting of very small solid particles distributed in a liquid dispersion medium.

SUSPENSOID SOL. See *colloidal solutions*.

SYLVINE. Natural potassium chloride, KCl, usually containing sodium chloride as an impurity. Important source of potassium compounds.

SYMBOL (chem.). A letter or letters representing an atom of an element; e.g. S = one atom of sulphur. Often loosely taken to mean the element in general, e.g. Fe = iron. See *formula*.

SYMMETRY. The correspondence of parts of a figure with reference to a plane, line or point of symmetry. Thus, a circle is symmetrical about any diameter; a sphere is symmetrical about a plane of any great circle.

SYNCHROTRON. Apparatus for accelerating electrons to energies greater than those obtainable with the *betatron* (q.v.), thus producing an appreciable increase in the mass of the electron (see *relativity, theory of*). Its design combines features of both the betatron and the *cyclotron* (q.v.).

SYNERESIS. Separation of liquid from a *gel* (q.v.).

SYNODIC PERIOD OF A PLANET. The period between two successive *conjunctions* (q.v.) with the Sun, as observed from the Earth.

SYNTHESIS (chem.). 'Putting together'; the formation of a compound from its elements or simpler compounds.

SYNTHETIC (chem.). Artificially prepared from the component elements or simpler materials; not obtained directly from natural sources.

T

TALC. Hydrated magnesium silicate, $3MgO.4SiO_2.H_2O$.

TALLOW. The rendered fat of animals, particularly cattle and sheep. Consists of various *glycerides* (q.v.).

TANGENT OF AN ANGLE. See *trigonometrical ratios*.

TANGENT TO A CURVE. A straight line touching the curve at a point.

The tangent to a *circle* (q.v.) at any point is at right angles to the radius of the circle at that point.

TANGENT GALVANOMETER. *Galvanometer* (q.v.) consisting of a coil of wire held in a vertical plane parallel to the magnetic field of the Earth, and a small magnetic needle pivoted at the centre of the coil and free to rotate in a horizontal plane. A direct current flowing through the coil produces a magnetic field at right angles to that of the Earth. The needle takes up the direction of the resultant of these two fields. The tangent (see *trigonometrical ratios*) of the angle of deflection of the needle from its equilibrium position parallel to the Earth's field is proportional to the current passing through the coil. The galvanometer may be used to measure current in absolute *electromagnetic units* (q.v.).

TANNIC ACID. White, amorphous, soluble solid extracted from gall-nuts; a class of similar substances widely distributed in plants. Ester-like (see *esters*) in chemical constitution, of high molecular weight. Used in *tanning* (q.v.) and in the manufacture of ink.

TANNING. The conversion of natural raw hide of animals into leather by the chemical action of substances containing *tannin* (q.v.), *tannic acid* (q.v.), or other agents.

TANNINS, THE. Class of organic substances of vegetable origin, of which *tannic acid* (q.v.) is representative.

TANTALUM. Ta. Element. A.W. 180·88. At. No. 73. Greyish-white metal, very ductile and malleable. S.G. 16·6, m.p. 2850° C. Occurs together with niobium in a few rare minerals; extracted by reduction of the oxide with carbon in an electric furnace. Used for electric lamp filaments, in alloys, in cemented carbides for very hard tools, and in electrolytic rectifiers.

TAR. Name given to various dark, viscous organic materials; e.g. *coaltar* (q.v.).

TARTAR. See *argol*.

TARTAR EMETIC. Potassium antimonyl tartrate,
$$2K(SbO)C_4H_4O_6.H_2O.$$
Used in medicine and as a mordant in dyeing.

TARTARIC ACID. $COOH.(CH.OH)_2.COOH$. Organic acid existing in four stereoisomeric forms (see *stereoisomerism*). The common form, *d*-tartaric acid, obtained from *argol* (q.v.), is a white, soluble, crystal-line solid, m.p. 170° C. Used in dyeing, calico-printing, and in making baking-powder and effervescent 'health salts'.

TARTRATE. Salt of *tartaric acid* (q.v.).

TAUTOMERISM, dynamic isomerism. The existence of a compound as a mixture of two *isomers* (q.v.) in equilibrium. The two forms are con-vertible one into another, and removal of one of the forms from the mixture results in the conversion of part of the other to restore the equilibrium; but each of the two forms may give rise to a stable series of derivatives.

TEAR GASES, lachrymators. Substances which can be distributed in the form of a vapour or smoke, producing an irritating effect on the eyes.

TECHNETIUM, masurium. Element. A.W. 100 approximately, At. No. 43. Very rare.

TELEGRAPH. A method of transmitting messages over a distance by means of electrical impulses sent through wires. By depressing a key at the transmitting end, a circuit is closed and a current flows through the conducting wire or cable to the receiver; the dots and dashes of the Morse code being obtained by varying the length of time for which the current flows. At the receiving end, the feeble electrical impulses are made to operate a *relay* (q.v.), which then closes a local circuit, carrying a larger current. This current either sounds a *buzzer* (q.v.), a telephone-receiver, or causes the dots and dashes to be automatically recorded.

TELEMETER. Apparatus for recording a physical event at a distance.

TELEPHONE. The circuit, which is closed when the line is connected, consists essentially of a transmitter and a receiver connected by an electrical conductor. The transmitter is usually a carbon *microphone* (q.v.), by means of which variable electrical impulses, depending on the nature of the sounds made into the microphone, are caused to flow through the circuit. In the telephone-receiver these impulses flow through a pair of coils of wire wound upon soft iron pole-pieces attached to the poles of a magnet; an iron diaphragm near these coils experiences variable pulls, and thus vibrates so as to produce sounds corresponding to those made into the microphone.

TELEPHOTO LENS. Combination of a convex and a concave *lens* (q.v.), used to replace the ordinary lens of a camera in order to magnify the normal image. The size of the image obtained on the photographic film varies as the *focal length* (q.v.) of the lens. The telephoto lens system increases the effective focal length without the necessity of increasing the distance between the film and the lens. See *camera; photography*.

TELESCOPE. Device for viewing magnified images of distant objects. In the *refracting telescope* the objective is a large convex lens which produces a small, bright, real image; this is viewed through the eye-piece, which is another convex lens, serving to magnify the image. In the *reflecting telescope* a large concave mirror is used instead of the objective lens to produce the real image, which is then magnified by the eye-piece. For terrestrial needs, these types of telescope are unsuitable, since the images formed are inverted; for terrestrial purposes telescopes are equipped with a further lens or prism which causes the image to be seen erect.

TELEVISION. The transmission of visible moving images by means of electro-magnetic wireless waves.

TELLURIUM. Te. Element. A.W. 127·61. At. No. 52. Silvery-white, brittle non-metal, resembling sulphur in its chemical properties. S.G. 6·24, m.p. 452° C. Exists in several *allotropic forms* (q.v.).

TEMPERATURE. The temperature of a body is a measure of its 'hotness' or 'coldness', primary physical ideas which themselves cannot be precisely defined. It may, however, be said that the change in temperature of a body is a measure of the change in energy of the atoms or molecules of which the substance is composed. Measured in degrees *Centigrade*, *Fahrenheit*, *Réaumur* or *absolute* (q.v.).

TEMPERATURE SCALE, INTERNATIONAL. A practical scale of temperature defined to conform as closely as possible to the thermodynamic Centigrade scale (see *thermodynamic temperature scale*). The *ice* and *steam* points are first assigned the values 0° and 100° C. respectively. Other reproducible equilibrium temperatures are assigned numerical values from measurements using the *gas thermometer* (q.v.). Any temperature is then determined on this scale by using the stated interpolation instrument for the temperature range under investigation; e.g. for the range 0° C.–660° C. the interpolation instrument to be used is the *platinum resistance thermometer* (q.v.). The instrument is calibrated at the fixed equilibrium temperatures according to a specified procedure.

TEMPERING OF STEEL. Imparting a definite degree of hardness to steel by heating to a definite temperature (which is sometimes determined by the colour which the steel assumes) and then quenching, i.e. cooling, in oil or water.

TEMPORARY HARDNESS OF WATER. Hardness of water, which is destroyed by boiling. See *hard water*.

TEMPORARY MAGNETISM, induced magnetism. Magnetism which a body (e.g. soft iron) possesses only by virtue of being in a magnetic field and which largely disappears on removing the body from the field.

TENACITY, tensile strength. The tensile (pulling) stress which has to be applied to a material to break it. Measured as a force per unit area; e.g. dynes per square centimetre; pounds or tons per square inch.

TENSOR. Quantity expressing the ratio in which the length of a *vector* (q.v.) is increased.

TENTH-METRE. *Ångström unit* (q.v.).

TERBIUM. Tb. Element. A.W. 159·2. At. No. 65. See *rare earths*.

TERMINAL VELOCITY. If a body free to move in a resisting medium is acted upon by a constant force (e.g. a body falling under the force of gravity through the atmosphere), the body accelerates until a certain terminal velocity is reached, after which the velocity remains constant.

TERPENES. Class of *hydrocarbons* (q.v.) occurring in many fragrant essential oils of plants. Colourless liquids, generally with a pleasant smell; include *pinene*, $C_{10}H_{16}$, the chief ingredient of oil of turpentine; and *limonene*, $C_{10}H_{16}$, found in the essential oils of oranges and lemons.

TERRESTRIAL MAGNETISM. See *magnetism, terrestrial*.

TERVALENT, trivalent. Having a *valency* (q.v.) of three.

TETRA-. Prefix denoting four, fourfold.

TETRAD. Element having a *valency* (q.v.) of four.

TETRAHEDRON. Four-faced, solid figure, contained by four triangles; a pyramid with a triangular base.

TETRODE. *Thermionic valve* (q.v.) containing four electrodes; a cathode, an anode or plate, a control grid, and (between the two latter) a screen grid. The screen grid serves to prevent interaction between the control grid and the anode.

THALLIUM. Tl. Element. A.W. 204·39. At. No. 81. White malleable metal resembling lead. S.G. 11·85, m.p. 303·5° C.

THEINE. See *caffeine*.

THEODOLITE. Instrument for the measurement of angles, used in surveying. Consists essentially of a telescope moving along a circular scale graduated in degrees.

THEOREM. A statement or proposition which is proved by logical reasoning from given facts and justifiable assumptions.

THERAPEUTICS. Healing; remedial treatment of diseases.

THERM. Practical unit of quantity of heat; 100,000 *British thermal units* (q.v.), 25,200,000 calories.

THERMAL DIFFUSION. If a temperature gradient is maintained over a volume of gas containing molecules of different masses, the heavier molecules tend to diffuse down the temperature gradient, and the lighter molecules in the opposite direction. This forms the basis of a method of separating the different *isotopes* (q.v.) of an element in certain cases.

THERMAL DISSOCIATION. See *dissociation*.

THERMAL NEUTRONS. *Neutrons* (q.v.) of very slow speed and consequently of low energy. Their energy is of the same order as the thermal energy of the atoms or molecules of the substance through which they are passing. Thermal neutrons are responsible for numerous types of nuclear reactions, including *nuclear fission* (q.v.).

THERMAL VALUE OF A CHEMICAL REACTION. The quantity of heat given out or absorbed in a chemical reaction, usually per gram-equivalent of reacting substances. See *Hess's law*.

THERMION. *Ion* (q.v.) emitted by a hot body.

THERMIONIC VALVE, tube. A system of electrodes arranged in an evacuated glass or metal envelope. For special purposes a gas at low pressure may be introduced into the valve. The electrodes are: (1) a cathode which emits electrons when heated; (2) an anode or plate maintained at a positive potential with respect to the cathode; the electrons emitted by the latter are attracted to it. Most valves also contain a number of perforated electrodes or grids interposed between the cathode and anode, designed to control the flow of current through the valve. The cathode can be in the form of a filament heated by an electric current passing through it, or an electrode heated indirectly by a separate filament. See *diode, triode, tetrode, pentode*.

THERMIONICS. Branch of science dealing with the emission of *electrons* (q.v.) from substances under the action of heat.

THERMISTOR. A *semi-conductor* (q.v.), the electrical resistance of which decreases rapidly with increase of temperature; e.g. the resistance may be of the order of 10^5 ohms at 20° C. and only 10 ohms at 100° C. Used as a sensitive temperature-measuring device.

THERMIT, thermite. A mixture of aluminium powder and the oxide of a metal, e.g. iron oxide. When ignited by magnesium ribbon, a chemical action begins in which the aluminium combines with the oxygen of the oxide, forming aluminium oxide and the metal. A great quantity of heat is given out during the action, the reduced metal appearing in the molten state. The mixture is used for welding iron and steel, and in incendiary bombs; the principle is applied in the extraction of certain metals from their oxides (see *Goldschmidt process*).

THERMOCHEMISTRY. Branch of physical chemistry dealing with the quantities of heat absorbed or evolved during chemical reactions. See *Hess's law*.

THERMOCOUPLE. Instrument for the measurement of temperature. Consists of two wires of different metals joined at each end. One junction is at the point where the temperature is to be measured and the other is kept at a lower fixed temperature. Owing to this difference of temperature of the junctions, a thermo-electric E.M.F. is generated, causing a current to flow in the circuit (see *Seebeck effect*). This current can be measured by means of a *galvanometer* (q.v.) in the circuit, or the thermo-electric E.M.F. can be measured using a *potentiometer* (q.v.).

THERMODYNAMIC TEMPERATURE SCALE. Temperature scale independent of the physical properties of any material substance and set up solely from the thermodynamical considerations of the heat exchanges in an ideal *Carnot cycle* (q.v.). An example is the scale of the *absolute thermodynamic temperature* (q.v.).

THERMODYNAMICS. The study of the general laws governing processes which involve heat changes.

THERMODYNAMICS, LAWS OF. 1. Heat and mechanical work are mutually convertible, and in any operation involving such conversion one calorie of heat is equivalent to $4 \cdot 18 \times 10^7$ ergs of mechanical work. 2. Heat cannot be transferred by any continuous, self-sustaining process from a colder to a hotter body. 3. The *absolute zero* (q.v.) of temperature can never be attained.

THERMO-ELECTRIC POWER. The rate of change of the thermo-electric E.M.F. of a *thermocouple* (q.v.) circuit with the temperature of the hot junction.

THERMO-ELECTRICITY. Electricity produced by the direct conversion of heat energy into electrical energy. See *thermocouple; Thomson effect*.

THERMOGRAPH. Self-registering thermometer; apparatus which records temperature variations during a period of time on a graph.

THERMOMETER. Instrument for the measurement of temperature. Any physical property of a substance which varies with temperature can be used to measure the latter; e.g. the volume of a liquid or gas maintained under a fixed pressure; the pressure of a gas at constant volume; the electrical resistance of a conductor; the E.M.F. produced at a thermocouple junction, etc. The property chosen depends on the temperature range, the accuracy required and the ease with which the instrument can be made and used. The common mercury thermometer depends upon the expansion of mercury with rise in temperature. The mercury is contained in a bulb attached to a narrow graduated sealed tube; the expansion of the mercury in the bulb causes a thin thread of it to rise in the tube. See also *gas thermometer; pyrometers; resistance thermometer; thermocouple*.

THERMOMETER, BECKMANN. See *Beckmann thermometer*.

THERMOMETER, CLINICAL. Mercury thermometer designed to measure the temperature of the human body, and graduated to cover a range of a few degrees on either side of the normal body temperature. A constriction in the tube near the bulb causes the mercury thread to break when the thermometer is taken away from the warm body, and the mercury in the bulb starts to contract. The thread thus remains in the tube to indicate the maximum temperature reached, until it is shaken down.

THERMOMETER, GAS. See *gas thermometer*.

THERMOMETER, MAXIMUM AND MINIMUM. Thermometer which records the highest and lowest temperatures reached during a period of time. Consists of a bulb filled with alcohol, which, by expansion, pushes a mercury thread along a fine tube, graduated in degrees. At each end of the mercury thread is a small steel 'index' which is pushed by the mercury; one is thus left at the farthest point reached by the mercury thread, corresponding to the maximum temperature, and the other at the lowest point.

THERMO-MILLIAMMETER. Instrument for measuring small alternating electric currents. The current passes through a wire made of *constantan* (q.v.) or platinum, which is in contact with or very close to a *thermocouple* (q.v.). The thermocouple is connected to a sensitive milliammeter, the heat of the constantan wire producing a thermo-electric current in the thermocouple; this current is recorded by the milliammeter. In a more sensitive instrument, the heater wire and thermocouple are arranged in an evacuated quartz envelope.

THERMOPILE. Instrument for detecting and measuring heat radiations. Consists of a number of rods of antimony and bismuth, connected alternately in series. When the junctions are exposed to heat, the thermo-electric current produced (see *thermocouple*) may be detected or measured by a sensitive galvanometer.

THERMOPLASTIC. Substance which becomes plastic on being heated; a plastic material which can be repeatedly melted or softened by heat without change of properties.

THERMOSETTING PLASTICS. *Plastics* (q.v.) which, having once been subjected to heat (and pressure), are resistant to further heat treatment.

THERMOSTAT. Instrument for maintaining a constant temperature, by the use of a device which cuts off the supply of heat when the required temperature is exceeded, and automatically restores the supply when the temperature falls below that required.

THIO-. Prefix denoting sulphur, in the naming of chemical compounds.

THIOKOLS. Rubber-like polymer materials of the general formula $(RS_x)_n$, where R is an organic bivalent radical, and x is usually between 2 and 4. Very resistant to the swelling action of oils. Undergo a form of vulcanization on being heated with certain metallic oxides.

THIXOTROPY. Defined as the rate of change of viscosity with time. Certain liquids, e.g. some paints, possess the property of increasing in *viscosity* (q.v.) with the passage of time when the liquid is left undisturbed. On shaking, the viscosity returns to its original value.

THOMSON EFFECT, Kelvin effect. A temperature gradient along a conducting wire gives rise to an *electric potential* (q.v.) gradient along the wire.

THORIUM. Th. Element. A.W. 232·12. At. No. 90. Dark grey radioactive metal, S.G. 11·2, m.p. 1845° C. Compounds occur in *monazite.*

THRESHOLD FREQUENCY. Light incident on a metal surface will give rise to the emission of electrons (see *photo-electric effect*) only if the frequency of the light is greater than a certain *threshold frequency*, which is characteristic of the metal used.

THULIUM. Tm. Element. A.W. 169·4. At. No. 69. See *rare earths.*

THYMOL, 3-hydroxy-*p*-cymene. $C_{10}H_{14}O$. Organic compound belonging to the *phenols* (q.v.). White crystals, m.p. 51·5° C., b.p. 233·5° C. Smells of thyme. Occurs in many essential oils; used as a mild antiseptic.

TIDES are caused by the attraction exerted upon the seas by the Moon, and to a lesser extent by the Sun. At full and new moon the tidal force of the Sun is added to that of the Moon, causing high *spring tides;* while at half-moons the forces are opposed, causing low *neap tides.*

TIMBRE. See *quality of sound.*

TIME MEASUREMENT. The unit of time is the *second* (q.v.), based upon the fundamental unit of the *sidereal day* (q.v.), to which all time-measuring devices are ultimately referred. Such devices include the *pendulum* (q.v.) and the *quartz clock* (q.v.). See also *year.*

TIN. Sn. (Stannum.) Element. A.W. 118·70. At. No. 50. Silvery-white metal, S.G. 7·31, m.p. 231·85° C. Soft, malleable and ductile. Unaffected by air or water at ordinary temperatures. Occurs in three *allotropic forms* (q.v.), below 18° C. passes into 'grey tin', causing 'tin plague'. Occurs as tin oxide, SnO_2, cassiterite or tinstone. Metal is

extracted by heating the oxide with powdered carbon in a reverberatory furnace. Used for tin-plating and in many alloys.

TIN PLAGUE. Allotropic change (see *allotropy*) in which white tin
changes into a grey, powdery form at low temperatures.

TIN PLATE. Iron coated with a thin layer of tin, by dipping into the
molten metal.

TINCAL. Impure form of *borax* (q.v.).

TINSTONE. See *cassiterite*.

TITANIUM. Ti. Element. A.W. 47·90, At. No. 22. Malleable and ductile
metal resembling iron. S.G. 4·5, m.p. 2000° C. Compounds are fairly
widely distributed in Nature, but the metal is difficult to extract.
Used in alloys. The oxide, TiO_2, is used as a white pigment.

TITRATION. Operation forming the basis of *volumetric analysis* (q.v.).
The addition of measured amounts of a solution of one reagent from
a *burette* (q.v.) to a definite amount of another reagent until the action
between them is complete, i.e. till the second reagent is completely
used up.

T.N.T. See *trinitrotoluene*.

TOLUENE, toluol. $C_6H_5CH_3$. *Hydrocarbon* (q.v.) of the benzene series.
Colourless, inflammable liquid with a peculiar smell. B.p. 110° C.
Occurs in coal-tar. Used as a starting-point in the preparation of dyes,
drugs, saccharin, and T.N.T.

TOLUIDINE. $CH_3.C_6H_4.NH_2$. Amine derived from toluene. Exists in
three isomeric forms. Used for making dyes.

TOLUOL. *Toluene* (q.v.).

TONE OF SOUND. See *quality of sound*.

TONNE. Metric ton; 1000 kilograms; 2204·62 lb., 0·9842 ton.

TOPAZ. Crystalline aluminium silicate and fluoride.

TORQUE. *Couple* (q.v.).

TORRICELLIAN VACUUM. Space, containing mercury vapour, which
is produced at the top of a column of mercury when a long tube sealed
at one end is filled with mercury and inverted in a trough of the metal.
The mercury sinks in the tube until it is balanced by the atmospheric
pressure (see *barometer*), the *Torricellian vacuum* being the space above
it. See Fig. 1.

TORSION. 'Twisting' about an axis, produced by the action of two
opposing *couples* (q.v.) acting in parallel planes.

TORSION BALANCE. If a wire is acted upon by a *couple* (q.v.) the axis of
which coincides with the wire, the wire twists through an angle
determined by the applied couple and the *rigidity modulus* (q.v.) of
the wire. The amount of twist produced can thus be used to measure
an applied force. In the torsion balance, the force to be measured is
applied at right angles to, and at the end of, an arm attached to the
wire.

TOTAL INTERNAL REFLECTION. When light passes from one medium
to another which is optically less dense, e.g. from glass to air (see

refraction and *density, optical*), the ray is bent away from the normal. If the incident ray meets the surface at such an angle that the refracted ray must be bent away at an angle of more than 90°, the light cannot emerge at all, and is totally internally reflected.

TOURMALINE. Class of natural crystalline minerals, consisting of silicates of various metals and containing boron. The crystals show some interesting pyro-electric, piezo-electric and optical effects.

TOXIC. Poisonous.

TOXICOLOGY. The study of poisons.

TOXIN. Poison; the name is generally confined to intensely poisonous substances produced by certain bacteria, which cause dangerous effects when they attack food or the human body.

TRACER. See *radioactive tracing*.

TRAJECTORY. The path of a *projectile* (q.v.).

TRANS-FORM. See *cis-trans isomerism*.

TRANSFORMATION CONSTANT, decay constant, radioactive constant. The decay of all radioactive isotopes (see *radioactivity*) is exponential; i.e. the number N of radioactive atoms of a given isotope present in a substance at time t is given by $N = N_o e^{-\lambda t}$, where N_o is the number of radioactive atoms of this isotope originally present ($t = 0$). The constant λ is characteristic of the particular isotope in question, and is called the *transformation constant* for that isotope.

TRANSFORMER. Device by which an alternating current of one voltage is changed to another voltage, without alteration in frequency. A step-up transformer, which increases the voltage and diminishes the current, consists in principle of an iron core on which is wound a *primary coil* of a small number of turns of thick, insulated wire; and, forming a separate circuit, a *secondary coil* of a larger number of turns of thin, insulated wire. When the low-voltage current is passed through the primary coil, it induces a current in the secondary (see *induction*) by producing an alternating magnetic field in the iron core. The ratio of the voltage in the primary to that in the secondary is very nearly equal to the ratio of the number of turns in the primary to that in the secondary. The step-down transformer works on the same principle, with the coils reversed.

TRANSISTOR. A device which may be used to amplify currents and perform other functions usually performed by the *thermionic valve* (q.v.). Consists essentially of a small block of germanium, which is a *semiconductor* (q.v.) with two closely spaced metallic point electrodes (termed the *emitter* and the *collector* electrodes) on the upper surface, and a plane electrode of large area (the *base* electrode) on the opposite surface. The emitter is maintained at a positive potential, and the collector at a larger negative potential, with respect to the base. The signal to be amplified is introduced into the emitter circuit and the amplified signal appears in the collector circuit.

TRANSITION TEMPERATURE. Transition point. The temperature at which one form of a polymorphous substance (see *polymorphism*) changes into another; the temperature at which both forms can co-exist.

TRANSLUCENT. Permitting the passage of light in such a way that an object cannot be seen clearly through the substance; e.g. frosted glass.

TRANSMISSION COEFFICIENT. When a beam of light passes through a medium the light is absorbed to a greater or less extent (depending upon the medium and the wave-length of the light) and the intensity of the beam decreases. The ratio of the intensity after passing through unit distance of the medium to the original intensity is called the transmission coefficient.

TRANSMUTATION OF ELEMENTS. Changing one chemical element into another. Once the aim of alchemy; subsequently held to be impossible; with the present knowledge of *radioactivity* (q.v.) and atomic structure it is seen that the process goes on continuously in radioactive elements. Artificial transmutation by suitable *nuclear reactions* (q.v.) forms the basis of experimental nuclear physics.

TRANSPARENT. Permitting the passage of light in such a way that objects can be seen clearly through the substance.

TRANSURANIC ELEMENTS. Elements beyond uranium in the periodic table; i.e. elements of *atomic number* (q.v.) greater than 92; e.g. neptunium, plutonium, americium and curium. Such elements do not occur in Nature, but may be obtained by suitable *nuclear reactions* (q.v.).

TRANSVERSE. Cross-wise; in a direction at right angles to the length of the body under consideration.

TRANSVERSE WAVES. Waves in which the vibration or displacement takes place in a plane at right angles to the direction of propagation of the wave; e.g. *electromagnetic waves* (q.v.). See also *longitudinal waves*.

TRAPEZIUM. *Quadrilateral* (q.v.) having two of its sides parallel. The area of a trapezium having parallel sides a and b units in length, and vertical height h units is given by $\dfrac{h(a + b)}{2}$.

TRIAD. Element having a *valency* (q.v.) of three.

TRIANGLE. Plane figure bounded by three straight lines. The three angles total 180°. The area of any triangle is given by the following expressions: 1. Half the product of one of the sides and the perpendicular upon it from the opposite vertex ($\frac{1}{2} \times$ base $\times$ height). 2. Half the product of any two of the sides and the sine of the angle between them ($\frac{1}{2} bc \sin A$). 3. $\sqrt{s(s - a)(s - b)(s - c)}$, where a, b and c are the lengths of the sides, and s is half the sum of a, b and c.

TRIANGLE OF FORCES. If three forces acting at the same point can be represented in magnitude and direction by the sides of a triangle taken in order, they will be in equilibrium.

TRIANGLE OF VELOCITIES. If a body has three component velocities which can be represented in magnitude and direction by the sides of a triangle taken in order, the body will remain at rest.

TRIBASIC ACID. An acid having three atoms of *acidic hydrogen* (q.v.) in the molecule, thus giving rise to three possible series of salts; thus, phosphoric acid, H_3PO_4, can give rise to trisodium phosphate, Na_3PO_4; disodium hydrogen phosphate, Na_2HPO_4, and sodium dihydrogen phosphate, NaH_2PO_4.

TRIBO-ELECTRICITY. See *electricity, frictional*.

TRIBOLUMINESCENCE. The emission of light when certain crystals (e.g. cane-sugar) are crushed.

TRIGLYCERIDES. See *glycerides*.

TRIGONOMETRICAL RATIOS. If a perpendicular *AB* is drawn from any point on arm *OA* of an angle *AOB* to the other arm, the following ratios are constant for the particular angle: *AB/AO*, *sine* (sin *AOB*); *OB/AO*, *cosine* (cos *AOB*); *AB/OB*, *tangent* (tan *AOB*); *AO/AB*, *cosecant* (cosec *AOB*); *AO/OB*, *secant* (sec *AOB*) and *OB/AB*, *cotangent* (cot *AOB*). See Fig. 17.

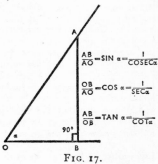

$$\frac{AB}{AO} = \text{SIN } \alpha = \frac{1}{\text{COSEC}\alpha}$$

$$\frac{OB}{AO} = \text{COS } \alpha = \frac{1}{\text{SEC}\alpha}$$

$$\frac{AB}{OB} = \text{TAN } \alpha = \frac{1}{\text{COT}\alpha}$$

FIG. 17.

TRIGONOMETRY. Branch of mathematics using the fact that numerous problems may be solved by the calculation of unknown parts (i.e. sides and angles) of a triangle when three parts are known. The solution of such problems is greatly assisted by the use of the *trigonometrical ratios* (q.v.).

TRILLION. 10^{18}, a million million million (British); 10^{12}, a million million (American).

TRINITROTOLUENE, T.N.T. $C_7H_5(NO_2)_3$. Pale yellow, crystalline solid, made by the *nitration* (q.v.) of *toluene* (q.v.). High explosive.

TRIODE. *Thermionic valve* (q.v.) containing three electrodes: an anode or plate, a cathode and a control grid.

TRIOLEIN, olein. $C_{57}H_{104}O_6$. Glyceride of *oleic acid* (q.v.); liquid oil which occurs in many natural fats and oils.

TRIPALMITIN, palmitin. $C_{51}H_{98}O_6$. Glyceride of *palmitic acid* (q.v.);

solid, fat-like substance which occurs in palm-oil and many other natural fats and oils.

TRIPLE POINT. The point at which the gaseous, liquid and solid phases of a substance are in equilibrium. For a given substance, the triple point occurs at a unique set of values of the temperature, pressure and volume.

TRISTEARIN, stearin. $C_{57}H_{110}O_6$. Glyceride of *stearic acid* (q.v.); solid, fat-like substance which occurs in natural fats; formed by the hydrogenation of triolein. See *hydrogenation of oils*.

TRIVALENT, tervalent. Having a *valency* (q.v.) of three.

TRONA. Natural crystalline sodium sesquicarbonate,
$$Na_2CO_3.NaHCO_3.2H_2O.$$

TROTYL. Trinitrotoluene, *T.N.T.* (q.v.).

TROUTON'S RULE. The ratio of the latent heat of vaporization (see *heat, latent*) per gram-molecule, to the boiling point in degrees Absolute is a constant for all substances. The rule is only approximate.

TROY WEIGHT.

1 grain = 0·0648 gram;
20 grains = 1 scruple;
24 grains = 1 pennyweight;
3 scruples = 1 drachm;
8 drachms = 1 ounce troy = 1·1 ounce avoirdupois.

TRYPSIN. *Enzyme* (q.v.) produced by the pancreas. In the process of digestion, breaks up proteins into *amino-acids* (q.v.).

TUBE OF FORCE. Theoretical concept. Tube formed by the *lines of force* (q.v.) drawn out into space through every point on a small closed curve upon the surface of a charged conductor.

TUNGSTEN. See *wolfram;* both names for this element were officially recognized in 1951.

TUNING, RADIO. Radio tuning is the adjustment of circuit elements to the resonant frequency (see *resonance*) of the wireless waves which it is desired to receive. The natural frequency of oscillation of an electrical circuit depends upon the *inductance* (q.v.) and the *capacity* (q.v.) of the circuit; either of these can be varied to achieve resonance.

TURBINE. Any motor in which a shaft is steadily rotated by the impact of a current of steam, air, water or other fluid directed from jets or nozzles upon blades of a wheel.

TURPENTINE, oil of turpentine. Liquid extracted by distillation of the resin of pine trees. B.p. 155° C.–165° C. Composed chiefly of pinene (see *terpenes*). Used as a solvent.

TURQUOISE. Natural basic aluminium phosphate, coloured blue or green by traces of copper.

TWADDELL SCALE of specific gravity of liquids. Degrees Twaddell = 200 (S.G. − 1); S.G. = 1 + Degrees Twaddell/200.

TYNDALL EFFECT. The scattering of light by particles of matter in the path of the light, thus making a visible 'beam', such as is caused by a ray of light illuminating particles of dust floating in the air of a room.

TYPE METAL. Alloy of 60% lead, 30% antimony and 10% tin. Owing to the presence of antimony, expands on solidifying and thus gives a sharp cast.

U

UDELL, aludel. Earthenware receiver for condensing iodine vapour; shaped like a short pipe with a constricted end.

ULTRA-CENTRIFUGE. High speed *centrifuge* (q.v.). Used in the determination of the molecular weights of large molecules in high polymers. See *polymerization*.

ULTRAMARINE. Artificial form of *lapis lazuli* (q.v.), made by heating together clay, sodium sulphate, carbon and sulphur.

ULTRAMICROSCOPE. Instrument, making use of the *Tyndall effect* (q.v.) for showing the presence of particles which are too small to be seen with the ordinary microscope. A powerful beam of light is brought to a focus in the liquid which is examined; suspended particles appear as bright specks by scattering the light.

ULTRASONICS. See *supersonics*.

ULTRA-VIOLET RAYS. *Electromagnetic waves* (q.v.) in the wave-length range of approximately 4×10^{-5} cm. to 5×10^{-7} cm.; i.e. between visible light waves and *X-rays* (q.v.). The longest ultra-violet waves have wave-lengths just shorter than those of violet light, the shortest perceptible by the human eye. Affect the photographic plate; their action on *ergosterol* (q.v.) in the human body produces vitamin D. Radiation from the Sun is rich in such rays; they may be produced artificially by the *mercury vapour lamp* (q.v.).

UMBRA. Region of complete shadow. See *shadows*.

UNCERTAINTY PRINCIPLE. It is impossible to determine with accuracy both the position and the *momentum* (q.v.) of a particle (e.g. an electron) simultaneously. The more accurately the position is known, the less accurately can the momentum be determined. The principle arises from the wave nature of matter. See *De Broglie wave-length*.

UNIAXIAL CRYSTAL. Doubly refracting crystal possessing only one *optic axis* (q.v.).

UNIT. A quantity or dimension adopted as a standard of measurement.

UNIT QUANTITY. E.g. unit length; a length of one, in whatever system of units is specified.

UNITY (math.). One.

UNIVALENT (chem.). Monovalent. Having a *valency* (q.v.) of one.

UNSATURATED COMPOUND (chem.). A compound having some of the atoms in its molecule linked by more than one *valency bond* (q.v.); a compound which can form *addition compounds* (q.v.).

UNSTABLE (chem.). Easily decomposed.

UNSTABLE EQUILIBRIUM. Defined under *stable equilibrium* (q.v.).

URANIUM. U. Naturally occurring radioactive element. A.W. 238·07, At. No. 92. Hard white metal, S.G. 18·68, m.p. 1850° C. Undergoes *nuclear fission* (q.v.) when bombarded by *neutrons* (q.v.).

URANUS (Astr.). Planet possessing four satellites, with its orbit lying between those of Saturn and Neptune. Mean distance from the Sun, 1783 million miles. Sidereal period ('year') 84 years. Mass approximately 14·6 times that of the Earth. Surface temperature, about $-180°$ C.

URAO. Natural crystalline sodium sesquicarbonate, $Na_2CO_3.NaHCO_3.2H_2O$.

UREA, carbamide. $CO(NH_2)_2$. White, crystalline, organic compound, m.p. 132° C. Occurs in the urine. The first organic compound to be prepared artificially.

URIC ACID. $C_5H_4O_3N_4$. Organic acid, belonging to the purine group; colourless, crystalline solid, slightly soluble in water. Occurs in very small amounts in urine. Sodium and potassium salts of the acid are deposited in the joints in cases of gout.

UROTROPINE. See *hexamethylene tetramine*.

V

VACUUM. Space in which there are no molecules or atoms. A perfect vacuum is unobtainable, since every material which surrounds a space has a definite vapour pressure. The term is generally taken to mean a space containing air or other gas at very low pressure.

VACUUM TUBE. See *thermionic valve*; *discharge in gases*.

VALVE, WIRELESS. See *thermionic valve*.

VALENCY. The combining power of an atom; the number of hydrogen atoms which an atom will combine with or replace. E.g. the valency of oxygen in water, H_2O, is 2.

VALENCY BOND. The link holding atoms together in a molecule. In the case of two univalent atoms joined together, a single valency bond holds them together; it is possible for an atom to satisfy two or three valency bonds of another atom, giving rise to a double or triple bond.

VALENCY, ELECTRONIC THEORY OF. An explanation of *valency* (q.v.) on the basis of modern views on atomic structure (see *atom, structure of*), and particularly on the assumption that certain arrangements of outer electrons in atoms (e.g. 'octets' or outer shells of 8 electrons) are stable and tend to be formed by the transfer or sharing of electrons between atoms. The chief types of linkage are: (1) *electrovalent* bonds formed by the transfer of electrons from one atom to another; the atom which loses an electron becomes a positive *ion* (q.v.), and the other a negative ion. This provides an explanation of the behaviour of *electrolytes* (q.v.). (2) *Covalent* bonds. The sharing of a pair of electrons, one being provided by each atom. This applies to many non-ionizable bonds, e.g. those in organic compounds. (3) *Co-ordinated* bonds. The sharing of a pair of electrons, both provided by the same atom. Many bonds possess electronic configurations intermediate between the above forms.

VAN DE GRAAFF GENERATOR. *Electrostatic generator* (q.v.) used for accelerating charged particles of atomic magnitudes, e.g. *protons* (q.v.), to high energies.

VAN DER WAALS' EQUATION OF STATE. $\left(p + \dfrac{a}{v^2}\right)(v - b) = RT$ for a gram-molecule of a substance in the gaseous and liquid phases where p = pressure, v = volume, T = absolute temperature, R = the *gas constant* (q.v.); $\dfrac{a}{v^2}$ is a correction for the mutual attraction of the molecules, and b is a correction for the actual volume of the molecules themselves. The equation represents the behaviour of ordinary gases more correctly than the 'perfect gas' equation $pv = RT$.

VAN DER WAALS' FORCE. Attractive force existing between atoms or molecules of all substances. The force arises as a result of electrons in neighbouring atoms or molecules (see *atom, structure of*) moving in sympathy with one another. This force is responsible for the term a/v^2 in *van der Waals' equation of state* (q.v.). In many substances this force is small compared with the other inter-atomic attractive and repulsive forces present.

VANADIUM. V. Element. A.W. 50·95. At. No. 23. Very hard white metal, S.G. 5·866, m.p. 1715° C. Occurs in a few rather rare minerals. Used in alloys.

VAPOUR. Substance in the gaseous state, which may be liquefied by increasing the pressure without altering the temperature. A gas below its *critical temperature* (q.v.).

VAPOUR DENSITY. A measure of the density of a gas or vapour; usually given relative to oxygen or hydrogen. The latter is the ratio of the weight of a certain volume of the gas to the weight of an equal volume of hydrogen, measured under the same conditions of temperature and pressure. Numerically this ratio is equal to half the molecular weight of the gas.

VAPOUR PRESSURE. All liquids and solids give off vapour, consisting of molecules of the substance. If the substance is in an enclosed space, the pressure of the vapour will reach a maximum which depends only upon the nature of the substance and the temperature; the vapour is then saturated and its pressure is the *saturated vapour pressure*.

VAREC, kelp. Ash of seaweed, from which iodine is extracted.

VARIABLE (math.). A symbol or term which assumes, or to which may be assigned, different numerical values.

VARIATION (math.). If a quantity y is some function of another quantity x, ($y = f(x)$), then, as x varies, y varies in a manner determined by the function. If $f(x) = x \times$ a constant, then y is said to vary directly as x, or to be directly proportional to x; $y \propto x$. If $f(x) = $ constant$/x$, y is said to vary inversely as x, or to be inversely proportional to x; $y \propto 1/x$.

VASELINE. See *petrolatum*.

VAT DYES. Class of insoluble dyes which are applied by first reducing them to *leuco-compounds* which are soluble in alkalies. The solution is applied to the material, and the insoluble dye is regenerated in the fibres by oxidation. *Indigo* (q.v.) and many synthetic dyes belong to this class.

VECTOR. Any physical quantity which requires a direction to be stated in order to define it completely. E.g. *velocity* (q.v.).

VECTORS, PARALLELOGRAM LAW OF. If a particle is under the action of two like vector quantities which are represented by the two sides of a parallelogram drawn from a point, the resultant of the two vectors is represented in magnitude and direction by the diagonal of the parallelogram drawn through the point.

VECTORS, TRIANGLE LAW OF. If a particle is acted upon by two vector quantities represented by two sides of a triangle taken in order, the resultant vector is represented by the third side of the triangle.

VELOCITIES, PARALLELOGRAM OF. A special case of the parallelogram of vectors. See *parallelogram of velocities*.

VELOCITIES, TRIANGLE OF. A special case of the triangle of vectors. See *triangle of velocities*.

VELOCITY. Rate of motion in a given direction; measured as length per unit time.

VELOCITY RATIO OF A MACHINE. The ratio of the distance through which the point of application of the applied force moves, to the distance through which the point of application of the resistance moves in the same time. For an 'ideal' machine which requires no energy to move its component parts, the velocity ratio is equal to the *mechanical advantage* (q.v.).

VELOCITY, RELATIVE. The velocity of one body relative to another is the rate at which the first body is changing its position with respect to the second. If the velocities of two bodies are represented by two sides of a triangle taken in order, their relative velocity is represented by the third side.

VENETIAN WHITE. A mixture of *white lead* (q.v.) and barium sulphate, $BaSO_4$, in equal parts. Used in paints.

VENUS (Astr.). Planet with its orbit between those of Mercury and the Earth. Mean distance from the Sun, 67 million miles. Sidereal period ('year'), 225 days. Mass, approximately 0·8 that of the Earth. There is no evidence of oxygen in the atmosphere of the planet, which is probably surrounded by a mass of clouds. The temperature is probably higher than that on the Earth.

VERDIGRIS. Green deposit formed upon copper; consists of basic copper carbonate or sulphate of variable composition.

VERMILION. Scarlet form of mercuric sulphide, HgS ; used as a pigment.

VERNIER. Device for measuring subdivisions of a scale. For a scale graduated in (say) inches and tenths, a vernier consists of a scale which slides alongside of the main scale, and on which a length of nine-tenths of an inch is subdivided into ten equal parts. Each vernier division is thus ·09 of an inch. If it is desired to measure a length *AB*, the main scale is placed with its zero mark at *A*, and the vernier scale is slid till its zero mark (the '*V*' of the vernier) is at *B*. By noting which division on the vernier scale is exactly in line with a division on the main scale, the second decimal place of the length *AB* is obtained. Thus, if *B* falls between 4·6 and 4·7 inches on the main scale, and the fourth division on the vernier scale is just in line with a main scale division line, the length *AB* is 4·64 inches. See Fig. 18.

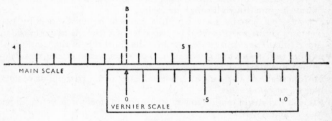

FIG. 18.

VERONAL. Diethyl-barbituric acid; member of the barbiturate group of drugs, used as a hypnotic.

VESICANT. Blister-producing.

VIBRATION, PLANE OF. See *polarization of light*.

VINASSE. Residual liquid obtained after fermentation and distillation of beetroot molasses. Used as a source of potassium carbonate ('potash').

VINEGAR. Liquid containing 3%–6% acetic acid (q.v.), obtained by the oxidation of *ethyl alcohol* (q.v.) by the action of bacteria on wine, beer or fermented wort.

VINYL GROUP. The unsaturated univalent radical $CH_2:CH$. Vinyl compounds, e.g. vinyl chloride, $CH_2:CHCl$, often readily undergo *polymerization* (q.v.) forming products from which important plastics and artificial textile fibres are made.

VIRTUAL IMAGE. See *image, virtual*.

VIRTUAL WORK. If a body, acted upon by a system of forces, is imagined to undergo a small displacement, then in general the forces will do *work* (q.v.), termed the *virtual work* of the forces. If the body is in equilibrium (q.v.), the total virtual work done is zero. This *principle* *of virtual work* is used to determine the positions of equilibrium of a body or a system of bodies under the action of given forces, and to determine relations between the forces acting on such a system in a given equilibrium position.

VISCOMETER. Instrument for the measurement of *viscosity* (q.v.).

VISCOSE. Thick, treacly brownish liquid, consisting mainly of a solution of cellulose xanthate in dilute sodium hydroxide. Made from *cellulose* (q.v.) by the action of sodium hydroxide and carbon disulphide. Used for the production of viscose *rayon* (q.v.) and of cellulose film, of the type used for transparent wrappings.

VISCOSE RAYON. See *rayon*.

VISCOSITY. The property of a fluid whereby it tends to resist relative motion within itself. If different layers of a fluid are moving with different velocities, viscous forces come into play, tending to slow down the faster-moving layers and to increase the velocity of the slower-moving layers. For two parallel layers in the direction of flow, a short distance apart, this viscous force is proportional to the velocity gradient between the layers. The constant of proportionality is called the coefficient of viscosity of the fluid.

VISCOSITY, KINEMATIC. The ratio of the coefficient of *viscosity* (q.v.) to the density of a fluid.

VISCOUS. Having high *viscosity* (q.v.); a liquid which drags in a treacle-like manner.

VISUAL PURPLE. See *rhodopsin*.

VITALISTIC THEORY. The view that life, and all consequent biological phenomena, are due to a 'vital force'.

VITAMINS. Accessory food factors. A group of organic substances, occurring in various foods, which are necessary for a normal diet. Absence or shortage leads to various deficiency diseases. Before the chemical nature of any of the vitamins was known, they were named by the letters of the alphabet. *Vitamin A*, $C_{20}H_{29}OH$, occurs in milk, butter, green vegetables and in liver, especially of fish. Deficiency causes 'night-blindness' (see *rhodopsin*) and ultimately more serious eye troubles; the resistance of the mucous membranes to infection also decreases. This vitamin can be made in the body from *carotene* (q.v.). *Vitamin B*, originally regarded as a single substance, has been shown to be a whole group of compounds termed the vitamin B complex; these occur in wheat-germ, yeast and other sources. B_1, *aneurin*, protects from neuritis, muscular weakness and digestive disturbances; serious deficiency causes beri-beri. B_2, *lactoflavin* or *riboflavin*, promotes growth in the young and probably plays an important part in the health of the skin. *Vitamin C, ascorbic acid* (q.v.), occurs in the juice of lemons and oranges and in fresh vegetables; deficiency causes scurvy. *Vitamin D, calciferol* (q.v.), occurs together with vitamin A; it is formed in the human skin by the action of sunlight. It controls the deposition of calcium compounds in the body; deficiency causes rickets. Absence of *vitamin E*, which occurs in green vegetables and wheat-germ, causes sterility in women. In addition to all these, numerous other vitamins have been discovered in recent years.

VITREOSIL (reg. trade mark). Translucent form of silica, SiO_2, prepared from sand. Used for making laboratory apparatus which is required to withstand large and sudden changes in temperature; does not crack at such changes owing to very low expansion.

VITRIOL. Concentrated sulphuric acid, H_2SO_4, oil of vitriol; copper sulphate, $CuSO_4.5H_2O$, blue vitriol; ferrous sulphate, $FeSO_2.7H_2O$, green vitriol; zinc sulphate, $ZnSO_4.7H_2O$, white vitriol.

VOLATILE. Passing readily into vapour; having a high *vapour pressure* (q.v.).

VOLT. Unit of electromotive force and potential difference. The *absolute volt* is 10^8 electromagnetic units of potential, and is that potential difference which, applied across the ends of a conductor having resistance of 1 absolute *ohm* (q.v.), causes a current of 1 absolute *ampere* to flow. The former *international volt* was similarly defined in terms of the international ohm and international ampere. 1 international volt = 1·0035 absolute volts.

VOLTAGE. The *electromotive force* (q.v.) of a supply of electricity, measured in volts.

VOLTAIC PILE. Earliest electric battery, devised by Volta. A number of cells joined in series, each consisting of a sheet of zinc and copper separated by a piece of cloth moistened with dilute sulphuric acid.

VOLTAMETER. Electrolytic cell in which a metal, generally silver or copper, is deposited by *electrolysis* (q.v.) of a salt of the metal upon the cathode. From the increase in weight of the cathode and a knowledge of the *electrochemical equivalent* (q.v.) of the metal, the quantity of electricity which has passed through the circuit may be found.

VOLTMETER. Instrument for measuring the *potential difference* (q.v.) between two points. In principle consists of an arrangement similar to an *ammeter* (q.v.) with a high resistance in series incorporated in the instrument, the scale being calibrated in volts. When the instrument is connected in parallel between the points where the P.D. is being measured, very little current flows through it, and a correct reading of the voltage is obtained.

VOLUME. The measure of bulk or space occupied by a body.

VOLUME, BRITISH UNITS OF.

> *Solids:* 1728 cubic inches = 1 cubic foot.
> 27 cubic feet = 1 cubic yard.
> (1 cubic inch = 16·387 c.c.).
> *Liquids:* 4 gills = 1 pint, 0·5682 litre.
> 2 pints = 1 quart.
> 4 quarts = 1 gallon, 4·546 litres.

VOLUME, METRIC UNITS OF.
1000 cubic millimetres = 1 cubic centimetre.
1000 c.c. = 1 *litre* (q.v.) very nearly.
1,000,000 c.c. = 1 stere.

VOLUMETRIC ANALYSIS. A group of methods of quantitative chemical analysis involving the measurement of volumes of the reacting substances. The amount of a substance present is determined by finding the volume of a solution of another substance, of known concentration, which is required to react with it. The added volume is measured by adding the reacting solution from a *burette* (q.v.); the completion of the reaction is often shown by a suitable *indicator* (q.v.).

VULCANITE. Hard insulating material made by the action of rubber on sulphur.

VULCANIZED RUBBER. Product obtained by heating rubber with sulphur.

W

WASHING-SODA. Crystalline sodium carbonate, $Na_2CO_3 . 10H_2O$.

WATER. H_2O. The normal oxide of hydrogen. Natural water (river, spring, rain, etc.) is never quite pure but contains dissolved substances.

WATER EQUIVALENT (phys.). See *heat capacity*.

WATER, EXPANSION OF. Water, on cooling, reaches its maximum *density* (q.v.) at very nearly 4° C. At this temperature its density is, by definition, 1·000 gm. per millilitre (1/1000 of a *litre*, q.v.); it then expands as its temperature falls to 0° C., the density at 0° being 0·99987; on freezing, it expands still further, giving ice with a density of 0·9168 at 0° C. This accounts for the bursting of water-pipes in frosts.

WATER GAS. Fuel gas obtained by the action of steam on glowing hot coke, giving carbon monoxide and hydrogen. The formation of water gas is accompanied by absorption of heat (an *endothermic* reaction); thus the coke is rapidly cooled and has to be re-heated at intervals by a blast of hot air, which causes partial combustion and makes the coke incandescent again.

WATER GLASS. Sodium silicate, Na_2SiO_3.

WATER OF CONSTITUTION. The portion of *water of crystallization* (q.v.) which, in some hydrated salts, is retained more tenaciously than the rest. Thus, copper sulphate, $CuSO_4 . 5H_2O$, when heated to 100° C. loses 4 molecules of water of crystallization and becomes $CuSO_4 . H_2O$, but the last molecule is retained till the temperature reaches 250° C.

WATER OF CRYSTALLIZATION. A definite molecular proportion of water chemically combined with certain substances in the crystalline state; e.g. the crystals of copper sulphate contain 5 molecules of water with every molecule of copper sulphate, $CuSO_4 . 5H_2O$.

WATER SOFTENING. Removal of the causes of hardness of water (see *hard water*). Generally depends on the *precipitation* (q.v.) or removal from solution of the metals the salts of which cause the hardness.

WATER VAPOUR. Water in the gaseous or *vapour* (q.v.) state, present in the atmosphere in varying amounts. See *humidity*.

WATT, THE. Unit of power; the rate of work done in *joules* (q.v.) per second; the energy expended per second by an unvarying electric current of 1 ampere flowing through a conductor the ends of which are maintained at a potential difference of 1 volt. Equivalent to 10^7 ergs per second. The power in watts is given by the product of the current in amperes and the potential difference in volts. 1000 watts = 1 *kilowatt*; 746 watts = 1 *horse-power*.

WATT-METER. Instrument for the direct measurement of the power, in watts, of an electrical circuit.

WAVE FRONT. The locus of adjacent points in the path of a wave motion which possess the same *phase* (q.v.).

WAVE GUIDE. Hollow metal conductor through which very short wireless waves (i.e. electromagnetic waves of wave-length approximately 1 cm.) are propagated. Used extensively in radar.

WAVE-LENGTH. The distance between successive points of equal *phase* (q.v.) of a *wave motion* (q.v.); thus, the wave-length of the waves on water could be measured as the distance from crest to crest. The wave-length is equal to the velocity of the wave motion divided by its *frequency* (q.v.).

WAVE MECHANICS. A development of the *quantum theory* (q.v.). Every particle is considered to be associated with a kind of periodic wave, whose frequency and amplitude are determined by rules which are derived partly by analogy with the propagation of light-waves, partly by *ad hoc* hypothesis from known quantum conditions, and partly from necessary conditions of continuity. These waves, however, are not conceived as having any real physical existence, the term 'wave' being really used only by analogy as a description of the mathematical relations employed, since in all but the simplest cases the waves would have to be imagined in a 'hyperspace' of very many dimensions.

WAVE MOTION. The propagation of a periodic disturbance carrying energy. At any point along the path of a wave motion, a periodic displacement or vibration about a mean position takes place. This may take the form of a displacement of air molecules (e.g. sound waves in air), of water molecules (waves on water), a displacement of elements of a string or wire, displacement of electric and magnetic vectors (*electromagnetic waves*), etc. The locus of these displacements at any instant is called the wave. The wave motion moves forward a distance equal to its *wave-length* (q.v.) in the time taken for the displacement at any point to undergo a complete cycle about its mean position. See *longitudinal waves; transverse waves*.

WAVE NUMBER. Number of waves in unit length. Reciprocal of *wavelength* (q.v.).

WAVE THEORY OF LIGHT. The theory that light is propagated as a wave motion (see *electromagnetic waves*); formerly the existence of a medium, the ether, was postulated for the transmission of light waves. Modern views suggest modifications in the classical wave theory of light, and do not assume the existence of the ether.

WAX. The true waxes (e.g. beeswax) are chiefly mixtures of *esters* (q.v.) of fatty acids and monohydric alcohols; the term is often loosely applied to solid, non-greasy, insoluble substances which soften and melt at fairly low temperatures; e.g. *paraffin wax* (q.v.).

WEIGHT. The *force* of attraction of the Earth on a given mass is the weight of that mass.

WEIGHT, BRITISH UNITS OF. Avoirdupois weights.

$$437\tfrac{1}{2} \text{ grains} = 1 \text{ ounce} = 28\cdot3 \text{ gm.}$$
$$7000 \text{ grains} = 16 \text{ ounces} = 1 \text{ pound.}$$
$$14 \text{ pounds} = 1 \text{ stone.}$$
$$2 \text{ stone} = 1 \text{ quarter.}$$
$$4 \text{ quarters} = 1 \text{ hundredweight.}$$
$$2240 \text{ pounds} = 20 \text{ cwt.} = 1 \text{ ton.}$$
$$2000 \text{ lb.} = 1 \text{ short ton.}$$

WEIGHT, METRIC UNITS OF.

$$1000 \text{ milligrams} = 1 \text{ gram} = 15\cdot432 \text{ grains.}$$
$$1000 \text{ grams} = 1 \text{ kilogram} = 2\cdot2046 \text{ lb.}$$
$$1000 \text{ kilograms} = 1 \text{ tonne} = 0\cdot9842 \text{ ton.}$$

WELDING. Joining of two metal surfaces by raising their temperature sufficiently to melt and fuse them together.

WESTON CELL, cadmium cell. Primary cell used as a standard of E.M.F.

WET AND DRY BULB HYGROMETER. Instrument for determining the *relative humidity* (q.v.) of the atmosphere. Consists of a pair of thermometers side by side, the bulb of one being surrounded by moistened muslin. This one will indicate a lower temperature than the other, on account of loss of heat by evaporation; the difference in the readings will depend upon the relative humidity, which can be found by reference to special tables calculated for the purpose.

WHALE OIL. Animal fat obtained from the fatty layer of *blubber* of true whales. After extraction it is divided into various fractions and used for soap manufacture and other purposes; on *hydrogenation* (q.v.) a hard, tasteless, edible fat is obtained.

WHEATSTONE BRIDGE. A divided electrical circuit used for the measurement of resistances. When no current flows from C to D, as indicated by the absence of deflection on the galvanometer G, $R_1/R_2 = R_3/R_4$, where R_1, etc., are resistances. See Fig. 19. This principle is applied in the *metre bridge*. A wire, AB, of uniform resistance and generally 1 metre in length, corresponds to R_3 and R_4 in the Wheatstone bridge diagram; for R_1 a standard resistance is used, while R_2 is the resistance to be measured. By a sliding contact a point of no deflection in the galvanometer is found along AB, the resistances R_3 and R_4 being proportional to the lengths cut off.

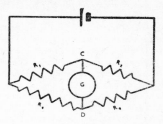

FIG. 19.

WHITE ARSENIC. Arsenious oxide, As_2O_3. Intensely poisonous white powder.

WHITE LEAD. Basic lead carbonate, $2PbCO_3.Pb(OH)_2$. Used in paints.

WHITE LIGHT. Light which can be resolved into a continuous *spectrum* (q.v.) of wave-lengths (i.e. colours); e.g. the light from an incandescent 'white-hot' solid.

WHITE SPIRIT. A mixture of petroleum *hydrocarbons* (q.v.) of boiling range 150° C.–200° C. Used as a solvent and in the paint and varnish industry.

WIEDEMANN-FRANZ LAW. The ratio of the thermal *conductivity* (q.v.) to the electrical conductivity is the same for all metals at a given temperature. This ratio is proportional to the *absolute temperature* (q.v.). Most pure metals obey the law with reasonable accuracy at ordinary temperatures.

WIMSHURST MACHINE. Laboratory apparatus for generating static electricity.

WIND. A large-scale movement of air, generally caused by a *convection* (q.v.) effect in the atmosphere.

WIRELESS. Communication by means of *electromagnetic waves* (q.v.). See *radio telephony*.

WOLFRAM. W. (Tungsten.) Element. A.W. 183·92. At. No. 74. Grey, hard metal, ductile, malleable and resistant to corrosion; S.G. 19·3, m.p. 3370° C. Occurs as *wolframite* or '*wolfram*', $FeWO_4$, and *scheelite*, $CaWO_4$. Obtained by converting the ore to the oxide and then reducing the latter. Used in alloys, in cemented carbides for hard tools, and for electric lamp filaments. The names *tungsten* and *wolfram* for this element were both officially recognized in 1951.

WOLFRAMITE, 'wolfram'. Natural ferrous tungstate, $FeWO_4$.

WOLLASTON PRISM. Prism for obtaining plane-polarized light (see *polarization of light*). Constructed of quartz, this prism, like the *Rochon prism* (q.v.), may be used for work in the ultra-violet. (See *ultra-violet rays*.)

WOOD NAPHTHA. See *methyl alcohol*.

WOOD'S METAL. Alloy of 50% bismuth, 25% lead, 12·5% tin, 12·5% cadmium. M.p. 71° C.

WORK (phys.). The work done by a force f when it moves its point of application through a distance s is equal to $fs \cos \theta$, where θ is the angle between the line of action of the force and the displacement. For units, see *erg*, *joule*, *foot-pound*, *foot-poundal*.

WORK FUNCTION. At the absolute zero of temperature, the free electrons present in a metal are distributed amongst a large number of discrete energy states E_1, E_2, etc., up to a state of maximum energy E. At higher temperatures a small proportion of the electrons have energies greater than E. The work function of a metal is the energy which must be supplied to free electrons possessing energy E, to enable them to escape from the metal.

WORT. See *brewing*.

WROUGHT IRON. Purest commercial form of iron; iron nearly free from carbon. Very tough and fibrous; can be welded.

X

XANTHATES. Salts of the series of *xanthic acids* which have the general formula ROCSSH. Cellulose xanthate is the important intermediate product in the manufacture of *viscose* (q.v.).

XENON. Element. A.W. 131·3. At. No. 54. *Inert gas* (q.v.) occurring in exceedingly minute amounts in the air.

X-RAYS, Röntgen rays. *Electromagnetic waves* (q.v.) of the same type as light, but of much smaller wave-length, in the range of 5×10^{-7} cm. to 6×10^{-10} cm. approximately. Produced when *cathode rays* (q.v.) (a stream of electrons) strike a material object. X-rays affect a photographic plate in a way similar to light. The absorption of the rays by matter depends upon the density and the atomic weights of the material. The lower the A.W. and density, the more transparent is the material to X-rays. Thus, bones are more opaque than the surrounding flesh; this makes it possible to take an X-ray photograph (*radiograph*) of the bones of a living person.

X-RAY SPECTRUM. Each element, when bombarded by cathode rays, emits X-rays of a characteristic frequency which depends upon the atomic number; a spectrum photograph of lines corresponding to various elements may thus be obtained from the X-rays emitted.

X UNIT. X.U. Unit of length, 10^{-11} cm. Used mainly for expressing X-ray wave-lengths.

XYLAN. A complex *polysaccharide* (q.v.) which occurs closely associated with *cellulose* (q.v.) in plants.

XYLENE, dimethylbenzene, $C_6H_4(CH_3)_2$. Liquid resembling *toluene* (q.v.); occurs in coal-tar. Exists in three *isomeric* (q.v.) forms. Mixture of these boils at 137° C.–140° C.

XYLOL. Xylene.

XYLONITE. Trade name for a plastic material of the cellulose nitrate type. See also *celluloid*.

Y

YARD. British unit of length. The *Imperial standard yard* is the distance, at 62° F., between the central traverse lines on two gold plugs in a certain bronze bar. 91·44 centimetres.

YEAR. Measure of time; commonly understood to be the time taken by the Earth to complete its orbit round the Sun. The civil year has an average value of 365·2425 mean solar days; 3 successive years consisting of 365 days, the fourth or leap year of 366. Century years do not count as leap years unless divisible by 400. The tropical or solar year, the average interval between two successive returns of the Sun to the first point of Aries, is 365·2422 mean solar days; the *sidereal year* (q.v.) is 365·2564 mean solar days.

YIELD POINT. If a wire or rod of a material such as steel is subjected to a slowly increasing tension, the elongation produced is at first proportional to the tension (Hooke's law). If the tension is increased beyond the *elastic limit* (q.v.), a point is reached at which a sudden increase in elongation occurs with only a small increase in tension; this is the *yield point*.

YOUNG'S MODULUS. *Elastic modulus* (q.v.) applied to a stretched wire or to a rod under tension or compression; the ratio of the stress on a cross-section of the wire or rod to the longitudinal strain.

YPERITE. See *mustard gas*.

YTTERBIUM. Yb. Element. A.W. 173·04. At. No. 70. See *rare earths*.

YTTRIUM. Y. Element. A.W. 88·92. At. No. 39. See *rare earths*.

Z

ZEEMAN EFFECT. When a substance which emits a *line spectrum* (q.v.) is placed in a strong magnetic field, the single lines are split up into groups of closely spaced lines. From the separation of the lines in these groups information on atomic structure can be deduced.

ZENITH (astr.). Highest point; the point on the *celestial sphere* (q.v.) directly overhead.

ZEOLITE. Natural hydrated silicate of calcium and aluminium, term also now applied to artificial substances used in softening *hard water* (q.v.) by the 'base-exchange' method. The calcium in the water replaces sodium in the zeolite; the process may be reversed and the zeolite restored by washing it with a solution of common salt.

ZERO. Nought; the starting-point of any scale of measurement.

ZERO POINT ENERGY. The energy possessed by the atoms or molecules of a substance at the *absolute zero* (q.v.) of temperature.

ZINC. Zn. Element. A.W. 65·38. At. No. 30. Hard, bluish-white metal; m.p. 419° C.; b.p. 907° C.; S.G. 7·14. Occurs as calamine, $ZnCO_3$, and zinc blende, ZnS. Extracted by roasting the ore to form the oxide, which is then reduced with carbon and the resulting zinc distilled. Used in alloys, especially *brass* (q.v.), and for galvanizing iron.

ZINC BLENDE. Natural zinc sulphide, ZnS. Important ore of zinc.

ZINC-COPPER COUPLE. Metallic zinc coated with a thin film of copper by immersing zinc in copper sulphate solution. Evolves hydrogen with hot water.

ZIRCONIUM. Zr. Element. A.W. 91·22. At. No. 40. Rare metal, S.G. 6·4, m.p. 1900° C. Used in alloys.

ZODIAC. Zone of the *celestial sphere* (q.v.) containing the paths of the Sun, Moon, and the planets. Bounded by two circles, equidistant from the ecliptic (q.v.) and about 18° apart; divided into 12 *signs of the zodiac*, named after 12 constellations.

ZONE OF SPHERE. Portion of the surface of a sphere cut off by two parallel planes. Area is given by $2\pi rd$, where r is the radius of the sphere and d the distance between the two planes.

ZONES OF AUDIBILITY. An intense sound, e.g. that due to an explosion, can usually be heard or detected at all points in a large area which includes the source of the sound, and also in distant *zones of audibility*, which are separated from that area by regions in which the sound cannot be detected. The sound waves reaching these zones do so by reflection down from the upper atmosphere.

ZONES, FRESNEL. See *half-period zones*.

ZOOLOGY. The scientific study of animals.

ZYMASE. *Enzyme* (q.v.) present in yeast; acts on sugar with the formation of alcohol and carbon dioxide (see *fermentation*).

Element	Symbol	At. No.	A.W.
Actinium	Ac	89	227
Aluminium	Al	13	26·98
Americium	Am	95	[243]
Antimony	Sb	51	121·76
Argon	A	18	39·944
Arsenic	As	33	74·91
Astatine	At	85	[210]
Barium	Ba	56	137·36
Berkelium	Bk	97	[245]
Beryllium	Be	4	9·013
Bismuth	Bi	83	209·00
Boron	B	5	10·82
Bromine	Br	35	79·916
Cadmium	Cd	48	112·41
Caesium	Cs	55	132·91
Calcium	Ca	20	40·08
Californium	Cf	98	[246]
Carbon	C	6	12·010
Cerium	Ce	58	140·13
Chlorine	Cl	17	35·457
Chromium	Cr	24	52·01
Cobalt	Co	27	58·94
Copper	Cu	29	63·54
Curium	Cm	96	[243]
Dysprosium	Dy	66	162·46
Erbium	Er	68	167·2
Europium	Eu	63	152·0
Fluorine	F	9	19·00
Francium	Fr	87	[223]
Gadolinium	Gd	64	156·9
Gallium	Ga	31	69·72
Germanium	Ge	32	72·60
Gold	Au	79	197·2
Hafnium	Hf	72	178·6

[*A.W.* values in brackets denote mass number of the most
stable known isotope.]

Element	Symbol	At. No.	A.W.
Helium	He	2	4·003
Holmium	Ho	67	164·94
Hydrogen	H	1	1·0080
Indium	In	49	114·76
Iodine	I	53	126·91
Iridium	Ir	77	193·1
Iron	Fe	26	55·85
Krypton	Kr	36	83·80
Lanthanum	La	57	138·92
Lead	Pb	82	207·21
Lithium	Li	3	6·940
Lutetium	Lu	71	174·99
Magnesium	Mg	12	24·32
Manganese	Mn	25	54·93
Mercury	Hg	80	200·61
Molybdenum	Mo	42	95·95
Neodymium	Nd	60	144·27
Neon	Ne	10	20·183
Neptunium	Np	93	[237]
Nickel	Ni	28	58·69
Niobium	Nb	41	92·91
Nitrogen	N	7	14·008
Osmium	Os	76	190·2
Oxygen	O	8	16·0000
Palladium	Pd	46	106·7
Phosphorus	P	15	30·975
Platinum	Pt	78	195·23
Plutonium	Pu	94	[242]
Polonium	Po	84	210
Potassium	K	19	39·100
Praseodymium	Pr	59	140·92
Promethium	Pm	61	[145]

[*A.W. values in brackets denote mass number of the most stable known isotope.*]

Element	Symbol	At. No.	A.W.
Protactinium	Pa	91	231
Radium	Ra	88	226·05
Radon	Rn	86	222
Rhenium	Re	75	186·31
Rhodium	Rh	45	102·91
Rubidium	Rb	37	85·48
Ruthenium	Ru	44	101·7
Samarium	Sm	62	150·43
Scandium	Sc	21	44·96
Selenium	Se	34	78·96
Silicon	Si	14	28·09
Silver	Ag	47	107·880
Sodium	Na	11	22·997
Strontium	Sr	38	87·63
Sulphur	S	16	32·066
Tantalum	Ta	73	180·88
Technetium	Tc	43	[99]
Tellurium	Te	52	127·61
Terbium	Tb	65	159·2
Thallium	Tl	81	204·39
Thorium	Th	90	232·12
Thulium	Tm	69	169·4
Tin	Sn	50	118·70
Titanium	Ti	22	47·90
Tungsten	W	74	183·92
Uranium	U	92	238·07
Vanadium	V	23	50·95
Wolfram (Tungsten)	W	74	183·92
Xenon	Xe	54	131·3
Ytterbium	Yb	70	173·04
Yttrium	Y	39	88·92
Zinc	Zn	30	65·38
Zirconium	Zr	40	91·22

[*A.W. values in brackets denote mass number of the most stable known isotope.*]